Schizophrenia and the Family

Monograph Series on Schizophrenia No. 7

SCHIZOPHRENIA AND THE FAMILY

Second Edition

Theodore Lidz, M.D.
Stephen Fleck, M.D.

with the collaboration of

Alice R. Cornelison

and

Yrjo A. Alanen, M.D.
Dorothy Terry Carlson, Ph.D.
Cynthia Wild Cowgill, Ph.D.
Sarah Schafer Feidelson, M.A.
Daniel X. Freedman, M.D.
Ruth W. Lidz, M.D.
Judith L. Ricci, M.A.
Bernice L. Rosman, Ph.D.
Margaret T. Singer, Ph.D.
D. Clint Smith, M.D.

INTERNATIONAL UNIVERSITIES PRESS, INC.

NEW YORK

Library of Congress Cataloging in Publication Data

Lidz, Theodore.
  Schizophrenia and the family.

  Bibliography: p.
  Includes index.
  1. Schizophrenics—Family relationships.
2. Schizophrenia—Etiology. I. Fleck, Stephen.
II. Title. [DNLM: 1. Family. 2. Parent-Child
Relations. 3. Schizophrenia—etiology.
WM 203 L715s]
RC514.L5 1985   616.89′82   85-10870
ISBN 0-8236-6001-X

Manufactured in the United States of America

To
The Memory
of Our Colleagues
Alice R. Cornelison
Cynthia Wild Cowgill

Contents

Acknowledgments

We wish to thank the many persons who helped carry out the lengthy investigations, particularly our deceased co-worker Alice R. Cornelison, who coauthored the first edition of this book. Her abilities to develop relationships with the relatives of patients and to help them with the burden of having a schizophrenic member of their families were remarkable and essential to the project. Other collaborators are listed on the title page of the book and the participation of each in a specific aspect of the work is noted at the beginning of each chapter. The contributions of Dr. Beulah Parker who helped start the project and of Dr. Dorothy Terry Carlson and Mrs. Sarah Schafer Feidelson who were members of the research team for many years extend beyond any specific chapters. The influence of our collaborator by correspondence, Dr. Margaret Thaler Singer, is apparent in several chapters.

Members of the staff of the Yale Psychiatric Institute between 1952 and 1965 aided our work by their cooperation, through reports provided, and by helping establish the therapeutic milieu which had been essential to the conduct of the investigation.

We are particularly grateful to Mrs. Catherine Molloy, Mrs. Hope Mag Appel, Ms. Doris Berndtson, and Mrs. Myrna Schwartz for patiently deciphering our handwritings, transcribing our voices, and for the many other secretarial tasks they have carried out.

Harriette Dukeley Borsuch prepared the manuscript and

ix

collated the references. We are greatly indebted to her for her many suggestions and her editing as well as her patience with our decisions and indecisions in making revisions. We wish once again to express our appreciation for her devotion to the task.

The following publishers and journals permitted use of articles which were originally published by them, as noted in footnotes at the start of the chapters: American Journal of Psychiatry, American Journal of Orthopsychiatry, AMA Archives of Neurology and Psychiatry, Archives of General Psychiatry, Journal of the American Psychoanalytic Association, Journal of Nervous and Mental Disease, Psychiatry, Brunner/Mazel, Inc., Grune & Stratton, and Plenum Publishing Co.

The investigations on which this volume is based were supported by grants from the National Institute of Mental Health, The Social Research Foundation, and the Supreme Council Thirty-Third Degree Masons, Northern Jurisdiction (Chapter II).

It follows from the nature of the facts which form the material of psycho-analysis that we are obliged to pay as much attention in our case histories to the purely human and social circumstances of our patients as to the somatic data and the symptoms of the disorder. Above all, our interest will be directed towards their family circumstances.

—FREUD (1905)

Introduction to the Original Edition

Over the past twelve years we have been conducting an intensive study of the intrafamilial environment in which schizophrenic patients grew up. During this time we have written and usually published papers dealing with various aspects of the complex data in order to analyze the material and work through theoretical problems as well as to report our findings. Confronted by a wealth of pertinent data in an almost virgin field and lacking a conceptual framework for analyzing and describing the material, we found the discipline of condensing data and formulating hypotheses extremely useful. Now that the prolonged exploratory phase of the work has ended and it becomes possible to formulate and investigate testable hypotheses, we are publishing the significant papers in one volume. The collection contains several previously unpublished papers that round out the study.

For the most part, each paper deals with a particular aspect of the data isolated from the totality to permit scrutiny and presentation. A grasp of the interrelationships of the different segments of the picture is essential for an appreciation of the significance of these family situations as a whole and of their impacts upon the offspring who became schizophrenic. As the published papers appeared in various journals over a span of nine years, only those persons who have specifically sought them out have been able to survey and properly assess our findings. The collection offers the reader the opportunity to follow us on a quest which we—and others—have found absorbing; which has provided a wealth of new insights; and which, we believe we may say, has done

1

much to change the conceptualization of schizophrenia, its etiology, and the approaches to its treatment.

We had considered writing a book that offered a comprehensive and carefully organized expression of the end results of the study and our current views on each aspect of it. There are a number of reasons for not doing so. We have not reached closure concerning our findings and even less concerning theory. Although our formulations seem to us to gain in clarity and comprehensivity, some earlier formulations may turn out to have greater pertinence than certain current views. We wish to present what we have done and how we have thought about the data, and think that the articles contain more freshness and challenge than would a retrospective survey. We do not wish to serve up a warmed-over stew. Perhaps, even more important, writing—at least for us—consumes time and effort, and we are far from the end of the road, engaged in ongoing studies provoked by what we are herein reporting. Lastly, we are turning from the analysis of seventeen families that form the core material of our study to other related studies not because we have exhausted the data but because it has exhausted us, and it is time for us to be finished with it.

The theoretical considerations that entered into the study and which influenced our perception of the data are presented in a general way in the paper, "An Orientation to the Role of the Family in Schizophrenic Disorders" and are amplified and developed as pertinent in each paper, and cannot be presented more concisely in this introduction. A separate volume, *The Family and Human Adaptation* (Lidz, 1963a) contains some of the reappraisal of the functions and functioning of the family that has been essential to the comprehension of our findings. This introduction will present only the reasons for embarking on the investigation; the approach and methods used, in order to be able to delete the repetition of such statements from the individual papers; some comments upon the problems encountered in analyzing and assessing the data; and finally a few notes concerning the papers themselves.

At the outset, the investigators were venturing into an area that had remained virtually unexplored. Aside from two studies (Chapter II; Reichard and Tillman, 1950), interest in the family had been confined to genetic studies and to concerns with mothers and their personality characteristics or psychopathology. During the past decade the picture has changed profoundly. Largely due to these studies and those of Jackson and Bateson; Wynne, Bowen, and their coworkers, and colleagues in the United States; Y. O. Alanen in Finland; and Delay, Deniker, and Green in France—but also with many others contributing—the importance of the family environment to the genesis of schizophrenia is now widely recognized, and in some settings even taken for granted. Concomitantly, recognition of the importance of the family as the primary social unit gave rise to conjoint family therapy, fostered notably by Ackerman (1958) and the group in Palo Alto (Jackson, 1959) which has contributed to the understanding of family dynamics and communication. The publication of Parson and Bales's *Family, Socialization and Interaction Process* (1955) was of particular moment to us because its theory meshed with our findings and thinking and offered other useful guidelines. While much remains to be done in clarifying the intrafamilial factors in the etiology of schizophrenia, the extent and magnitude of the problems within these families have now been documented and the nature of the difficulties delineated.

ORIGINS OF STUDY

Observations concerning the peculiarities of the parents of psychotic patients are nothing new. Almost a hundred years ago both Griesinger and Ideler (Delay et al., 1957) had noted the frequency of eccentric and strange parental behavior and commented that aside from genetic influence, the environmental or educational influences of such parents upon their children must be taken into account. However, the dominant orientations concerning the etiology of schizophrenia directed attention away from the topic and the potential importance of the observations. Until Adolf Meyer (1906) who seriously suggested that schizophrenia could be a "habit deterioration" or a "reaction type," psychiatrists virtually without exception sought to follow the lead of the remainder of medicine in searching for a specific structural, infectious, or biochemical cause of schizophrenia—a trend fortified by the discovery of the cause of general paresis. This conviction was not even countered in any definitive manner by psychoanalysts who continued to believe in a toxic or genetic etiology of the condition. Dynamically oriented psychiatry—psychobiology as well as psychoanalysis—concentrated upon the development of the individual patient, and not upon the setting in which it occurred. Analysis directed attention to the earliest mother-child relationships following Abraham's (1908) concept that schizophrenia indicated a fixation and regression to the earliest oral phase, and also to the problem of unconscious homosexuality following Freud's (1911) analysis of the Schreber case but with the tacit implication that the homosexuality was a constitutional matter. In H. S. Sullivan's (1925-26) early writings an appreciation of the importance of the family configurations and interrelationships can be found.

Although our intensive investigation of the families of schizophrenic patients was started in 1952, one of us (T. L.) had begun studying the topic in 1940. As a resident in charge of Adolf Meyer's private male service, he had considerable contact with the relatives of the small number of patients on the unit. Still inexperienced, he did not yet know what was considered germane to the study and treatment of schizophrenic reactions. He became impressed by the personality problems of the immediate relatives of the schizophrenic patients and the extremely devastating family milieu in which these upper-class patients had been reared. Even without consideration of other factors such as genetics, metabolic disorder, brain anomaly, or, of chronic masturbation, homosexuality, etc., it seemed unlikely that these persons could have grown up without becoming seriously disturbed. The impression was heightened when the uncle of one youth declined the customary explanation that his nephew suffered from a condition of unknown origins; he had come to describe and explain why the boy was ill. He carefully depicted the serious and enduring conflict between the parents; the mother's depression and apathy following the patient's birth; her efforts to cling to this child to give some meaning to her unhappy marriage; the father's rigidities and paranoid sensitivities; the patient's feelings of being overwhelmed when his self-aggrandizing father failed in business, etc. Soon thereafter the sister of another patient spent many hours detailing how her brother had been expected to live up to the image of their father, a ruthless financier who presented a grandiose model, but at the same time had been sissified by a doting mother who sought to woo him from the father's influence and from developing into a callous person like her husband. The sister went on to explain how her childhood had been unhappy in this disturbed household, but she had not been burdened with the unrealistic expectations placed upon her brother, and as she had resented her mother's preference for her brother, she had been able to liberate herself from the family in adolescence. A paper describing the family settings of a small series of schizophrenic patients failed to elicit enthusiasm from his senior colleagues and remained unpublished because it was so removed from current concepts that the writer considered that he may have been concerned with a coincidence of unusual cases. However, to broaden the base and to learn whether such family situations might have pertinence to the etiology of schizophrenia, a more structured study was carried out with Dr. Ruth Lidz in 1941. The family histories in the charts of fifty consecutively admitted schizophrenic patients and fifty psychotically depressed patients were compared. The War and prolonged overseas service precluded completion of the analysis of the data, and the findings were not published until 1949. The paper, included as Chapter II of this volume, appears to be the first concerned with the total family setting: it drew attention to notable differences in the family backgrounds of the two groups of patients, and indicated that further attention to the area was warranted.

During the years between 1945 and 1950, the experiences of several psychiatrists in Baltimore with analytically oriented therapy of schizophrenic patients verified prior impressions, for all of these patients had disturbed parents and disorganizing family backgrounds. How such data became a central issue in treatment was indicated in a paper (Lidz and Lidz, 1952) which points out some of these implications of the mother's use of the child to complete her life and her inability to establish boundaries between herself and the child—a finding that had also been made by Reichard and Tillman (1950) in their highly significant paper on parent-child relationships in schizophrenia.

Now, other reasons also directed to a need to focus on the patient's early family environment. A series of studies[1] of patients with a wide variety of brain pathology and metabolic and toxic impairments of cerebral functioning had further demonstrated that the thought disorders of all such patients differed from those of schizophrenic patients. Patients with known brain dysfunctions that affected their thinking suffered a degradation of intellectual potential. Both tests and psychotherapeutic work with schizophrenic patients indicated that they retained their intellectual potential but used it in distorted ways. As the child receives his basic training in the meaning of words and in ways of communicating, reasoning, and thinking within his family of origin, it seemed reasonable to believe that a study of the intrafamilial influences upon the child's development might provide a useful approach to the problem of schizophrenic thinking.

Further, the individual's reactions in all subsequent group and interpersonal situations rest upon the foundations pro-

[1]Lidz (1939, 1942, 1949); Lidz, Carter, Lewis, and Surratt (1952); Lidz, Gay, and Tietze (1942); Lidz and Kahn (1946); Lidz, Miller, Padget, and Stedem (1949); Newell and Lidz (1946).

vided within the family. Yet the family has its own needs, which may take precedence over its educational functions. It may be deviant from the remainder of society, set mutually exclusive demands upon the child, provide inconsistent emotional experiences, teach paralogical ways, and in many other areas provide faulty schooling. Although the family is not the only influence upon the developing ego, it provides the most consistent or consistently inconsistent set of influences impinging upon the child. It seemed imperative to scrutinize the family milieu for determinants of schizophrenic reactions, but an investigation of the influence of the family and its members upon the emergent generation presented very grave methodological and conceptual difficulties. Neither suitable techniques nor an adequate conceptual framework for a dynamic study of family transactions existed. Preliminary studies indicated the need to examine the entire family situation rather than some segment of it. The father appeared to be seriously disturbed just as often as the mother, and the vicissitudes of the family life as a whole appeared of potential importance. The basis for the belief that schizophrenia is determined by events in the early, oral phase of development is purely hypothetical, unsupported by evidence that the earliest mother-child relationships are more deleterious that those of certain other psychiatric patients. The cardinal symptomatology of schizophrenia would seem to indicate that later developmental periods also have critical significance. The symbolic distortions, the interpenetration of reality by fantasy, the confusion of sexual identity, the concerns over incestuous impulses, the attribution of omniscience and omnipotence to parental figures are all significant problems of the early oedipal or late preoedipal phases of development. Although it may be considered that disturbances in the oral phase are essential to the development of schizophrenia, they may only establish a potential for mental illness, whereas subsequent events may determine the degree and form of the individual's adjustment or maladjustment.

After lengthy consideration it became evident that circumscribed testable hypotheses could not be formulated until clearer ideas emerged concerning just what within these families might have particular significance to the etiology of schizophrenia. A careful examination of the family environments in a search for something within this sphere that might contribute to knowledge of the nature and origins of schizophrenia seemed an essential initial step. We decided not to be deterred because we could not conduct a methodologically rigorous investigation, but to carry out the necessary exploratory work. We have, therefore, conducted a study that is basically an exploration; and, by analogy, an exploration that seeks to describe and map unknown terrain, for such measures must precede efforts to compare the region with other areas.

METHODS OF STUDY

The approach adopted, despite its obvious shortcomings, was the intensive exploration of what had transpired within the family from its inception through the time of study. The core material was obtained from the long-term study of the families of patients who were hospitalized in the Yale Psychiatric Institute. This institute is a forty-four bed private university hospital in which seriously ill psychiatric patients are treated with individual analytically oriented therapy and group therapy, and in which the hospital milieu and patient-staff transactions are considered essential elements in treatment (Fleck, 1962). The Institute was in the process of being transformed into a place particularly suited to the therapy of schizophrenic reactions and other serious personality disorders of adolescents and young adults. Only families of unmarried patients between the ages of fifteen and thirty were included in the study as the parents and other members of the family had to be available. The diagnosis had to be clearcut and beyond reasonable dispute. The series contains no cases of "borderline" or "pseudoneurotic" schizophrenia. The only other criteria for inclusion in the series were the presence and availability for study of the mother and at least one sibling. Direct study of the mother seemed essential because of the crucial position she fills in child rearing as well as because of studies and theories that indicated her potential import in the etiology of schizophrenia. A sibling was needed both to provide information about the family from the view of a member of the childhood generation, and also to provide a type of inner control through study of a person reared within the family who had not become schizophrenic. Because of the frequency with which families of schizophrenic patients are broken by the death or mental hospitalization of one parent, or by separation, the availability of both parents was not established as a requirement. However, only three of the seventeen families were broken, two by death and one by divorce, and in all but two of the cases, the fathers were available and participated in the study. Toward the end of the inclusion of cases into the series, we asked colleagues to refer patients from families which they considered to be reasonably stable and well integrated. We hoped that such families with less diffuse family pathology might provide better leads to factors that might have specific relevance to schizophrenia. However, the several families included with this criterion turned out to be just as disturbed as the remainder. Seventeen families were studied—nine of male and eight of female patients. An additional three originally included were discarded because the patients were withdrawn from the hospital within the first two months. Fourteen families were upper- or upper-middle class and capable of supporting a member in a private hospital for a prolonged period and three families were emerging from lower-middle class status. The sample had a decided bias toward intact families with status and even prestige in their communities. The bias was desired to safeguard against inadvertent inclusion of families because of their disorganization or partial dissolution, and to lessen the complexities created by economic distress and disturbed extrafamilial social environments. However, as the studies of Hollingshead and Redlich (1958) have shown, generalizations from one social class to another can be made only with great care and reservation. Indeed, we know that the families in this series are more intact than families of schizophrenic offspring in general. The incidence of homes broken before the patient's nineteenth birthday in our series is 18 per cent, about the incidence in the general population in the 1950s, whereas several studies have shown that about 40 per cent of families of schizophrenic patients are broken by this time (Chapter II; Oltman et al., 1952; Wahl, 1954). The study of Delay et al. (1957, 1960, 1962) which dealt with French families of lower socioeconomic levels reports even more blatant family pathology than our study.

Multiple techniques were utilized in an attempt to re-create the personalities of the family members, their interactions, the family patterns and the atmosphere. The primary source of data was gained from repeated interviews with all members of each family by the social worker and the psychiatrists. In some families, one member—usually the mother or father—was the most important source of information and was interviewed weekly for many months or even for several years. The other relatives were seen less often or only sporadically; but in some families all members were seen repeatedly. At times, a sibling, particularly one who had been in psychotherapy because of his own difficulties, was a major source of information concerning the family transactions. The social worker saw all members of all families, and thus served as one fixed point in comparing the families and their members. One of the two psychiatrists also saw almost all of the members of the families on at least one occasion to permit some check upon the social worker's impression, and usually one of the psychiatrists saw one or more members of each family on a number of occasions. In some families when it seemed unwise for the social worker to follow both parents, or when some special difficulty interfered, one of the psychiatrists saw a parent regularly. In some instances the social work and investigative relationship turned into a therapeutic relationship because of the intense need. Aside from two of the first families who were followed and studied for less than six months, all families were studied for at least one year and some for five years or longer. Whenever possible, less immediate relatives, old family friends, nursemaids, and former teachers of the patient were also interviewed. Home visits were made, in some cases on a number of occasions. Diaries kept by mothers, photograph albums and family movies, and various childhood productions of the patients were examined.

The utilization of such extensive contacts with the family for gathering material needed for the research presented problems that required study. Some of these considerations are discussed in an article, "Casework Interviewing as a Research Technique" (Cornelison, 1960). Obviously, potential prejudices of an interviewer or other members of the research group concerning a family member had to be noted and discounted when they could not be overcome. The psychiatric social worker became an object of investigation, and her reactions to people, her likes and dislikes and her prejudices were a constant topic of discussion and study in order to keep these variables controlled as far as possible.

The interaction of family members with one another as well as with the members of the research team and hospital staff was observed under a variety of conditions. During the lengthy period of study special circumstances usually occurred that permitted observation of these persons under new types of stress; sometimes there were marked changes in the family circumstances, and we could observe how the various persons in the family reacted under such conditions. Toward the end of the study, greater emphasis was placed upon observing the family interacting as a group, particularly during recorded conjoint family sessions.

A battery of projective tests (Rorschach, TAT, Figure Drawing, and Sentence Completion) was administered to all family members whenever possible, aside from the first four families studied. The tests helped gain understanding of the patients and the members of their families, checking impressions gained through interviews and other contacts, and offering potential new insights. Initially, a major purpose of the testing was to seek out patterns and styles common to family members, to learn whether aspects of a child's identification with a parent could be noted in the tests, and to examine relationships of the styles of approach, perception, and thinking in parents and children. These were new uses for projective techniques which presented problems of such magnitude that they were of limited value. However, after Margaret Thaler Singer started analyzing the protocols as a consultant and in conjunction with similar work she was carrying out with Wynne (Wynne and Singer, 1963a, 1963b), new potentialities opened. Working blindly with coded material, she successfully matched the protocols of six male patients to those of their parents without error, and then did the same with four female patients. In some instances, Dr. Singer constructed descriptions of the patient's personality and problems solely from the parents' test protocols with an accuracy and breadth akin to that obtained from patient test protocols. These results together with related work at the National Institute of Mental Health led to a new series of explorations of relationships between parental styles of thinking and the offspring's thought disorder, which are still in progress both at the National Institute of Mental Health and at Yale. Dr. Singer's test analyses have been utilized primarily in the papers on the siblings and the mothers (Chapters III and XII).

The material gained from family members and other sources was augmented by careful use of data emerging during the patient's therapy. However, no data offered by any person were by themselves taken as factual, but instead were evaluated in the light of total information. Efforts were made to continue gathering material until the various versions and opinions interdigitated adequately. Divergent views were, of course, in themselves a type of factual data that could be extremely pertinent.

The interviews, particularly after the initial sessions with each individual, were "open ended." They were not recorded, but the interviewer dictated lengthy notes concerning the material and her impressions of the subject immediately after the interview. The story of the family, the relationships between members, and the feelings of each member to all other members, etc., were gradually filled in by placing questions as opportunities arose. Gradually the different views and opinions of the various informants began to fit together, and the discrepancies became understandable in terms of personality differences, defenses, and divergent ways of viewing the world, etc. It is particularly important to note that little reliance could be placed in material obtained during the first interviews or even during the first months. The information often changed very appreciably as the informant gained confidence in the interviewer and the hospital, and as guilt feelings and initial anxieties diminished. The collection of data could not be pushed and hastened. At first it was discouraging when material emerged after months or even after a year or longer that completely altered the understanding of the family history and situation. Although one can gain an impression of a family from a few interviews, it was the experience of our group, probably as skilled as most investigative teams, that we arrived at some very erroneous concepts unless the work continued for many months.

Any such procedure for studying the family has shortcomings. Any attempt to reconstruct the life of a family over a period of fifteen to thirty years must contain limitations. Even though we collected far more extensive material than we had originally intended, important data concerning some of the families eluded our efforts—particularly as we sought to base our study upon reasonably ascertained data with minimal theoretical interpolations. Nevertheless, it is highly likely that the studies of these seventeen families contain the most complete, dynamically comprehensive, and personally meaningful material ever gathered about any series of families for any purpose.

The extensive material concerning each family was condensed into comprehensive summaries of the history of the family, the life and personality of each member, the interrelationships and transactions among members, the organization and atmosphere of the family as a unit; its relationships to the parental families and to the community, etc. An effort was made to include each member's views on the interrelationships among family members. As the study progressed, an increasing amount of material concerning the grandparents and even earlier generations was obtained.

The study of the seventeen families forms the core of the project; most papers in this volume are derived from the study of these families. We avoided embellishment by illustrations drawn from other experiences, unless specifically stated, lest we slant or accentuate certain trends. However, other experiences entered into our thinking. During the project over 200 other schizophrenic patients were treated in the Yale Psychiatric Institute under the supervision of the project psychiatrists, and social work with families and group therapy with parents of patients became increasingly comprehensive. The psychiatrists were also conducting analytic psychotherapy of schizophrenic patients and with some siblings of schizophrenic patients. The material gained from these sources was confirmatory of the findings of the core study.

We have been chided for not reporting a study of a control series of families. We must hope that the reader realizes that we are as aware of the shortcoming as he is. However, a study of a real control series rather than carrying out a pretense for the sake of scientific respectability presented problems which we could not surmount. The term "control" series is in itself incorrect, but we could use a "comparative" series. Yet, the use of a series of families without emotionally disturbed offspring would serve little. It is apparent from general psychiatric experience that the families of schizophrenic patients differ in many ways from the families of mild neurotic or relatively normal persons. But which of the differences would be significant to the problem? Perhaps even more pertinently, individuals and families must be strongly motivated to work as long and intensively as did the patients' relatives, and to be willing to seek after material they have sought to conceal from themselves as well as from others. A primary motivation was the furtherance of the treatment of a family member, and other motives were such personal matters as wishing help with their own problems, justifying the self while condemning a hostile spouse, etc. A comparable study of a comparative series requires that the situations in which the families find themselves are reasonably similar.

We have conducted an intensive study of a series of ten families with a sociopathic offspring. We had decided after considerable scrutiny of the problems that these families were in situations closely analogous to the families in our original series and presumably had similar motivation to cooperate and concerns about a hospitalized offspring. A series of upper- and upper-middle-class delinquents were admitted to the Yale Psychiatric Institute for this purpose. We had intended to delay publishing this volume until we could compare the families of the two series. However, a variety of problems has made this impractical if not impossible. The families were not altogether comparable. We could not collect a series of families of delinquents and eliminate adopted children or parents with multiple marriages—neither of which occur in our schizophrenic series. The symptomatic differences between male and female delinquents are more striking than between male and female schizophrenics as the young male delinquents are in trouble for stealing, aggressive and hostile behavior, etc., whereas the females are almost all sexually delinquent. We were unable to retain many of the delinquents in the hospital for a year or longer. Parents tended not to be as cooperative, an important difference in motivation, but an uncontrollable variable. These are salient findings—or may be—but they make comparisons difficult. The main problem, however, was that the study and understanding of the families of delinquents is as arduous and complex as the study of the schizophrenic families which has taken over a decade. The matter is so complex that we decided that we must finish the work with the schizophrenic families before we could concentrate sufficient attention and energy on the delinquent families. We hope that at some future but still far from proximate date, we shall compare the two series. At present, we can state only that despite some resemblances, we have strong indications that there are profound differences between these types of families—though obviously overlap occurs—an impression also held by Morris and Wynne (1965) who believe they can differentiate these types of families by the analysis of samplings of conjoint family therapy sessions. Though differentiating families of schizophrenic patients from those of sociopathic subjects would mark a major advance in psychopathology, it is not the same as defining what is critical to the genesis of schizophrenia, but simply an assurance that our study findings are not dealing with factors common to families which give rise to offspring with a variety of emotional disturbances.[2]

Alanen and his coworkers (1966) have compared the family environments in which a series of schizophrenic and neurotic patients grew up. The preliminary reports indicate very marked differences and in general substantiate our findings concerning schizophrenic patients.

The project plan provided for one type of control—the comparison of the influences impinging upon the patient with those affecting one or more siblings. Whereas such comparisons do not illuminate differences between families, they can help clarify what factors within a family are critical. The results of the comparisons will be found in the chapter, "Schizophrenic Patients and Their Siblings." Among other findings, the study emphasized the differential effects of family configurations upon male and female offspring and the need to differentiate between the family situations of male and female patients.

---

[2]*We also studied some families which had no member with a known psychiatric or emotional disorder through interviews and psychological testing, including tasks for the family to solve conjointly. These families increased our appreciation of how different these families were from the families with schizophrenic offspring or sociopathic offspring we had been studying but we did not formulate just what these differences were beyond those indicated in this volume.*

Problems of Analysis

The study of seventeen families did not require a dozen years. The understanding of the accumulated data has taken time, study, and re-evaluation of our psychoanalytically oriented concepts of personality development. In particular, we have had to broaden our perspectives concerning the family's influence upon the emergent personalities of its children. Psychiatric theory had been suited to the study of the individual and his intrapsychic problems, or to the interpersonal transactions between two individuals. An approach to the understanding of the dynamics of the family group did not exist in psychiatry, and sociological studies of the family were rarely suited to furthering the understanding of the individual. We have sought conceptualizations that permitted presentation and analysis of the findings: the papers in this volume indicate the searching.

Initially, we hope that we might find some elements or factors within the family that led to schizophrenic development of an offspring. A plethora rather than a paucity of findings of potential significance created the problem. In each aspect of the family life which we examined something was seriously amiss. The parental personalities, the parents' marital interaction, the relationship of each parent to the child, the verbal and nonverbal communication within the family, the essential adherence to parental and childhood generation tasks and roles, the structure of the family as a unit, the parents' gender-linked roles, the transmission of the culture's techniques of adaptation, the relatedness of the family to the community: these and other facets were all seriously disturbed in our judgment—and various authorities who examined the protocols agreed. Further, it was not a matter of statistics, that is to say, finding that more families were disturbed in each area we examined than were not, but rather that each of the families was disturbed in virtually all of these respects—some more and some less in various areas. We examined the material in a variety of ways and sought to isolate core problems.

Now, it is evident that the various factors we studied are interrelated. We examined the individuals, the dyadic relationships, the group transactions. Rightly or wrongly, we eventually ceased looking for a specific etiological factor or factors, and instead asked what must a family provide to assure the integrated development of an offspring. As schizophrenia, no matter what else may be involved, is a gross failure to achieve or maintain a workable personality integration or ego integration, the question we asked seemed worth asking. When we reached an answer—insofar as one was achieved—we found in a somewhat circular fashion that these families did not provide the requisites. (Constellations more specific to the etiology of schizophrenic disorders are presented in this revised edition.)

Our findings led increasingly to a new appreciation of the extent to which the family shapes the personalities of its children and the inordinate complexity of the process by which it does. The family's influence upon the child cannot be considered in terms of maternal love or nurturance, nor through the transfer of a parent's superego to the child, nor the relationship of one or even both parents to the child, nor any other such single factor, even though it alone may be difficult enough to study. These and other elements are in themselves, of course, vitally important but insufficient. The family is a social system and its structure is also important; and it is a subsystem of the larger society holding the responsibility —albeit often unwittingly—for the enculturation and socialization of the new generation. But it has other functions both for parents and the society which influences how the family rears its offspring, and which must also be taken into account (Lidz, 1963a).

Once the question is asked, "What is the family's role in human adaptation and integration?" a new phase of investigation of personality development and maldevelopment opens. It is a phenomenon that is apt to occur whenever something that is so omnipresent that it is taken for granted is questioned and subjected to scientific scrutiny. New doors open and significant questions rush in. Although the topic is considered in many of these papers, and more globally in the book *The Family and Human Adaptation* (Lidz, 1963a), little more than a start has been made. The role of the family in personality development requires, and is first beginning to receive, the intensity of scrutiny such as has been given to the unfolding of the embryo, to the directives that provide for the proper sequence of its nurturance, and to how its environment influences it.

Although the study of the role of the family in the etiology of schizophrenia requires such extensive and detailed knowledge of the functions of the family and of family functioning, the attainment of this knowledge is clearly beyond our capacities. It must await the combined and lengthy studies of many future investigators. Such ignorance has set limits upon our study, but the study has served to focus the spotlight upon this ignorance.

The papers present evidence of our changing, expanding concepts of the family. Herein we focus upon three general areas in assessing the family's influence upon a child. (1) The parental nurturance and how it alters to provide for the changing needs and capacities of the child as he matures, and how the parental nurturance influences the offspring's achievement of autonomy. (2) The family structure and how it influences the structuring of the personality of the child by channeling drives, providing relatively conflict-free areas and roles within the family into which the child can develop and motivating him to do so. We consider the family structure in terms of the parental coalition, the boundaries between the generations, and the parents' maintenance of their gender-linked roles. (3) The transmission of the basic instrumentalities of the culture, including social roles and societal institutions, but particularly a foundation in the society's system of linguistic meanings that the child requires for learning, collaborative interaction and thinking and without which no real ego functioning is possible. We wish, however, to state clearly that these constructs are tentative and not fully satisfactory. We simply consider them an advance, for they provide a means of making more comprehensive analyses of a family's influences upon its offspring, and form a basis for making comparisons between families. They permit us to formulate testable hypotheses, and with the achievement of such hypotheses, the exploratory phase of our investigations comes to a close.

POSTSCRIPT

It will become apparent that we have utilized other parameters in assessing the family's influence on the child. Among these are: the nature and style of the intrafamilial communications; the boundaries between the family and the larger social system; the models provided by parents as objects for identification and primary love objects; the atmosphere of the home, particularly concerning hopefulness, meaningfulness, cooperation, and mutual acceptance.

Introduction to the Revised Edition

It is almost twenty years since we published *Schizophrenia and the Family*, a collection of papers derived from our lengthy and intensive study of seventeen families in which schizophrenic patients grew up. These studies not only had a profound effect on the understanding of schizophrenic disorders and their treatment but also were a major stimulus to the development of family psychotherapy. It now seems appropriate to extend our findings and conceptualizations of how the family milieu is a critical factor in the development of schizophrenic offspring. The material in the original edition was limited to the seventeen families. We were constrained from including material from other families as we recognized it might well distort our findings. The papers, with one or two exceptions, were presented in order of their publication to enable readers to follow the development of our thinking and why, in 1965, we had come to conceptualize schizophrenic conditions as "deficiency disorders" —deficiencies of the family to provide few, if any, of the requisites for the integrated personality development, including cognitive development, for the offspring who became schizophrenic.

Time has passed and we have gained additional knowledge from treating schizophrenic patients, supervising the intensive psychotherapy of numerous patients and their families, and following the course of hundreds of others. We have, helped by the contributions of other investigators, sharpened our understanding of the functions and functioning of families, developed greater understanding of the nature of the thought disorders that are the hallmark of schizophrenic conditions, and developed a more definitive understanding of just what in these disturbed or distorted families may be specific to schizophrenic disorders. We have been aided by our unpublished studies of the families of delinquent offspring and more specifically of the families of upper-middle-class persons addicted to various drugs (Lidz et al. 1976). In this new edition we present most of the original papers in a more meaningful sequence, delete some of the original articles that are not of critical pertinence, and add some of the papers which are not limited to material obtained from the original seventeen families that we have published during the past twenty years. We add comments to the original articles to bring them up to date or reflect our altered views and what others have contributed that is of pertinence. Finally, we present a more tightly knit theory of the etiology of schizophrenic disorders derived from our more recent studies and continuing contemplation of the topic.

The publication of a revised and amplified edition of our book also seems timely in view of the developments in the field. It had long been apparent that strong familial factors exist in the transmission of schizophrenic disorders. The familial incidence had usually been attributed to genetic influences, in part because of the faulty studies of Kallmann (1946) concerning the concordance rates of schizophrenic disorders in monozygotic and dizygotic twins. Studies implicating the family environment were considered a challenge to the concept that schizophrenia was essentially a genetically determined biological disorder. Of course, there need not be a conflict between genetic and environmental influences. One might consider that the intrafamilial difficulties are due, in part, to genetically transmitted emotional disorders or neurochemical vulnerabilities in the patient's relatives. Our own approach was to study that which had never been explored previously; namely, what the family environment might have to do with the etiology of schizophrenic disorders. However, we also noted the extremely high proportion of first- and second-degree relatives who were schizophrenic, paranoid or borderline—even though none of the parents of our patients and very few of the siblings had ever been hospitalized for psychiatric disorders. Our intensive studies of the families had revealed far more serious psychopathology in the families than had genetic studies, which were usually based either on hospital records or a single interview with the relatives. We came to pursue the hypothesis that the intrafamilial problems could explain the origins of the disorder irrespective of genetic factors or some prior neurochemical imbalance.

Several important developments that have drawn attention away from the intrafamilial milieu back to genetic and neurochemical factors in the etiology of schizophrenic disorders now appear to have run their course, or at least the limitations of the expectations they aroused are beginning to be recognized. The discovery of neuroleptic drugs gave rise to a widespread belief that a cure for schizophrenia had been discovered, or, minimally, that the pharmacologists and neurochemists were well on the road to finding a drug that would do for schizophrenia what streptomycin had done for tuberculosis. It has gradually become apparent that the various antipsychotic agents ameliorate symptoms and make it possible for a number of patients to make reasonable social adjustments but they do not cure. Indeed, the restraining and dulling effects of prolonged, heavy medication may impede the chances of recovery; they may contribute to the social breakdown syndrome that previously had been attributed to the stultifying atmosphere of many mental hospitals. Furthermore, prolonged usage of the neuroleptics now available can cause irreversible disfiguring dyskinesic side effects. New knowledge of the chemistry of neurotransmission in the central nervous system together with the belief in the efficacy of the neuroleptics led to the "dopamine hypothesis" and the belief by some leading investigators that the cause of schizophrenic disorders had been uncovered. The hypothesis has now been discarded, just as have countless earlier metabolic and biochemical theories.

On the basis of the utility of various pharmaceutical agents in the treatment of anxiety and depressive states, as well as schizophrenic psychoses, much of psychiatry has returned to an outdated "medical model" and has attempted to isolate clear-cut entities to replace the more diffuse diagnoses formerly utilized by a large proportion of American psychiatrists. A new classification of psychiatric disorders was developed with the hope that symptomatic or phenomenologic diagnoses would guide to specific types of therapy, primarily the use of the proper medication or combination of medications. It is doubtful that the system is succeeding. Lithium therapy, originally considered specific for manic disorders or manic-depressive conditions, is now widely used in the treatment of schizophrenic patients, and, when beneficial, the patients are rediagnosed as schizoaffective. Neuroleptic drugs considered specific for schizophrenic disorders are being used in a variety of agitated states including manic disorders and deliria; antidepressive agents are used to treat phobia, etc. In brief, although pharmaceutical agents have been very helpful in the treatment of schizophrenic disorders, they have also brought about a number of new problems because of their role in the deinstitutionalization programs that are leaving so many schizophrenic patients without care. Whereas the many discoveries concerning the neurochemistry of the brain have brought about a new era in neurophysiology and neuroanatomy, these researches thus far have contributed little to our basic understanding of schizophrenic disorders.

As we have noted, it is difficult to differentiate the genetic and intrafamilial environmental factors in the etiology of schizophrenic disorders. The belief in the importance of genetic factors rested very heavily upon concordance rates in twins. It became apparent, however, that the high concordance rates found by Kallmann for monozygotic twins, eighty percent or higher, in contrast to approximately ten percent for dizygotic twins were due to case finding from hospital records which usually do not note if a patient is a twin unless the co-twin is also schizophrenic. It was also noted that in

Kallmann's and other studies the concordance rate for female dizygotic twins was almost as high as the rate for monozygotic twins; and that Kallmann's report that both twins in five sets of monozygotic twins reared apart became schizophrenic was erroneous. Other, more rigorous studies (Gottesman and Shields, 1975; Kringlen, 1964; Tienari, 1975) provided concordance rates for monozygotic twins ranging from seventeen to fifty percent, the figures depending on the spectrum of disorders diagnosed as schizophrenic, and the manner in which the calculations are made. Without seeking to analyze these studies here, it becomes apparent that the findings of twin studies leave considerable room for environmental factors.

It is theoretically possible to separate genetic and familial environmental factors by the study of the children of schizophrenic parents who were adopted-away at an early age and raised in reasonably stable families; or by the study of relatives of schizophrenic patients who had been adopted at an early age as compared with relatives of a control series of adopted children. Such studies are very difficult to carry out. Heston (1966) found that the adopted-away children of hospitalized schizophrenic mothers became schizophrenic as frequently as children raised by their biological schizophrenic mothers. However, many of the "adopted" children were raised in foster homes or institutions, and the high incidence of criminality in the group would suggest a common genetic etiology for schizophrenia and criminality, a finding no other study justifies. Heston's study may well have been marred by the problem of what sorts of parents adopt a child of a hospitalized schizophrenic mother. Rosenthal et al. (1968, 1971) carried out a more carefully controlled study of the adopted-away children of schizophrenic parents in Denmark and, their claims notwithstanding, failed to replicate Heston's findings (Lidz et al., 1981; Kety et al., 1968, 1975) studied the biological and adoptive relatives of adopted-away children who became schizophrenic and compared them to a series of controls. They, too, claimed definitive evidence of a strong genetic factor in the etiology of schizophrenic disorders and conveyed that their findings indicated that schizophrenia was essentially a genetic disorder and their claims were widely accepted. However, the studies of Lidz and Blatt (1983) indicate that their data and methodologies had not been carefully examined before their results were acclaimed. The studies actually provide little clear-cut evidence of a significant genetic factor in the etiology of schizophrenic disorders.

With the uncertain status of genetic and neurotransmitter aberrations in the etiology of schizophrenic disorders, and with the failure of neuroleptic drugs to live up to expectations, there is renewed reason to believe that the search for a neurophysiological or neurochemical cause of schizophrenic disorders has erroneously preempted the direction of research. We believe that the only consistent finding, and a finding that has been apparent to everyone who has studied the families of schizophrenic patients carefully, is that schizophrenic patients always emerge from severely disturbed and distorted families. It therefore seems timely to refocus attention on this clear-cut lead, following facts rather than theoretical bias and preconceptions. Herein lies the purpose of this new edition of our earlier book.

Our neurophysiologically oriented colleagues have maintained that a focus on the family runs counter to a "biological" or "medical" orientation. We believe, on the contrary, that those who neglect the family milieu have an erroneous concept of human biology. Although the family is a social rather than a biological structure, it is a necessary concomitant of the human biological makeup. The human species is unique for through the acquisition of a brain and neuromuscular system capable of language and the invention and use of tools, it did not have to evolve genetically to adapt to a variety of environments. Instead, it altered environments to suit its physiological limits, and evolved different cultures—each ethnic group developing different sets of techniques of adaptation, including symbolic systems, suited to its physical and social environment. Homo sapiens is the unique species that must assimilate a culture in order to survive, and, among its other tasks, the family is everywhere the major instrument for conveying the culture's techniques to the new generation, a task that it never carries out perfectly, and all too often very inadequately.

* * * * * * * *

In order to delimit the size of the volume, we have deleted the following chapters, which can be found in the first edition:

Therapeutic Considerations Arising from the Intense Symbiotic Needs of Schizophrenic Patients

Casework Interviewing as a Research Technique in a Study of Families of Schizophrenic Patients

The Interaction between Hospital Staff and Families

The Prediction of Family Interaction from a Battery of Projective Tests

Psychiatric Hospitalization as a Family Experience

The Relevance of Family Studies to Psychoanalytic Theory

Family Studies and a Theory of Schizophrenia

Perspectives

In this volume we have included the following articles published since the first edition:

Homosexual Tendencies in the Mothers of Female Schizophrenic Patients

Interrelated Schizophrenic Psychoses in Fraternal Twins

The Influence of Family Studies on the Treatment of Schizophrenia

Family Studies and a Theory of Schizophrenia

Some Observations on the Nature and Value of Psychotherapy with Schizophrenic Patients

and added a new chapter:

Beyond Schizophrenia

I

An Orientation to the Role of the Family in Schizophrenic Disorders

(1957)

The paper in substantially the same form was presented at the Second International Congress of Psychiatry in Zurich, Switzerland in September, 1957, under the title "Schizophrenia and the Family." Although the entire Congress was devoted to the topic of schizophrenic disorders, this was the only plenary presentation that considered the family milieu. It presented our early general orientation that we sharpened as the studies of the families and our study of the problems progressed. At the time, a larger proportion of American psychiatrists held a psychodynamic orientation concerning the nature of schizophrenic disorders than currently, and almost all European psychiatrists held a biological orientation. The paper took a stand against the organicist and genetic orientation prevalent at the meeting, and held that a reorientation of psychiatric thinking concerning the nature of human adaptation was required in order to grasp the nature of schizophrenic disorders. It proceeded to sketch how humans who depend on language and tools must assimilate a culture to survive, which differentiates them from all other organisms, and leads to the expectation that some persons will fail in this essential process and become schizophrenic as one type of anticipated developmental anomaly.

Theodore Lidz: Schizophrenia and the Family. *Psychiatry*, Vol. 21, 1958, pp. 21-27. Copyright © 1958, The William Alanson White Psychiatric Foundation, Inc. This paper, in substantially the same form, was presented at the Plenary Session on the Social Psychiatry of Schizophrenia at the Second International Congress for Psychiatry in Zurich, Switzerland, September, 1957.

The second International Congress for Psychiatry, devoted to the problems of schizophrenia, opened with an address by Manfred Bleuler which emphasized the dilemma created because virtually no two schools of contemporary psychiatry agree concerning the nature and the etiology of schizophrenia. The proceedings of the Congress confirmed his concern, and, in particular, made it clear that some American and English groups who have pursued intensive psychotherapy with schizophrenic patients regard the condition very differently from the way in which Continental psychiatrists view it. As I listened to my European colleagues at the Congress—at times with enthusiasm, and occasionally with astonishment—I became more impressed than ever that the difficulties in achieving areas of agreement do not simply follow upon different conceptualizations of schizophrenia, but stem from the more basic problem of widely divergent views concerning the nature of man and how he becomes an integrated person.

I do not believe that a satisfactory orientation for the study of schizophrenia can be achieved simply by synthesizing all approaches of possible relevance. A major task of the scientist is to seek to simplify through achieving laws or principles that unify and bring order to complex and seemingly contradictory phenomena. The present state of knowledge as indicated by the presentations at the Congress indicated a great need for a reorientation that will bring new insight, clarity, and direction.

I wish, therefore, to try to present a different way of regarding man and schizophrenia. I say "man and schizophrenia" pointedly, to suggest that schizophrenia, instead of being a *process* that has inserted itself into a person and possessed him, depriving him of reason, is rather one of the potential fates to which man is subject in his efforts to find a way of life as an independent person amid the many potential hazards that beset his path from infancy to maturity. Further, I believe that the study of schizophrenic reactions has an importance to the science of man that even transcends the relief of myriads of suffering patients. There are indications that a satisfactory understanding of schizophrenia will be synchronous and synonymous with the opening of vast new insights concerning the integration of man and his emotional homeostasis. Yet I do not consider that all is darkness and mystery even now, if we psychiatrists can but accept some facts that confront us rather than insist upon perceiving only what fits into preconceptions handed to us from our professional forebears.

In the hope of contributing to the clarification of issues involved, I have sought to set down what I consider fundamental to the study of schizophrenia as succinctly as possible and as simply as possible—for I believe that simplicity provides a test of clarity of conceptualization. I do not know if many—or any—of my countrymen will agree with me; it is my orientation, and it may also be theirs. This presentation certainly differs from the tradition generally followed in many other countries, and followed by many in the United States. But when strenuous and persistent efforts, pursued for almost a hundred years, only lead in circles, it is time to raise the question: Are the concepts and premises which guide the search sufficient?

Those who study schizophrenia as a problem of aberrant personality development, or as a type of failure to achieve a workable ego integration, are accustomed to hear that they neglect the brain and problems of physiological homeostasis. I believe, in contrast, that many of my neurologizing and chemically oriented colleagues are the ones who do not properly take into account the human brain and the nature of human physiological integration. The human brain, after all, differs from that of animals and bestows upon man a uniqueness in the way he adapts to his environment. It is just this uniqueness that must be considered in an illness that is specifically human because it involves distortions of the symbolic processes.

I consider that the critical characteristic of schizophrenia lies in the aberrant symbolic processes—in the distortion of perception, meaning, and logic. Such disturbances are usually, and even conventionally, taken to indicate dysfunctions of the brain, although careful studies and even casual observations show that the schizophrenic disorders of mentation differ critically from any produced by known toxic or deficit states, which include degradations of mental capacity along with any distortions. Schizophrenia is considered as a condition in which the patient escapes from an untenable world and his insoluble conflicts by altering his internal representation of reality. Unable to move into the future, and even unable to regain security through regression, he withdraws, and by changing the world autistically and by renouncing the logic of his culture, finds some living space and some semblance of self-esteem. The condition tends to be self-perpetuating because the patient has abandoned testing of the utility of his ideas in terms of their capacity to help him to master his environment or to further his communication with others. Since this self-contained way of life is often precipitated by fear of loss of control of incestuous, homosexual, or homicidal impulses, panic increases the disorganization of the interpersonal disorientation, but restitutive measures to re-establish some way of relating usually follow, because man cannot live in isolation.

Consideration of a few critical problems of human adaptation leads to an expectation that a schizophrenic outcome is a possibility inherent in the developmental process which must be anticipated, rather than a condition to be regarded as incomprehensible or as the manifestation of a disordered cerebral apparatus.

Man's inordinate adaptability depends upon a brain that permits abstract symbolization, including communication and its internal counterpart, mentation. Because he can communicate, man has built up over countless generations ways of doing and reacting which are termed the instrumentalities of his culture. These include his language, his ways of perceiving and thinking, and his mores and sentiments, as well as the actual tools that he has slowly accumulated. These acquisitions, of course, are not transmitted from one generation to the next within the germ plasm. Medicine has sought, by and large, to confine its considerations to the biological unfolding of the genetically endowed man, and the maintenance of his homeostasis in relation to his physical environment. Unless one understands that man is endowed with two heritages, a genetic inheritance and a cultural heritage, one can never understand him or his physiological functioning correctly. Unless the infant grows into and assimilates the instrumentalities of the culture in which he is raised, he will be no more a person than his pre-Stone Age progenitors, and no more capable of living in society. Man has, after all, developed not so much through genetic mutation as through his acquisition over generations of new and more helpful ways of living.

The infant is born with countless potentialities, but virtually no inborn direction; he learns ways of communicating, doing, and thinking through the long years of dependency necessarily provided because, unlike the lower animals, he has been freed of inborn—or instinctive—patterns of adaptation. He must find ways of solving the tasks presented at each stage of growth in order to move on to the next phase with security. By the end of adolescence or in early adult life he is expected to have assimilated patterns of adaptation in a way that is sufficiently integrated for him to leave his parental guidance, to achieve an identity of his own, and to find a role in life and a path into the future. These do not come to him as part of his biological development simply because he has matured physically, but through learning, and particularly through his interaction with the parental models with whom he must identify and whom he introjects. The process can proceed with reasonable smoothness only if these models are not impossible to follow, if they are not mutually contradictory, and if they have transmitted useful ways of living in the society into which the youth must emerge.

There are endless chances for misdirection, confusion, and conflict. The child, who must constantly gain more independence in the normal course of development, is prey to insecurity and anxiety and repeatedly seeks dependency and the security it provides despite its confinements. Repression and the relegation to the unconscious of impulses and wishes unacceptable to real or introjected parental figures are part of a development which requires delimitation and channeling to permit integrated ego growth. Regression, as well as progression, is an essential part of development. The child grows in relation to others, requiring them for his security, and man is never free of his need for others. He is moved to regain the lost union of childhood, even as he grows from it. The need gains compulsive moment because of his sexual drives. He can never be considered as an isolate, for even in isolation he is supported by his bonds to others, which are no less real because they are intangible. The loss of such bonds brings catastrophe. Nor can he be ever understood separated from the culture which he carries within him, for he has grown into it, and it has become incorporated in him.

Indeed, the problems with which psychiatry proper deals can be defined in just such terms—those problems that arise because the infant, biologically endowed with inborn drives but not with inborn direction, must assimilate the instrumentalities of his culture to become a person. Also because this assimilation must be sufficiently harmonious to permit him to function in an integrated way, it depends to a very great extent upon what is incorporated of and from the persons who raise him.

The two paths of maturation, the unfolding of his genetic endowment and the assimilation of the culture, are inextricably intertwined. His biological nature establishes certain imperatives—such as the complete dependency of the infant and the late occurrence of pubescence—and each culture must take these into account. The value systems and meanings inherent in each culture set imperatives also, to insure that each new member will be able to live in and to transmit the culture—imperatives which profoundly affect physiological functioning. Simply illustrated, a Christian's appetite and gastric juices may be stimulated by pork, but a Mohammedan will be repelled by it. In pursuit of contemporary dynamic and analytic principles one cannot afford to forget the essence of Adolf Meyer's psychobiology—that the human being is integrated at a symbolic level, and that the way in which he thinks and feels influences the functioning of the entire organism down to the cellular level.

Now, the very mechanism which permits man's inordinate adaptability contains a major vulnerability, for he depends primarily upon the instrumental utility of his thinking to master the many divergent environments in which he has learned to live in widely differing fashions. Meanings are not inborn, nor is man endowed with an innate system of logic. The brain permits thinking, but it does not guarantee its rationality. Indeed, what is considered rational varies with time and place, as history has amply demonstrated. Meanings develop through communication with others and from sorting out life's experiences, but perceptions and meanings alter in the service of emotional needs, as well as in the service of learning a utilitarian adaptation to the environment. They alter not only in the attempt to maintain a satisfactory image of oneself but also a satisfactory image of the persons who are essential to one's security. When a person's acceptability to himself and others is threatened, many self-deceptions can arise to ward off anxiety. After all, such nonperceptions or self-deceptions are what are referred to as the mechanisms of defense. When these defenses are of no avail, when essential expectations are mutually conflicting, when the path into the future is barred, and even regression is blocked because the persons upon whom one would depend cannot be trusted, there is still a way. One can simply alter his perception of his own needs and motivations and those of others. He can abandon causal logic, change the meanings of events, retreat to the period of childhood when reality gave way before the fantasy of his wish, and regain a type of omnipotence and self-sufficiency. In short, he can become schizophrenic. Perhaps not everyone can resort to such devices;

they may only be open to those who have been poorly grounded in reality and who have actually been trained in irrational ways in their childhood. Indeed, this path is so clearly open to man, and so often used in culturally approved and therefore nondelusional ways, that if this analysis of man's adaptability is even approximately correct and if investigators did not know of a syndrome such as schizophrenia, they would have to search for it, as an anticipated anomaly of the developmental processes.

With this general orientation it has been natural to turn to the careful study of the family environment in which the patient grows up in a search for determinants of schizophrenic reactions. The family provides the primary schooling in social living; the person's experience in all other group and interpersonal interactions rests upon the foundations constructed within the family. Knowingly or unknowingly the family has the task of transmitting the basic instrumentalities of the culture to the offspring, including ways of reasoning and reacting emotionally, and of communicating verbally and empathically. It usually provides the models for identification which will be introjected, and the models of love objects that will pattern emotional relationships.

While the family is not all, and is not the only influence upon ego development, it provides the most consistent—or consistently inconsistent—set of influences impinging upon the maturing child. The emphasis upon the intrafamilial object relationships is not inconsistent with other analytic or dynamic approaches. It includes an interest in causes of ego weakness, of blurring of ego boundaries, of narcissistic withdrawal after object loss, of regression to infantile omnipotence and security, of withdrawal to a world free from the confines of reality testing, and so forth. However, it is considered that the ego develops in relation to objects—particularly to the parental figures—and in a world of the family created largely by the interaction of the parental figures.

Eventually a research group undertook intensive explorations of the lives of the families in which schizophrenic patients were raised. The study utilized multiple techniques in an effort to re-create the personalities, the dynamics, and the atmosphere of these family groups. I shall not attempt to review the findings here; they were unexpectedly striking. Not one family of a schizophrenic patient was found to be reasonably well integrated, although a few had difficulties which came to light only after many months of investigation.

Such studies cannot be confined to the interaction between a parent and the schizophrenic offspring. The family is a true small group with an organic life and unity of its own, and with a set of imperative functions which it must fulfill in order to raise a new generation. Such imperatives have scarcely been designated or studied as yet. The family provides a shelter for its members within and against the remainder of society. The welfare of the family, more than of any other group, requires that each member give an unspecified degree of precedence to the needs of the family above his own needs and those of outsiders. The actions of any one member affect all, producing reaction and counteraction. Roles are assigned, according to generation and sex, which cannot be violated without distorting the emergent personalities. Roles also develop to fit the emotional needs of the members, and these roles must relate reciprocally for the entire group, or leave one or several members in a state of imbalance requiring pathological defenses.

Stated in too summary a fashion, the family is viewed as a shaping force upon the offspring's personality. The family provides the constitutional basis for the personality through heredity, and constantly contributes to it by example, by teaching, and by the interaction of its members as a social unit; within this unit the child is prepared for existence in relation to other persons and social groups.

Thus it becomes apparent that a mother's attitude toward a child is not simply a reflection of her capacities to mother him, but also, for example, of her attitude toward the marriage. The father exerts direct and indirect influences upon her ability to mother, as well as upon the children. Yet we find in our studies that all of the marriages upon which these family structures rest are gravely disturbed. There is either a schismatic conflict between the parents that divides the family into two camps and that results in each spouse's destroying the worth of the other, or the family is distorted by the passive acceptance of the serious psychopathology of the dominant spouse by the other, with masking of the serious problems that arise, creating an aberrant environment that confuses the child.

It is difficult to discuss the more subtle influences affecting the child in such families, for it would require neglect of the very gross problems that are surprisingly aberrant to anyone who has not become involved in such studies. In each of these families at least one parent suffers from serious and crippling psychopathology. Even though in this series, because of a bias in selection, no parent had ever been in a mental hospital, in contrast to the many genetic studies that may be cited, minimally 60 per cent of the patients had at least one parent who was an ambulatory schizophrenic or was clearly paranoid. Still others were chronic though unadmitted severe alcoholics, or severe obsessives, and some were extremely passive-dependent—indeed "children" of their spouses and not "parents." The fathers were as pathological as the mothers, and often the more serious disturbing influence in the family. I cannot now go into the complex dynamics of the distorted relationships and the very faulty models for identification in these families, or how these disturbances, which help to determine the nature of specific symptomatology, are reflected in the way the offspring experience the world. Suffice it to say that these families in many ways provide training in irrationality. I wish to remark somewhat parenthetically, in response to a question raised repeatedly, that the problem of why one child among several in a family becomes schizophrenic does not appear to be insurmountable when one grasps the dynamics of role relationships within the family, the vicissitudes of the family, and the different stresses linked to being a member of one sex or the other in the given family.

Many persons have made contributions from clinical observations, and our particular group is no longer the only
one pursuing systematic studies in this area.[1] In contrast to
the difficulties of communicating in many areas at the International Congress, it was noteworthy that at the session
concerned with the family environment, people from seven
or eight countries, speaking in three languages, found common ground and meaningful exchange, for they were dealing
with tangible clinical findings, to which theory and specula-
tion were secondary. Even though the family varies from one
country to another, the findings seemed basically similar
from Israel to the United States, and from Greece to Finland.
There are no other such consistent findings of potential significance to the etiology of schizophrenia—whether interpreted genetically or environmentally—or findings which
promise to give so much structure and meaning to the understanding of what the schizophrenic patient is experiencing. True, the pursuit of such leads requires that the
psychiatrist become familiar with sociology, anthropology,
and genetics, as well as psychiatry, rather than with biochem-
istry and neuropathology, but it seems incumbent to follow
where facts lead rather than to cling to past training and
predispositions. Now I should say that of course there are
areas concerning schizophrenia that are best studied through
scrutiny of the central nervous system or the metabolic processes, or through animal experimentation. One takes exception to such studies only when they seek to simplify problems
concerning human behavior by confining attention to a small
segment of the field, hoping thus to avoid the complexities
that arise in considering human problems in terms of problems in living.

The studies of family environment to which I have referred
have had many practical effects upon our therapeutic efforts—but this forms a topic in itself. The support and understanding offered these parents has led to striking changes

[1]See, for example, Alanen (1958); Bowen et al. (1957); Delay et al. (1957); Wynne
et al. (1957).

in the marital relationship and in the attitudes toward the children. At times the parents have benefited more than the patients, but in other cases, changes in the parents have been followed by striking improvement in the patients. Communication between therapist and patient is fostered, for the meaning of what the patient seeks to communicate and what he seeks still to conceal may become apparent from knowledge of the family life and troubles. Perhaps, however, the essence of the benefit lies in the tangible meaning which the patients' behavior and symptoms take on, so that work with them becomes less evanescent and more capable of being translated into terms of concrete interpersonal difficulties with which both patient and therapist can work.

After all, the psychiatrist who wishes to learn about schizophrenia can be taught more by the patient than by laboratory samples of him. The therapist who can respect his patient as a person and can listen and dare to hear will eventually gain insights which make it an exciting privilege to work with schizophrenic patients. A Dadaist author whose identity I do not know said that to be insane is to forsake reason—to forsake reason but not truth, for the madman often speaks the truth while the sane hold their tongues.[2] And parents and siblings also have much to tell—sometimes including uncanny insights—as is shown by the profound communications concerning schizophrenia that have been offered by authors, and particularly by playwrights, who have had schizophrenic siblings.

Our family studies continue. I have sought to offer the reasons, both theoretical and empirical. We do not think that we have begun to solve the problems of schizophrenia—but we constantly find tangible and intriguing new leads to follow, and no longer feel that we grope in the dark in hopes of somehow stumbling onto the path. We begin to think that we see the path to follow through the labyrinth; at times we dare to hope—in our dreams—that we have grasped Ariadne's thread. But the way is long and help is needed.

[2]Quoted by Henry Miller in *Tropic of Capricorn*. Paris: Obelisk Press, 1956, p. 307.

Postscript

The paper, written five years into our study when we were struggling to formulate ways of organizing the material we were uncovering, presents conceptualizations that gained form and constancy as the study progressed and moved toward a clearly transactional systems orientation. As will become apparent, our concepts of what was pertinent to the etiology of schizophrenia broadened to encompass the global deficits of these families, before it then narrowed down to focus on fairly specific family configurations that are likely to produce schizophrenic offspring.

The paper states "perhaps the path to become schizophrenic may only be open to those who have been poorly grounded in reality and have actually been trained in irrational ways in their childhood." Our chapter (VII) on "The Transmission of Irrationality," Bateson and Jackson's concept of the "double-bind" (Bateson et al., 1956), and Wynne and Singer's (1963a, 1963b; Singer and Wynne, 1965a, 1965b) documentation of the amorphous and fragmented styles of thinking pursue this concept. However, it is possible that only persons with some still undetermined neurophysiologic endowment: for example, reticular activating systems with low thresholds to stimuli, are likely to become schizophrenic. The threshold need not lie outside the normal distribution curve, but toward the lower limit of the normal curve. Such vulnerability may or may not depend upon a specific genetic anomaly. It should be realized that category formation also serves to filter out extraneous stimuli, both by maintaining a focus on what is under consideration and by repressing thoughts and associations that lie between categories, as will be discussed in Chapters XVI and XIX.

II

The Family Environment of Schizophrenic Patients

(1942)

The following study was not part of the research carried out at Yale, but a preliminary investigation based on records of patients admitted consecutively to the Henry Phipps Psychiatric Clinic. The authors had been comparing the first fifty schizophrenic patients treated with insulin shock therapy with the last fifty patients treated prior to the institution of insulin therapy (there was little difference in outcome), and were struck by the large numbers of schizophrenic patients who had been deprived of a parent before the end of adolescence, as well as the frequency of serious intrafamilial problems. The observations fused with the impression gained from the families of patients they had been treating. The study was carried out to ascertain if the clinical impression was warranted. The actual survey was made in 1941, but the analysis of the data could not be completed until 1946 because of World War II.

The material demonstrates why the investigators were led to believe that an intensive study of the families of schizophrenic patients was imperative.

It was noted during the treatment of a small series of schizophrenic patients that they had frequently been deprived of at least one parental figure early in life; and also that the parental home was usually markedly unstable, torn by family schisms and constant emotional turmoil, and frequently pat-

Ruth Wilmanns Lidz and Theodore Lidz: The Family Environment of Schizophrenic Patients. *American Journal of Psychiatry*, Vol. 106, 1949, pp. 332-345. Copyright © 1949, American Psychiatric Association.

terned according to the whims of grossly eccentric and abnormal personalities. This study, a survey of fifty case histories in the records of the Henry Phipps Psychiatric Clinic, was then undertaken to evaluate the frequency with which broken homes or seriously disturbed family environments had been noted in those histories of schizophrenic patients.

The influence of the total family life upon schizophrenic patients has been considered in at least two books. Terry and Rennie (1938) emphasized the role of the family along with other features in the developmental process. They noted that difficulties between parents or the deprivation of a parent seemed to contribute to the insecurity of the children, and that a large number of patients in their study had been in daily contact with psychotic, eccentric, or unstable parents. They stated, "It is impossible to study this material without being impressed by the importance of the family constellations and of the effect of the maladjustments within the family in contributing to the growing timidities and insecurity of the children." Pollock, Malzburg, and Fuller (1939) in their statistical search for hereditary or environmental factors in the causation of dementia praecox and manic-depressive psychoses found, among the most striking contrasts between the two groups, "that the social life of the parents [of schizophrenic patients] was singularly restricted during the childhood of the patients; [and] that there was a certain instability of the home indicated by the absence of one or both parents during the formative years."

The early family environment is commonly accepted as a critical force in personality development both normal and abnormal. Numerous other factors, some of which may be of shattering intensity, may disturb the process of personality development, but few can be as long-lasting and as pervasive as the intrafamilial relationships. Here the basic attitudes toward later interpersonal relationships are established: the formation of the projective systems by which the individual perceives the world is begun. It was considered probable, on the basis of preliminary impressions, that there might be, in general, a relationship between the severity of the personality maladjustment and the degree of the family maladjustment, and that schizophrenic patients would be found to have emerged from early family environments that were very seriously disturbed.

The material in this survey was not expected to yield detailed information with which one could trace in detail how the dynamics of the family configuration influenced the patient's personality development because these case records were compiled by different psychiatrists with differing interests. It had the advantage of being material gathered prior to the investigation, free from the bias of the investigators. As the case histories in the Henry Phipps Psychiatric Clinic usually contain reasonably detailed information concerning the parental home, most offer sufficient data to permit judgment as to the character of the family setting. This study was undertaken as a gross survey of the topic to check preliminary impressions.

METHODOLOGY

The case records of fifty schizophrenic patients, in whom the psychosis had become manifest prior to the age of twenty-one, consecutively admitted to the clinic, were utilized for the study. The series was limited to patients who were youthful at the time of onset of the psychosis because their case records contained more information concerning the family environment than did records of older patients. The age limit of twenty-one was arbitrarily adopted to eliminate the necessity of further selection of records. No record was discarded other than those of a few patients who left the clinic within a few days of admission and before the admission work-up could be completed.

The fifty cases included twenty-seven males and twenty-three females. Subdivision of the data by sex did not reveal any significant or constant differences. No subclassification of schizophrenia has been made for a variety of reasons, but primarily because little value is placed upon such differentiation, particularly in youthful patients.

The case records were sifted for all information pertinent to the background afforded the patient by the family. Charts were constructed (see Chart 1) which permitted a rapid survey of the significant factors in each case, and statistical data were compiled. The topics selected for tabulation were limited to influences which seemed significant and which, when placed in apposition, would afford an impression of the background furnished by the home. Only such material as could be estimated with a fair degree of reliability was utilized. Therefore, attention was focused upon objective situations in the background of the patient rather than upon the personal reactions to situations; and single traumatic incidents as well as minor disturbances in the family life were disregarded even though they may have exercised considerable influence upon the patient's development. In particular, the obsessive, oversolicitous patterns of mothers were not taken into special consideration unless the mother's behavior reached bizarre extremes.

The division of the material into headings is obviously arbitrary, and data could often have been placed in a different column equally well. For example, instabilities of parents may be most clearly manifest in peculiar ways of raising a child, or in marital incompatibility due to peculiar choice of a mate, or in the reactive behavior of the marital partner. The loss of a parent may be due to emotional instability (suicide or divorce) but may have the serious result of changing the mode of raising of the patient. However, it is believed that the headings will serve to indicate the presence of one or several chronic conditions which adversely affected the patient. The headings utilized are as follows:

1. *Deprivation of a Parent* prior to the nineteenth birthday. The arbitrary age limit was selected as an age at which most children have gained a reasonable degree of independence from the parents. The frequency of the loss of a parent had been apparent from a preliminary survey of the material.

2. *Chronic Instability of a Parent or Foster Parent.*—Occasional and lesser neurotic disturbances and mild to moderate alcoholism have largely been disregarded, and only serious and long-standing personality disorders which clearly affected other members of the family are included.

3. *Chronic Hostility or Serious Friction Between Parents.*—The more usual degrees of friction between married couples have been overlooked in favor of estimating the general compatibility of the parents.

4. *Serious Deviations from Cultural Norms in Child Rearing.*—The topic is closely related to the stability of the parents, particularly the mother, but in some cases the eccentric methods of raising the patient were most clear-cut, and in other cases unusual circumstances led to unusual means of raising the patient. The topic deals only with clear-cut deviations from the social norm or eccentricities, such as treating a boy as a girl; extreme forms of obsessive oversolicitude or rejection; inculcation of repugnance to any contact with the opposite sex, etc. While deviations of early habit training and various more subtle influences of parents are considered of great significance, they could rarely be assayed from the case histories and are not considered in the charts.

5. *Mental Illness in the Family Tree.*—While not a real concern of this study, the data are included both to permit a general impression of the stability of the families and to allow comparison with environmental data. The information is considered reasonably accurate as one or more relatives were always questioned concerning mental illness in the family.

All patients included in the study were manifestly psychotic prior to the age of twenty-one. The ages given in the charts are the ages at the time of admission to the clinic, rather than an attempt to estimate the precise time of onset of the psychosis, which is often difficult in youthful schizophrenic patients.

The sequence in which the cases are listed in Chart 1 follows a general pattern though a precise arrangement is not possible because of the overlapping of the variables involved:

1. Patients who had been deprived of a parent by death (cases 1-14) starting with the six who also had a psychotic parent.

2. Patients whose parents had been divorced or separated (cases 15-20).

3. Patients whose parents had been seriously incompatible (cases 21-27).

4. Patients whose homes were marred by fairly serious incompatibility, an unfriendly atmosphere, or unusual modes of raising the patient (cases 28-35).

5. Patients not previously listed who had a psychotic parent (cases 36-38).

6. Cases in which insufficient information for a sound evaluation of the home situation could be gained from the histories (cases 39-45) including three in which there was fairly good evidence that the home was unfavorable to normal development (cases 39-41).

7. Cases whose family environment, despite some aberrations of parents or marital difficulties, appears from the records to have been adequate or good (cases 46-50).

ILLUSTRATIVE CASE ABSTRACTS

To enable the reader to judge how the material was evaluated and also to grasp how the various chronic disturbances in the family life impeded the maturation of the patient, the environments afforded by the families of ten patients are presented in brief form.[1] These ten abstracts are unselected, though not including any of the six cases in which insufficient data were available to form evaluations. Two of the ten are examples of relatively satisfactory homes. Although selected at random, the ten cases are typical of the fifty, though not including some in which the family environment seemed most disorganized.

---

[1]Three case abstracts presented here were not included in the original publication.

CASE 1. W. O. is a nineteen-year-old girl, the second of four siblings whose father suicided when she was fifteen. The mother had suffered a "nervous breakdown" after bearing the oldest child and had continued to worry and be obsessively apprehensive, particularly concerning her daughters, whom she had made excessively dependent upon her. The sisters aged twenty-three and thirteen, and the brother aged eighteen, are reputedly stable.

The family was well to do and the home life relatively congenial until the patient was ten. The children were educated in fashionable private schools and became accustomed to luxury. Then the father lost his money and became depressed, sullen, and alcoholic. His repeated ventures to start anew failed. The home became gloomy, filled with recrimination, and disturbed by the father's habitual drunkenness. The children shifted to public schools and later took stenographic positions.

When fifteen years old, the patient became severely upset when, alone in the house, she found her father's body. Little is known of the subsequent family life. The children were tied to the mother who impressed the psychiatrists as a silly, ineffectual person.

Comment.—The father ceased to be an effective parent five years before his suicide, leaving the burden of the family to the ineffectual, obsessive mother. The home was morbid during the patient's adolescence.

CASE 8. B. R. is a nineteen-year-old youth, handicapped by a high degree of bilateral deafness, whose father died when he was four. The vigorous mother sought to dominate the lives of the children of whom she was very demanding. A sister, aged twenty-five, had married and left home as soon as possible. The brother, aged twenty-two, openly revolted and secretly married at nineteen, but the mother had the marriage annulled.

The father had been a successful attorney, but the modest income he left dwindled with the years. The older children were educated mainly in private schools, whereas the patient had to walk four miles to high school to save carfare. Money was a prime concern and a source of constant discord. The brother openly expressed hope that the mother would die and leave him his inheritance. He constantly demanded money to entertain his fiancée, and when refused, stole articles from the home and pawned them. The brother was antagonistic to the patient, stressing his faults to gain preference with the mother. The home was frequently in turmoil with open conflict and physical strife between the brothers. The mother drew the handicapped patient to her, confiding her unhappiness to him, but gave him little in the face of the brother's demands. B. R. became dependent upon his mother because of his deafness but deeply resented her domination. He tried to mimic his brother's rebelliousness by running around with girls whom his mother disliked. His attempts were halfhearted and he accepted his mother's expectation that he would support her after completing school. Deafness made it difficult to secure a position. He suffered serious guilt over his ambivalence toward his mother.

Comment.—The father's guidance ceased at an early age. The handicapped patient became extremely dependent upon his demanding mother whose domination he resented. He became guilty when unable and rather unwilling to live up to the demands placed upon him. As the youngest he felt most heavily the burden imposed by the diminishing income and the increasingly unpleasant atmosphere.

CASE 9. F. A. is a twenty-year-old youth whose mother died when he was a year old. The patient and his six-year-old sister were taken and raised by a paternal aunt, while a three-year-old brother remained with the father. F. A. rarely ever saw his father and brother, and little of the sister after he was twelve. When his aunt died when he was thirteen, he refused to join his father who had by then married an ill-tempered woman. Instead he went to a boarding school where another maiden aunt was employed, partially supporting himself by working after school. At sixteen he was sent to a more exclusive school which his father and brother had attended. Both aunts had "spoiled" him, expecting and demanding little, catering to his desires. An attack of rheumatic fever at eight had confined him to bed for six months and thereafter prevented athletic activities. When F. A. first spent several months with the father when sixteen, he was openly hostile. He felt upon realistic grounds that his father had discriminated against him in favor of his brother, withholding similar advantages. Both the sister and brother emphasized the difference in upbringing, believing that the patient, raised by maiden aunts, was not as capable as they in combating obstacles and stating that the father had obviously rejected the patient.

Comment.—Paternal guidance was singularly lacking even though it was the mother who had died. The home life afforded by the foster parent was disrupted by her death when the patient was adolescent. The father's rejection engendered serious hostility.

CASE 10. C. H. is an eighteen-year-old youth whose life and environment differed markedly from those of his siblings because of his severe asthma. Little is recorded concerning the home life, probably because the patient spent little time there. When C. H. was eight the family moved to the country because of the father's tuberculosis but as the climate appeared to aggravate the patient's asthma, he was sent to boarding school. Thereafter the patient was rarely at home, even during summer vacations. The father, who died when the patient was thirteen, came from a prominent family and had been a successful engineer. He was a very rigid man, incapable of compromise, who expected everyone to do precisely what was right. The mother had been a trained nurse. She tended to be oversolicitous and, even though the patient was away from home, he depended upon her for affection and help. The family, proud of its ancestors, expected the patient as the only male descendant to preserve the tradition of achievement. C. H. expected to become a famous statesman but blamed his lack of scholastic prowess upon his asthma. His limited intellectual endowment was apparent to his teachers, who finally advised that he abandon hope of a college education.

Comment.—There was little home life for this patient after the age of eight, and the father died when he was thirteen. High rigid standards were established but little guidance given. The high expectations of the family were not tempered by recognition of his intellectual limitation and physical handicap.

CASE 20. M. A. is a sixteen-year-old youth whose conception forced the parents to marry. Both parents had immigrated from Germany during adolescence. They separated shortly after the patient's birth, reunited after a year, but there were several subsequent separations. There was little pretense of family life and no companionship between the parents, who both stated that they remained together only for the sake of the son. The father consorted regularly with prostitutes with the wife's knowledge. He is a milkman who provided for the patient financially but never showed any interest in him. The mother, a waitress in an ice cream parlor, is considered a shallow, flighty person who tried to do her best but had no understanding of her brilliant, scholarly son.

Comment.—No information was obtained from the catatonic patient during the brief hospital stay. It is evident that the patient had a father in name only, and very little home life.

CASE 21. B. I., a fourteen-year-old Jewish boy, had a sister six years his junior. Both parents were raised and educated in Russia. They led an active social life until they married, bought a grocery store, and isolated themselves from outside companionship. The patient was born the following year and then, according to the family physician, "they concentrated all their efforts on cramming knowledge into the boy. They coaxed and encouraged him in all possible ways to skip grades, make high marks, and to keep ahead of his classmates, without any apparent opportunity for relaxation for themselves or for the boy. For fourteen years they might just as well have lived 500 miles from the city." B. I. completed high school at thirteen with the highest grades in his city, but he was eccentric, poorly socialized, and puzzled.

The parents' lives were embittered as well as narrowed. Constant strife prevailed in the rooms behind the store in which they lived. The father was an uncouth man with a terrible temper despite an unusual education for a man of his occupation. He had left home at an early age because he could not get along with his father and stepmother. At fifteen he had not talked for a year because he had heard it would improve his singing. When the patient was ten the father was depressed following financial reverses. He began to grow paranoically suspicious of his wife's fidelity. He became frenzied when the patient brought a gentile friend into the home, and once threw both his son and wife out of the home because he found the patient in the company of a gentile. The mother, though kindly, pushed the boy, centering her life about her hopes for a genius son. She confided her unhappiness to the patient and sought his help. When the patient was thirteen she left her husband but, unable to remain away from the children, begged the boy to threaten suicide unless the father brought her back home. B. I. was the hub around which the quarrels revolved. The mother, extremely orthodox, was raising him to be a rabbi, whereas the atheist father belittled all religious belief and filled the boy with poorly digested philosophical concepts. The patient resented his parents but felt bound to them by their efforts to make him great. The mother made a suicidal attempt when the son was hospitalized and the father became seriously depressed.

Comment.—The home, shut off from social relations, was filled with conflict, suspicion, and confused thinking. The unstable parents drove the boy to excel but pushed in opposite directions. The patient found no acceptable pattern in the home and came to have extremely ambivalent feelings toward both parents, who were making each other and the patient miserable.

CASE 24. W. I. is a sixteen-year-old girl who grew up in a home with complicated interrelationships. The second of three children and the older daughter, she appeared to be the favorite of both parents. However, the family lived in the home of the divorced paternal grandmother, a fiery-tempered woman with a whip for a tongue who hated her daughter-in-law and the patient. She had opposed the son's marriage as she had made him promise to remain single and support her. The patient, as the father's favorite, became the target of her enmity. She nagged and belittled the child constantly.

The father, a heavy drinker with a violent temper, was paranoically jealous of his wife. He was afraid to sleep alone, and insisted that both the wife and the patient sleep in the room with him. When they were away the butler had to sleep in the room. He was inconsistent with all of the children, whipping them for trivialities and indulging them foolishly. The mother, supposedly of a relatively even disposition prior to the marriage, was unable to control herself when her husband and his mother lost their tempers, and violent quarrels took place almost every day.

W. I. was indoctrinated by her father from an early age with the idea that petting and pregnancy were revolting. He insisted that he would never permit her to go with boys. Her first parties created violent scenes. The father would whip her when she returned home a few minutes late, and threatened to kill the mother if the patient became pregnant. The girl had been attached to her father until this dissension started. She asked to be sent to boarding school and gained her ends with the mother's help. However, just before she was to leave, the mother and the patient learned that the father had been keeping a mistress for years. Divorce proceedings were started but were discontinued because of the father's threats.

Comment.—The home was inordinately filled with enmity, instability, and contradictory behavior. The patient, as the favorite of the father, was more subject to the family conflicts. The father's demands upon her and the mother in regard to sexual behavior were suddenly contrasted with his own infidelity.

CASE 35. S. I., a nineteen-year-old college girl, was born fourteen years after her sister and twenty-two years after her half-sister. The parents were both forty-two at the time, and the pregnancy continued only after abortifacients had failed and several doctors had refused to perform an abortion. The mother hid the pregnancy which led to gossip that the patient was the illegitimate child of the half-sister. The parents took no interest in the unwanted child and left her to the care of an elderly divorced aunt who lived in the home. The aunt hated the patient's mother, and taught S. I. to hate her by informing her at an early age of the attempts at abortion and the gossip about her birth. The child was never permitted to play with other children but was taken to teas at which elderly ladies gossiped. The aunt taught the child to spy upon the mother, read her mail, and report everything she heard. The aunt and the mother were openly hostile, at times having physical encounters. The aunt died when the patient was thirteen.

The family was wealthy and the parents, who led an active social life, preferred to let the patient have her way rather than be bothered. She received neither affection nor training. The family physician reported that she had not been taught to brush her teeth until the age of fifteen. Teachers, years later, recalled her as a child who had been pathetically neglected. Both the family physician and the teachers tried to intervene, but the mother only became insulted when it was suggested that the child was not being raised properly.

S. I. never had a friend during childhood, and her isolation was increased by slight lameness, the result of osteomyelitis, improperly treated because the mother had removed the patient from the hospital as she was not eating well.

Relatively little is known about the parents, but the mother was obviously a peculiar person who had been suffering from hyperthyroidism for years but refused operation. She insisted, when giving the anamnesis, that she knew nothing of sex, even though she had three children. She had placed great emphasis upon shielding S. I. from sexual contact by refusing to permit her out of the house after 10 P.M., but evidently paid no attention when the girl, at the onset of her overt psychosis, invited dozens of undesirable men into the home who broke furniture, stole, and took turns at having sexual relations with the patient.

Comment.—The rejection of the patient started prior to birth and continued to an unusual degree. The only guidance came from the unwholesome relationship with the aunt whose death when the patient was adolescent left her completely friendless. Animosity toward the parents was not only reactive but actually fostered by the aunt.

CASE 47. Z. A. is a fifteen-year-old boy, the oldest of four children. The father was an instructor in a preparatory school who treated the boy as an equal, offering little guidance. The mother dominated the home, but seemed to be a rather good-natured woman. She had suffered from emotional difficulties during adolescence and revolted against the socialite home by becoming a trained nurse. After each of her four pregnancies she had been overactive, and at other times there had been periods of mild depression.

The home life was free of friction and the parents devoted considerable time to the children without being unduly oversolicitous. The patient's preoccupation with his relationship to his parents seemed more the result of specific interpersonal difficulties rather than a reflection of an unstable home. He resented the lack of guidance by the father, and the fact that the home was indistinguishably merged with the school that he attended.

Comment.—Although the mother suffered from moderate manic-depressive mood swings, she appeared to have been a relatively adequate parent. For the purposes of this study the family environment is considered to have been good, even though difficulties in the father-son relationship existed.

CASE 48. N. I. is the twenty-year-old, only daughter of a college professor. According to both parents, and from information given by close friends, the parents were devoted to each other, and the home life was congenial. The parents were sociable, kindly persons who endeavored to guide their child sensibly. Difficulties for the patient arose from the father's position. She had been much attached to him during early childhood and paid little attention to the mother. As she grew up the father became prominent and had less and less time to devote to his daughter. N. I. resented the fact that she was only known as her father's daughter and that great expectations were held for her by the college community. At adolescence she became antagonistic toward her father and grew closer to the mother.

A factor difficult to assay was the burden of mental illness in the mother's family. She learned of the suicides of her grandfather and uncle with great shame. A schizophrenic aunt lived with the family until committed when the patient was seven. N. I. expressed the opinion in childhood that it was only a matter of time until she would become insane like the aunt.

The psychotic material all centered about the family relationships. The patient insisted that she was the illegitimate daughter of an uncle; and that her father abused the mother.

Comment.—Although the existence of intrafamilial difficulties might be assumed from the patient's delusional beliefs, the difficulties do not appear to have arisen from overt difficulties within the home or from gross eccentricities of the parents. The role of the schizophrenic aunt in the patient's development could not be estimated. For the purposes of this study the family environment is considered adequate.

The ten cases which have been abstracted are fairly typical of the entire group. Eight of the ten grew up amidst family relationships which were overtly disturbed and obviously deleterious to integrated personality development. Four had lost a parent during childhood: two of these (F. A. and C. H.) had little parental guidance and no consistent home life thereafter, one under circumstances that fostered deep resentment toward the remaining parent; and the other two lived in homes which became increasingly unpleasant. Two patients (M. A. and S. I.) had homes in name only, having been unwanted and rejected children in uncongenial homes. Two (B. I. and W. I.) had been favorite children, but in homes marred by constant strife which focused about them, insecure because of repeated threats of separation fostered by the fathers' paranoid tendencies. The remaining two patients came from homes which were considered reasonably amicable and constant, even though some sources of insecurity were found. The scrutiny of these synopses permits an understanding of the type of data from which the chart was constructed, the manner in which the material was evaluated, and an impression of how the more abstract data in the chart fit together.

ANALYSIS OF THE CHART

1. *Loss of a parent.*—Data were available for all cases. Fourteen patients had lost a parent by death, and an additional six had lost a parent from the home environment by divorce or separation before the patient was nineteen. Thus, 40 per cent had been deprived of at least one parent. Pollock et al. (1939) reported a comparable figure (37.7%) in their statistical survey of 175 schizophrenic patients. As this item could be readily checked in the case records of older patients, fifty histories of schizophrenic patients whose psychosis had become manifest after the age of twenty-one were reviewed, and it was found that 36 per cent had been deprived of at least one parent prior to their nineteenth birthday. A control survey on Phipps Clinic case records of fifty psychotically depressed patients gave a figure of 20 per cent. Pollock et al. (1939) reported 16.7 per cent in a series of 155 manic-depressive patients. Of sixty-nine medical students, twelve or 17.4 per cent had been deprived of a parent during the same age period.

These figures are highly significant, and this problem has therefore been subjected to closer scrutiny. Although it seemed reasonable to assume that the loss of a parent deprived the child of necessary guidance or might have produced unfavorable home conditions, it did not seem plausible that such deprivation could in itself bear a direct relationship to the production of schizophrenic reactions. Indeed, the possible implication of these figures was a principal reason for undertaking this study. Analysis of the data alters the emphasis. Four, and possibly five, patients had lost a parent because the parent was psychotic and committed suicide. In addition, the divorce or separation of parents was largely due to the psychotic or grossly unstable behavior of at least one parent in five of the six cases. Thus the loss of a parent in nine and perhaps ten of the twenty cases was due to the serious emotional instability of a parent.

In the control groups only one parent of a depressive patient had suicided, and none of the parents had been permanently separated. Of the medical students, three had lost a parent through permanent separation, but it is not known if any of these had been psychotic or grossly unstable.

The striking difference between the schizophrenic group and the control groups is seen to be largely a result of the psychotic or severely unstable behavior of parents which led to suicide or permanent separation.

2. *Incompatibility of Parents.*—Information adequate to form a definite impression was available in thirty-three cases. As has been noted, incompatibility led to divorce or separation (permanent or repetitive) in seven cases. An additional seven sets of parents had been seriously incompatible (cases 21-27). Four more patients had parents who were moderately but clearly incompatible, while the marriage in two other instances was considered obviously uncongenial. Thus, of the thirty-three cases in which sufficient information was available for judgment, twenty or 61 per cent had homes that had been marked by strife. Actually only seven of the thirty-three patients had the benefit of being raised by congenial parents as four had lost a parent by death, and two had been raised in homes kept free of strife only because the father had given in and pampered the eccentric and dominating mother.

Of the remaining seventeen marriages concerning which information was deemed inadequate to judge the compatibility, six had been terminated by the death of one partner.

Although none of the remainder ended in divorce, it was fairly definite that many were uncongenial, and it does not seem likely that further information would appreciably alter the calculation of the percentage of uncongenial marriages.

3. *Extreme Instability of Parents.*—Data were available for at least one parent in forty-eight cases. Twenty-three patients (48%) had twenty-nine parents who were either psychotic or chronically and seriously neurotic or psychopathic. The mother alone was unstable in nine cases, the father alone in eight cases, and both parents were markedly unstable in six. As information is not always given, this is clearly a minimal figure.

4. *Unsuitable and Unusual Raising.*—Estimation is particularly difficult for this item. Data are completely absent in six cases. The pattern of raising was bizarre or extremely faulty according to conventional standards in at least eighteen (41%) of the forty-four cases where the information permitted some evaluation. Ten patients had been rejected by at least one parent to an extreme degree such as can be noted in Cases 9, 20, and 35.

COMMENT ON DATA FROM CHARTS

The analysis of the data gives a statistical summary of some of the adverse influences to which the patients had been subjected in the early home environment, but it fails to convey the heaping up of deleterious factors which occurred in most cases. There were ten patients in whom none of the various items studied appeared to play a significant role, but these included five cases in which no information or relatively little information concerning the home life was available. The other forty patients were exposed to many injurious influences. These forty patients had been deprived of the guidance of fifteen parents by death and thirteen by separation; they had been exposed to the behavior of twenty-nine grossly unstable parents; and to the insecurity of twenty-one clearly incompatible marriages; and eighteen had been raised in unusual and eccentric fashion.

Stated conversely, only five of the fifty schizophrenic patients could be said to have clearly come from reasonably stable homes in which they had been raised by two stable and compatible parents according to fairly acceptable principles of child rearing.

DISCUSSION

A statistical or semistatistical survey cannot afford an understanding of the developmental dynamics gained through the careful study of individual cases. The ten case abstracts barely indicate the influences within the family which weigh upon the individual and help mold him, and the charts can only offer a glimpse of the manner in which the several factors studied impinge upon each of the fifty cases. Sibling relationships, often extremely significant, have been evaluated in but a few cases, and extrafamilial influences and the idiosyncrasies of individual development have been carefully screened out of the study. The study of the histories of these patients impresses forcefully that one patient after another was subjected to a piling up of adverse intrafamilial forces that were major factors in molding the misshapen personality, and which repeatedly interfered with the patients' attempts at maturation in a most discouraging fashion. The survey has been confined to the grossest features of the family environment. In their evaluation the prejudices of the individual physician caring for the patient, or of the writers, play a relatively small role. The intention has been precisely this: to call attention to the unusually poor family settings in which most schizophrenic patients gain their start in life, and which play a major role in the formation of interpersonal relationships, the projective systems, and the basic attitudes with which they face life and upon which they must build.

There has been an increasing tendency of late, more so than appears in the literature, for those interested in the psychotherapy of schizophrenic patients to lay stress upon the pernicious influence of the mothers, the severely rejecting mother, the so-called schizophrenogenic mother (Fromm-Reichmann, 1948). The origins of the schizophrenic reaction pattern have been sought in the infantile relationship with the mother who empathetically conveys her feelings of rejection to the infant (Rosen, 1948). The authors do not mean to detract from the importance of early maternal rejection. However, similar rejection or even more serious maternal rejection may be found in other psychiatric syndromes including certain psychosomatic configurations. If the type and degree of rejection suffered by schizophrenic patients can be differentiated from the rejection to which other patients are exposed, it has not yet been made apparent. This study indicates that less subtle early influences warrant careful attention. The data which have been reported here would appear to indicate a high frequency of grossly abnormal parental influences during the childhood of schizophrenic patients. It is suggested that there may well be a direct relationship between the degree of abnormality of the early environment and the seriousness of the emotional illness.

The suggestion is offered that, whereas infantile relationships may start the patient in the direction of asocial development or form an Anlage for later regression to infantile patterns, it may be the serious difficulties that are chronically present through childhood which prevent the patient from fitting into the pattern offered by society. In our data it is apparent that the paternal influences are noxious as frequently as are the maternal. The study of some of the cases leaves the impression that, had there been a stable father to offer guidance or to serve as a source for stable identification, the patient would not have been so seriously affected by the mother's difficulties. The conflict within the patient concerned with ambivalent feelings toward one or both parents, the divided loyalties, the unstable identifications, the incorporation of hostility directed toward one or the other parent—all these are often due to the influences of both parents. In the study of individual patients the gross abnormalities of the family background are not to be disregarded in favor of the more subtle interpersonal relationships, but should serve as background information which may throw light upon the reasons why the patient's emotional illness takes the drastic form.

It is recognized that the study can be taken to indicate that the instability of schizophrenic patients is hereditary. Although all the adverse familial influences are not directly to be attributed to the emotional instability of the parents, the differences between this group as a whole and some group of patients with another ailment might possibly be shown to be largely a matter of the frequency of serious instability of the parents. The problem is difficult to resolve: unstable parents tend to form unsuitable marriages and provide unstable homes. The cycle perpetuates itself. The topic will not be debated here. The emphasis of the paper, however, has been upon the survey of the environmental situation.

The question why one child in the family becomes schizophrenic when all have been subjected to similar adverse influences is frequently propounded. The problem diverges from the major emphasis of the paper, but it can be indicated that careful attention to the ten case abstracts will show that eight patients had siblings. Six of these were considered to have come from adverse environments, and all six were clearly brought up under markedly different influences from their siblings.

POSTSCRIPT

At the time of this study, psychodynamic theories concerning the etiology of schizophrenic disorders had largely focused on the patient's mother and the early mother-child interaction. The findings of the study drew our attention to the frequency of many other factors that seemed to have impeded the patient's development: the psychopathology of fathers, the parental discord, the loss of a parent, the aberrant child-rearing techniques, and to the continuation of deleterious influences over many years. However, the material gained from records was spotty and left the impression that the patients had been subjected to a piling up of unfortunate circumstances. Death of a parent, divorce, mental illness of a parent, conflict between parents, aberrant child rearing had not occurred in every case, and none of these factors by itself could explain the etiology of schizophrenic disorders. Could something specific to the origins of schizophrenic conditions be found? To us, the important outcome of the study was that it indicated that careful studies of the transactions of the family of origin were warranted.

It seems important to note that in the Danish-American studies of the biological and adoptive relatives of adoptees who became schizophrenic, Kety et al. (1968) found from the study of records that only three of sixty-three biological parents were sufficiently disturbed to warrant a "spectrum" diagnosis and that none was clearly schizophrenic. In the study we are reporting here that is also based on records, twenty-three patients (48%) had twenty-nine parents who were deemed to have been very seriously disturbed, including at least several who were clearly schizophrenic or paranoid. Either the records they studied were faulty or the biological parents of adopted-away schizophrenics are much less frequently disturbed than biological parents who raise their schizophrenic offspring. The findings of Kety et al. (1975) based on interviews show a similar discrepancy (Lidz and Blatt, 1983).

CHART 1

No.	Pt.	Age	Sex	Loss of parent	Incompatibility of parents	Instability of parent	Raising	Mental illness in family
1.	W.O.	19	F	Father suicided when patient was 15.	•	Father depressed and alcoholic for 5 years. Mother had "nervous breakdown" after first pregnancy.	Wealthy until aged 10; morbid surroundings thereafter as father was never stable after loss of wealth.	Father was depressed. Mother had "nervous breakdown."
2.	M.E.	21	F	Father suicided when patient was 15.	....	Father depressed prior to suicide.	Patient strongly attached to father.	Father depressed.
3.	S.T.	20	F	Mother absent with tuberculosis when patient 4. Father died when patient 9.	Unknown.	Father psychotic for 2 years prior to death.	Raised in orphanages from 4 to 17.	Father psychotic.
4.	M.U.	20	M	Father died of "nervous breakdown" when patient 15.	Unknown.	Father had "nervous breakdown."	Pampered excessively by mother who would not let him out of sight. Youngest sibling by 7 years. A "sissy not allowed to play with others."	Father had "nervous breakdown."
5.	R.U.	19	M	Mother suicided when patient 6.	Little known but apparently an adequate home.	Mother depressed before suicide. Aunt who raised patient "queer" and suffered an agitated depression.	....	Mother depressed. Mat. aunt depressed.
6.	W.E.	19	M	Mother died when patient 18.	Peculiar marriage of poor Protestant barber to wealthy Catholic heiress who was disowned and disinherited.	Father severely obsessive and incapacitated for 5 years by depressive illness when patient 5 to 10.	Patient was mother's favorite and confidant of her disappointments; closely bound to her, he lived to make her happy by becoming wealthy.	Father obsessive with depressive episodes.
7.	K.I.	17	F	Mother died when pt. 14. Parents separated when she was 3 and divorced when pt. was 8.	Very marked, and pt. greatly upset by separation.	....	Lived with mother from 3 to 8 and then awarded to father by court.	A paternal cousin suicided in a "tantrum."

• The dotted line indicates that the record contained no pertinent data.

CHART 1 (CONTINUED)

No.	Pt.	Age	Sex	Loss of parent	Incompatibility of parents	Instability of parent	Raising	Mental illness in family
8.	B.R.	19	M	Father died when pt. was 4.	Constant strife between older brother and mother.	....	Mother domineering and older sibs revolted but pt. was deaf and dependent.	....
9.	F.A.	20	M	Mother died when pt. was 1½. Aunt who raised pt. died when pt. was 13.	....	....	Raised by aunt while brother was raised by father. After 13 raised in boarding school where aunt worked. Pampered by both aunts.	
10.	C.H.	18	M	Father died of tuberculosis when pt. was 12.	Unknown.	....	Pt. asthmatic and raised differently from sibs, usually at schools away from home.	....
11.	B.A.	14	F	Mother died when pt. was 11.	Little known of first home, second apparently congenial.	....	Father remarried when pt. was 12, but was away from home half the time. Pt. jealous of kindly stepmother. Pt. was Catholic and father and stepmother were Protestant.	....
12.	M.O.	18	F	Mother died when pt. was 7.	Unknown.	....	Youngest of 10 sibs who was raised by older sisters. Father had no time for family but was very strict when home.	....
13.	R.A.	21	M	Father died when pt. was 2.	Unknown.	....	"Spoiled" by the maternal grandmother who helped raise pt.	Mat. grandfather was in state hosp. for 40 years.

CHART 1 (CONTINUED)

No.	Pt.	Age	Sex	Loss of parent	Incompatibility of parents	Instability of parent	Raising	Mental illness in family
14.	G.R.	20	M	Orphaned in infancy.	No data.	No data.	No data.	No data.
15.	H.E.	16	M	Permanent separation when patient was 5.	Extreme open conflict between mother and grandmother and between grandparents who raised pt.	Father extreme alcoholic. Mother an irresponsible psychopath. Maternal grandmother paranoid.	Extremely wealthy boy given no benefit of wealth or position, but subject to high expectations of family. Very abnormal surroundings with vindictiveness between members of family.	Father alcoholic. Mother psychopath. Mat. grandmother paranoid. Paternal line—many severe alcoholics and eccentrics.
16.	B.R.	18	M	Permanent separation when pt. was 8.	Extreme incompatibility. Family fled to Europe to be free of father who followed and caused terrible scenes.	Father severe alcoholic who was committed several times.	Only boy with four sisters and an aggressive mother. Peculiar education in Jesuit schools in several foreign countries.	Father alcoholic. Pat. grandmother and uncle were schizophrenic.
17.	C.R.	13	F	Separated when pt. was 11.	Family was completely disorganized. Father was alcoholic and cruel.	Father paranoid and alcoholic. Mother had screaming spells and was probably feeble-minded.	Family lived in a tumble-down shack. Aunt ran a bawdy house.	Father paranoid.
18.	B.A.	16	F	Divorced when patient was 6.	Extreme incompatibility. Mother would disappear for long periods. Pt. greatly concerned over incompatibility.	Mother paranoid.	Father abusive to wife and children. Pt. as youngest of seven was most exposed to difficulties in home.	Mother diagnosed as paranoid. Brother suffered a "nervous breakdown."
19.	H.F.	19	F	Divorced when pt. was 1.	Father Jewish and mother gentile. Pt. was unwanted and father unfaithful. Mother remarried when pt. was 9 but no information of this home.	....	Patient very spoiled and sheltered by the mother. Patient a feeding problem from infancy.	Paternal cousin suicided. Many divorces in family.

CHART 1 (CONTINUED)

No.	Pt.	Age	Sex	Loss of parents	Incompatibility of parents	Instability of parent	Raising	Mental illness in family
20.	M.A.	16	M	Sporadic separations.	Parents married only because of the pregnancy. No mutual life. Father took no interest in pt. and found interests out of home. Mother silly.	....	Little known.	Paternal grandmother in mental hospital for short time with "nervous breakdown."
21.	B.I.	14	M	Temporary separation when patient was 13.	Marked discord especially on all issues concerning patient.	Father had a "nervous breakdown" when 15 and again when patient was 8. Mother committed in agitated depression after patient became ill.	Brought up to be a genius, pushed by parents whose happiness depended on patient's future greatness. Strife between parents concerning patient's raising.	Father had depressive episodes. Mother an agitated depression.
22.	R.I.	20	M	....	Gross incompatibility. Remained married only "because of opinion of others."	Mother moody, thoughtless, rigid.	Little known.	Paternal aunt had "nervous breakdown." Pat. grandfather died in state hospital at 62. Mat. cousin and great-aunt schizophrenic.
23.	R.J.	18	M	....	Marked parental strife and pt. very sensitive of these fights.	Mother was depressed when pt. was 8 and remained hypochondriacal.	Excessively pampered by nervous mother.	Mother depressed.
24.	W.I.	16	F	....	Father had mistress which caused marked dissension. Strife between parents over pat. grandmother who dominated the home.	Father highly neurotic with phobia.	Patient was favorite child, spoiled particularly by father but squelched by jealous grandmother and restricted by fearful father.	Father neurotic. Mat. aunt "unstable." Mat. great-uncle had two depressions.

CHART 1 (CONTINUED)

No.	Pt.	Age	Sex	Loss of parents	Incompatibility of parents	Instability of parent	Raising	Mental illness in family
25.	P.O.	19	F	....	Parents never got along together. Father involved in suit for alienation of affection with much scandal.	....	Mother an "unfortunate person," very solicitous for patient but devoid of affection for her.	Mat. great-uncle suicided.
26.	H.O.	17	M	....	Marked parental strife which was patient's major concern.	Mother "nervous" and quarrelsome.	Little known.	....
27.	B.B.	22	F	....	Much quarreling and suspicion between parents which caused patient concern.	....	Oldest of four and very jealous of siblings.	Maternal great-aunt depressed.
28.	P.H.	19	F	....	Parents were not compatible; friction but not serious. Father a sort of handyman around mother's farm—a man who "never grew up."	Mother a chronic worrier, a "gloomy person." Father "immature."	Mother gloomy about children's heredity and thought them fated to insanity. Told patient that she was frigid. Mat. grandmother dominated the home.	A mat. aunt and uncle schizophrenic. A mat. aunt seclusive and suspicious. Pat. grandmother had violent and unreasonable temper. Four pat. aunts unstable and all divorced.
29.	D.A.	24	F	....	Some overt friction and patient worried about manner in which mother treated father.	....	No warmth or companionship in home. Mother a distant and aloof woman who supported and dominated family.	Maternal great-aunt was psychotic.
30.	K.E.	13	F	....	Parents never got along well. Father home but one day a week. Older sisters removed patient from home as it was "unsuitable."	Mother very peculiar, ? a socialized schizophrenic.	Mother excitable and was always at extremes using poor judgment. Very strict and overly concerned with sexual life of the children.	Mother ? Maternal second cousin schizophrenic. Pat. great-aunt in state hospital.

CHART 1 (CONTINUED)

No.	Pt.	Age	Sex	Loss of parents	Incompatibility of parents	Instability of parent	Raising	Mental illness in family
31.	L.A.	21	M	....	Not known.	Father had "nervous breakdown" and remained irritable.	Irritable father pushed patient and nagged continually.	Father had "nervous breakdown."
32.	B.L.	18	M	....	Little known but not congenial.	Father hypochondriacal and mother always "nervous" and irritable.	Not known.	Father hypochondriacal. Mat. grandmother paranoid and mat. aunt schizophrenic. Pat. second cousin schizophrenic.
33.	S.L.	17	F	....	Considerable friction but no open breaks. Both heavy drinkers with emphasis on social life rather than home.	Mother "neurotic."	Army officer family with many changes in residence and schools. Patient and identical twin became psychotic at same time with religious folie à deux.	Identical twin schizophrenic. Mother "neurotic." Mat. cousin had a religious "crack-up."
34.	T.R.	21	F	....	No overt break but a gloomy, unfriendly home with no compatibility between parents and no affection shown the children.	....	Father a physician with peculiar overconcern about patient's virginity. Would wish to perform pelvic exam. after her dates. Mother distant and uninterested in family.	Pat. uncle died of "softening of the brain."
35.	S.I.	19	F	....	Extreme hostility, suspicion and back-biting between mother and aunt who raised patient.	Aunt who raised patient was "peculiar."	Youngest sibling by 12 years who was rejected and neglected by parents who left her raising to a peculiar maiden aunt. No home life for patient despite wealthy home.	....

CHART 1 (CONTINUED)

No.	Pt.	Age	Sex	Loss of parent	Incompatibility of parents	Instability of parent	Raising	Mental illness in family
36.	J.O.	18	M	....	Fairly good as father humored mother's eccentricities.	Mother had several "nervous breakdowns," very eccentric and perhaps a socialized schizophrenic.	Mother permitted the patient no independence of action or thought, dictating all trivia. Brother left home in revolt. Patient was bound to mother but resentful.	Mother had "nervous breakdown." Two maternal aunts were peculiar and one may have been psychotic.
37.	M.O.	16	M	....	Not known.	Mother very odd. Neighborhood children would write on sidewalk, "Mrs. O. is crazy."	Patient youngest of 6 siblings by 7 years and most subject to mother's increasing eccentricity.	Mother ?
38.	D.E.	17	M	....	No information other than that older brother, a psychopath, caused much trouble in the home.	Mother mildly but chronically depressed for several years.	Father, a rather alcoholic policeman, was very strict and rigid. Mother was moody, irritable, and worrisome.	Mother depressive. Mat. aunt schizophrenic. Mat. uncle depressive. Mat. grandfather senile psychosis. Two pat. aunts and a pat. cousin suffered depressions.
39.	H.G.	22	M	....	Little known but probably fairly congenial.	Mother a "worrier."	Mother pampered the patient and shielded the 325-pound youth from his father who did not understand his "artistic" temperament. Brother's suicide affected family.	Brother suicided at 28. Sister depressed after the suicide. A mat. and a pat. uncle in state hospital.
40.	C.A.	23	F	....	No friction. Father subdued by aggressive mother.	....	Mother ambitious for patient socially and pushed her very aggressively.	....

CHART 1 (CONTINUED)

No.	Pt.	Age	Sex	Loss of parent	Incompatibility of parents	Instability of parent	Raising	Mental illness in family
41.	M.D.	21	M	....	Not known.	Mother depressed when patient was born "because of her figure."	Patient the retarded son of a university professor, raised as if normal and much out of place at home and in schools.	Pat. grandmother "nervous breakdown." Pat. uncle suicided. Pat. uncle mentally retarded. Pat. cousin and mat. aunt were schizophrenic.
42.	B.R.	16	F	....	Not known.	Mother a nervous worrier.	Spoiled by mother who always let patient have her own way. Patient married at 16 in opposition to parents.	Mother neurotic.
43.	D.O.	24	M	....	Not known.	....	Little known but patient had not talked to father in years. Rather wealthy and successful but patient looked down on parents because of lack of education.	Maternal uncle hospitalized with "nervous stomach."
44.	B.U.	19	M	....	Not known. Older brother estranged because parents would not meet his wife.	....	Rigid parents.	....
45.	C.C.	21	M	....	Not known.	Not known.	Not known.	Paternal grandmother hospitalized with "depression." "Insanity in her line." Paternal great-uncle and great-grand-uncle both insane.

CHART 1 (CONTINUED)

No.	Pt.	Age	Sex	Loss of parent	Incompatibility of parents	Instability of parent	Raising	Mental illness in family
46.	J.E.	19	M	....	Happy but odd home centering about invalid mother with father a detached research worker.	....	Patient much attached to invalid mother and jealous of any attention to siblings.	....
47.	Z.A.	15	M	....	Apparently congenial, offering good background.	Mother had severe adolescent difficulties and later brief period of depression and mild elation.	Father a prep. school teacher and home was fused with school.	Mother—brief depression.
48.	N.I.	21	F	....	Good with occasional slight friction.	....	Patient concerned about expectations for only child of a college dean and about imagined incompatibility of parents. Schizophrenic aunt in home for several years.	Maternal aunt schizophrenic. Mat. grandfather and uncle suicided in depressions.
49.	M.B.		F	....	Good home life.	....	....	Pat. grandmother had a mild depressive illness.
50.	U.L.		F	....	Good home life.	....	Both parents oversolicitous and ambitious for patient. Mother a meticulous and apprehensive person.	....

III

The Mothers of Schizophrenic Patients

(1964)

The chapter on the mothers of schizophrenic patients, now placed at the head of our studies of various aspects of the intrafamilial environment, was, for several reasons, among the last written. At the time we launched our study, the idea that schizophrenogenic mothers were a major cause of schizophrenic disorders was widespread; and a good deal had been written about them. It soon became apparent to us that the mothers in our study could not be stereotyped and other influences within the family were also important and sometimes more important. Although all the mothers had serious shortcomings as mothers, and some were very seriously disturbed, not all were "rejecting," not all were "incorporating or strangling," and only two could be considered "malicious." It was also apparent that some were less disturbed and less damaging than their husbands, and several might well have been rather adequate mothers if not for their disturbed husbands. Nevertheless, even though the mother is but one factor in the family milieu, she is usually the dominant influence on the young child and often the major influence in establishing the milieu, and we wished to be as certain as we could be in our analysis of our material concerning the mothers.

Placing the chapter that we wrote last at the beginning of this revised edition has caused some imbalance and difficulties. We did not repeat some material pertaining to the mothers that had appeared in prior papers, as, for example, their role in the "transmission of irrationality" (Chapter VII) or in impeding their children's extra-

Theodore Lidz, Alice R. Cornelison, Margaret T. Singer, Sarah Schafer, and Stephen Fleck. This paper was originally published in the first edition of this book.

familial relationships (Chapter XV) and their failure to provide adequate role models for daughters (Chapter XI); and we did not provide sketches of some very bizarre mothers because descriptions of them and their influence upon their families are found in other chapters.

The chapter remains essentially as it was in the first edition except for one major change. We now consider that the process of mothering is divided into four major components rather than three, and have done so by moving a major footnote concerning the mother as an object for identification and as a primary love object into the text.

Considerable attention had been paid to the personalities of mothers of schizophrenic patients and their ways of relating to the offspring before the start of our project though the descriptions are often contradictory (Abrahams and Varon, 1953; Gerard and Siegel, 1950; Lidz and Lidz, 1952; Kasanin et al., 1934; Prout and White, 1950; Reichard and Tillman, 1950; Sullivan, 1925-1926; Tietze, 1949). Then Hill (1955) provided a remarkably insightful though somewhat inconsistent portrayal and discussion of mothers of schizophrenic patients. His concepts of the devastatingly overpossessive love that was not rejecting but unrealistic and conditional stood in direct contrast to J. Rosen's (1953) convictions that maternal rejection during the first year of life formed the significant causative factor of schizophrenia. Alanen's (1958) excellent monograph provided a careful review of all prior studies and some significant new findings that were in accord with our own emerging data. As our studies were uncovering serious difficulties in all areas of the transactions in these families, we preferred to bring balance to the topic by directing attention to the total situation before focusing upon the mother. Our various papers contain numerous references to the deficiencies of these women as mothers and wives, but we required a more coherent theory concerning the importance of the family upon the development and maldevelopment of its children before we could seek to assay the mother's place and role in the genesis of schizophrenia.

The task presented greater difficulties than some other aspects of our study because the mother was both a cardinal informant and a central object of study in each family, and we were confronted by a mass of data which was extremely complex and which seemed, at times, paradoxical. We wished to evaluate, as far as possible, how often and to what extent the mother's difficulties arose in response to an abnormal child and whether or not they antedated the marriage and the birth of the child. The influences of spouses on each other are particularly difficult to assess. It appeared that in some families the mother's behavioral pattern had been well established prior to the marriage and more or less dictated the selection of a spouse, whereas in others the influence of the husband brought certain traits of the mother to the fore, crystallizing, so to speak, a configuration in a personality that had been more fluid prior to the marriage. In any case, it was apparent that the interaction of many of these women with their children was affected adversely by their efforts to cope with extremely difficult, disturbed, or inadequate husbands. Nevertheless, whatever the reasons, all but two or three of the seventeen mothers studied were seriously disturbed and strange women. Any study of the family milieu in which these patients grew up must pay particular attention to the mothers.

Describing these seventeen mothers and their impact upon their families and offspring presents difficulties. They cannot be categorized into a single group according to personality or way of relating to the schizophrenic offspring. Some fitted readily the description of the "schizophrenogenic" mother found in the literature (Hill, 1955; Lidz and Lidz, 1952)—the mother with nebulous ego boundaries who treats the child as an extension of herself, intruding but impervious to the child's needs and wishes as a separate individual. Other mothers fitted the category of the "rejecting" mother who did not want and could not cathect the child, a factor which has been described as causative of schizophrenia. The boundaries of such groupings, of course, are not fast—and merge into less clear-cut types of mothers whose difficulties and those they create for their children are recognized and understood through appreciation of similarities to the more extreme types. Several seemed to possess reasonable potential as mothers, but their husbands' serious psychopathology dominated the family life and thus affected the children directly and impaired the mothers' relationships with their offspring. There were mothers who could relate reasonably well to a son but not to a daughter, and an occasional mother who could interact more salubriously with a daughter. Some mothers had extremely little to do with the patient during the first years of his life as the nurturant functions were given over to nursemaids, and yet these were very disturbed mothers who clearly had a profoundly deleterious influence on their offspring. Consideration of the mother's influence could not be confined to the first year or two of life. We cannot describe *the* mother of the schizophrenic patient. An adequate survey of these mothers and their influence upon their children presented the problem of understanding some very different types of women and their effect upon their families as well as the patient over many years. We shall seek to convey some understanding of these women—all of whom were seriously handicapped by their own faulty upbringing and usually by the unfortunate marriages in which they had become enmeshed—and how they contributed to an offspring's failure to achieve a workable integration.

Before turning to a scrutiny of these mothers, it will be useful to recall some of the complexities of the task of being a mother. Motherhood is not an entity. It is not a quality that can be instilled into a woman by prenatal classes, natural childbirth, rooming-in or breast feeding. The functions of a mother extend over many years and are a compound of various emotions and attitudes, a series of interrelated skills, ways of communicating, etc., and involve the woman's relationships with her own parents and siblings, with her husband and her other children as well as with the specific child under study. Too often, particularly in studies pertaining to schizophrenia, the functions of a mother have been considered primarily in terms of her nurturant and empathic qualities during the first year or two of the child's life, as if her major function, if not her sole task, were to provide her offspring with a wholesome start by supplying his oral needs and thus inculcating a basic and lasting trust in the world and the people who inhabit it.

COMPONENTS OF MOTHERING

We cannot here attempt to review the many functions of a mother and the many capacities she is expected to possess. We believe that the process of mothering includes at least four major components. We can seek to convey something of the complexity and the interrelationships of these tasks, and then scrutinize how the mothers of the patients managed these functions.

The Maternal Nurturant Relationships

In providing nurturance for the infant, the mother requires a number of skills and a sense of security in her own ability to handle the helpless and fragile baby. To meet the child's demands upon her, she needs properly to cathect the infant almost as an extension of herself. The investment contains narcissistic components but also includes derivatives from her affection for her husband. The investment of the infant demands a priority over her other relationships but should not exclude, or be excluded by, attachments to her husband and her other children. The ability to feel warmly nurturant may well depend upon having experienced such nurturant care in her own early childhood. It involves her feelings of worth and capabilities as a woman. For some, only a male child will bring a sense of completion, whereas others can only feel close to a girl with whom they can empathize. Most mothers in giving of themselves to an infant require replenishment from sources of affection and esteem—usually from the husband. Then as the child moves into the second half of infancy, he requires an increasing responsivity to his smiles, babbling, reaching out, etc., from the mother who becomes important as a specific individual. A particularly difficult transition occurs for many mothers when the child begins to ambulate, express initiative, and get into things. Some women, who can feel secure as long as they can control their babies completely, cannot allow them to separate. They find it difficult to tolerate the disorder the child creates, or to cope with the almost inevitable anxiety that he will hurt himself. Efforts to limit and control the noncomprehending child can limit the child's initiative, direct toward undue passivity, and foster distrust in his own abilities. If there is conflict over control, it commonly focuses upon bowel training or feeding, areas in which the child can assert himself through negativism. Such struggles foster ambivalences in both mother and child, and at this time the mother's frustrations with her marriage, loss of a career, etc., are particularly likely to influence her handling of her child.

Such considerations of the first eighteen months of life can obviously be greatly amplified, and similar issues arise with each new phase of development requiring different capacities from the mother and arousing attitudes from her past that are influenced by her current life situation. The child's feeling of worth as a member of his or her sex is influenced by the mother's acceptance of the child's sex, her own feelings of worth as a woman, by how her husband fosters such feelings, and by her attitudes toward her husband. The consistency of the mother's responses to the child and the reliability of what she says affects the child's trust in the validity and usefulness of verbal communication. With the child's progression through the oedipal phase the mother needs to frustrate gradually the eroticized and sensuous components of the child's attachment and yet permit temporary regressions when the child becomes insecure or frustrated in his increasing independence. The child's security in venturing into peer groups and starting school depends upon having a firm base at home from which he can move outwards, and a mother who will expect the child to have disappointments and difficulties but who can encourage him to surmount them rather than convey her anxieties or her own distrust of the larger world. The child's transformation at puberty with increasing movement into the extrafamilial world, and his interests in members of the opposite sex can accentuate old problems in the mother-child relationship as well as create many new ones involving the mother's abilities to cope with the erotic components of her attachments to the child, the recrudescence of problems of her own adolescence, her concerns over aging, over being left isolated with her husband, etc.

This sketchy perusal of the mother's role in the child's developmental process with indications of the many factors that enter into her capacities to relate to her child salubriously at each phase of development should suffice to indicate the complexity of the simple task of providing adequate "mothering." Yet the mother exerts important influences in still other ways.

The Mother and the Family Structure

The mother-child interaction transpires within a family social system which it influences and by which it is influenced. The dynamic structure of the family, particularly of the isolated nuclear family characteristic of contemporary American life, depends primarily upon the nature of the marital relationship of the parents. The family must achieve certain structural requisites to direct the child's development into an integrated pattern. The development of a family social system suited for adequate child rearing rests upon the abilities of the parents to form a parental coalition, to maintain boundaries between the generations, and to adhere to their respective sex-linked roles. We have discussed the effects of the parents' marital relationship upon their children's personality development elsewhere (Chapters V and VI). The mother's capacities as a wife and her ways of relating as a wife clearly influence the structuring and integration of her children's personalities. Thus, a woman who cannot achieve a coalition with her husband and find reciprocally interrelating roles with him deprives the child of unified directives and of the opportunity of assimilating the benefits of marital and family mutuality: if she conveys her dissatisfactions with her husband, she undermines his worth as an object for a son's identification, or his value to a daughter as a model of a love object; if, because of her inadequacies as a wife, or even because she cannot meet a husband's unreasonable expectations, she becomes an object for her husband's contumely, her worth as an object of identification and love to the children is diminished. A mother who breaches the generation boundaries by seeking her major source of emotional support and a sense of completion from a son rather than from her husband not only impedes the formation of boundaries between herself and the son, but also confuses the child's passage through the oedipal phase. The woman who assumes the male role in the family, or who cannot fill the feminine expressive-affectional role disturbs a child's apprehension of masculinity and femininity and his achievement of a secure sexual identity. In general, we may say that the provision of a relatively conflict-free area within the family in which the child can feel secure, and the opening of the proper channels for him to move into and gain rewards for doing so, depend upon the creation of a suitable family structure by the parental interaction. The mother's role as a wife exerts a pervasive influence upon her children throughout their formative years.

The Mother as a Transmitter of Instrumental Techniques

A child's development into an individual capable of directing his own life depends upon the acquisition of countless adaptive techniques and the conscious and unconscious assimilation of the institutions of his culture. The fundamentals are gained within the family with the mother as a basic teacher. The fundamentals extend beyond the skills of primary socialization and include complex patterns of relating appropriately to different categories of persons and the as-

similation of a variety of social institutions. Basic to all but
the simplest tasks is the acquisition of the language and meaning systems essential for learning, communicating, and self-
direction. The learning of language is particularly pertinent
in a consideration of schizophrenia, an illness distinguished
by distortions of the symbolic processes. Mothers who fail to
respond to the child's early efforts, who respond inconsis-
tently, whose nonverbal and verbal communications are contradictory, who place the child in insoluble "binds," who
respond to their own feelings or needs projected onto a child,
whose promises or bribes are forgotten after they have
achieved their purposes, who blur and fragment meanings,
who obliterate meaningfulness, etc., confuse the child's development of meanings. As the ability to categorize experience depends upon possessing the words that indicate the
categories, and because the meanings of words provide pre-
dictability, confusions of linguistic meanings impair ego functioning (Lidz, 1963c). Inculcation of distrust in the usefulness
of verbal communication as well as teaching to use words to
avoid the implications of events can prepare a child to attempt
to solve conflicts by breaking through the confines imposed
by the culture's meanings and logic.

The Mother as a Primary Object for Identification and as a Basic Love Object

Consideration of these aspects of being a mother is not
meant to neglect the importance of the mother as an object
for identification and as a love object to the child. Much of
the child's personality development depends upon internalization of characteristics of the mother and other objects, and
much of the direction and the "leverage" for directing the
child's socialization comes from the child's wish and need to
gratify the love object. This is not the place to attempt to deal
with a highly involved topic that has been further complicated
by theoretical confusions. The integrative value of the mother
as an object depends upon all sets of functions discussed as
well as other factors. The mother is both the primary object

for identification and primary love object for children of both sexes—becoming more of the first for a daughter and more of the second for a son. Initially she is neither when the child is still in symbiosis with her: with differentiation the mother divides or is divided into an identification object that is internalized and a love object with whom the infant seeks an equilibrium and from whom he later seeks love and approbation. In this manner, the problem of identification, internalization, and object relationship relates to ego, superego, and ego-ideal formation, and also to what must be repressed into the unconscious. Adequate consideration of the topic requires an exploration of basic psychoanalytic theory. For present purposes, it suffices to recognize that the mother's security and self-esteem enter into the child, as also does the father's esteem for the mother. In addition, the father's value as an object for identification and as a love object also involves the mother's way of relating to him, as will become apparent in the illustrations. Harmonious and integrated personality organization probably requires harmony between the object for identification and the love object. A son's father who is the object of the boy's identification should also be desired as a love object by the mother.

We believe it useful to note how these women carried out the four sets of maternal functions that we have just designated: (1) to provide maternal nurturance and relate to the child in a manner that fosters a sound foundation for the development of ego autonomy; (2) to contribute to the formation and maintenance of a family system that provides integrating directives to the child's developing personality; (3) to transmit the basic adaptive techniques of the culture to the child, particularly the inculcation of the shared system of meanings and logic of the culture; (4) to form an object for identification and "internalization" and a primary "love object" for the child. None of these mothers filled any of these functions competently, and all were gravely deficient in at least one of these areas—a deficiency uncompensated by assets in the other areas, and aggravated by the father's characteristics and behavior.

CASE ILLUSTRATIONS

The series of seventeen mothers contains some very discrepant personalities. There is no one set of characteristics common to all, but certain patterns recur frequently, with some of the mothers having very similar ways of relating to both their husbands and children, and having become caught up in very similar family situations. A division of the mothers according to the sex of the psychotic child helps clarify some of the discrepancies in the literature in the descriptions of the mothers of schizophrenic offspring. The developmental tasks of boys and girls differ, and certain types of parents are more detrimental to children of one sex than to children of the other (see Chapter IX). However, some notable differences also exist among mothers of schizophrenic children of the same sex, particularly among the mothers of schizophrenic sons.

Rather than continue to deal with abstractions, we shall describe some mothers with differing characteristics. Viewing their ways of relating and communicating as mothers and wives together with their own developmental and marital problems will help avoid placing undue emphasis upon certain isolated characteristics, and may also provide a modicum of understanding of these women as persons.

Mothers of Schizophrenic Sons

We shall first consider a schizophrenic boy's mother who can serve as a paradigm of the "schizophrenogenic mother." The deleterious nature of her behavior and personality seems apparent. It is difficult to imagine how a son she raised would not be seriously disturbed, if not schizophrenic. She provides an example of a woman who can devote virtually all of her energies to rearing her children to their detriment. The gross and apparent disturbances in such mothers guide toward the recognition of similar difficulties in less disturbed mothers.

Two excellent private hospitals had refused to retain Jack Newcomb as a patient because their personnel could not tolerate his mother's constant and insistent intrusions into her son's therapy. She would dogmatically insist that he suffered from an endocrine deficiency and hound the staff to use a preparation that allegedly had cured a boy she knew. The separation from Jack caused her intolerable anxiety, but her frequent visits clearly aggravated his condition. No one other than she could understand her son and care for him properly. Her capacity to deny the obvious was remarkable. When, upon her insistence, a hospital had permitted Jack to spend a week at home, he had made unwelcomed advances to a girl whom he knew slightly. Despite the girl's complaints, Mrs. Newcomb insisted that she was leading her son on. When stopped from trailing the girl, Jack became refractory. An ambulance was called to return him to the hospital and when he became combative, the police were required to help subdue him. Thereafter, Mrs. Newcomb steadfastly maintained that Jack had done very well at home until the police appeared and mistreated him. On another occasion, a nurse saw Jack strike his mother on the back, almost knocking her down. Mrs. Newcomb expressed surprise at the nurse's concern, and insisted that her son had only tapped her playfully. Interviews with the Newcombs were extremely frustrating. They were dominated by Mrs. Newcomb, and even when questions were specifically directed toward her husband, Mrs. Newcomb answered, and like a cracked record repeated assertions and questions that had been discussed hundreds of times before. If an interviewer did not agree with her, Mrs. Newcomb seemed to believe that she could not have been understood properly, and rephrased her remark. When Mr. Newcomb was seen without his wife, he still served primarily as a spokesman for her. Mrs. Newcomb's bland expression gave little indication of feelings, but she readily became anxious and depressed. Her entire life and sense of well-being were wrapped up in her son. She refused to relinquish hope that he would eventually return home, and all of her energies and the family resources were devoted to this end—to the neglect of her daughter's needs and interests. Mrs. Newcomb thought of her son throughout the day and eventually confided that she feared that she would forget him if she did not think of him constantly. In actuality, her persistence over many years despite the discouragement of many psychiatrists finally won out.

Mrs. Newcomb had been successfully pursuing a career in commercial art when her husband, several years her junior, proposed marriage. She was taken by surprise, not having realized that he was at all interested in her. Mr. Newcomb, orphaned in early childhood, had been raised by friends of his parents. He behaved like an orphan with his wife, grateful for her attention and deferring to her leadership and judgment. The Newcombs considered their marriage to be almost ideal: disagreements were rare for Mr. Newcomb rarely dissented, partly because he had learned that his wife's ideas could not be changed by reasoning. Mrs. Newcomb was delighted when she gave birth to a son about a year after they were married. However, she was extremely insecure in handling the baby, and her husband had to bathe the child because of her fears that she might accidentally drown her son. A daughter born two years later was also welcomed. Mrs. Newcomb was overly concerned and protective of both children. During her frequent and prolonged incapacitations by a variety of ailments, a maid took care of the children. Although most of her complaints seem to have been neurasthenic and hypochondriacal, she also suffered from severe menorrhagia, but she deferred having her uterus removed for many years, unable to tolerate the idea of losing her womb even though no more children were desired.

The children were virtually isolated from other children during their preschool years. They played in a fenced-in yard where they would be safe and where they could run about in the nude for their health. The family lived in a rather isolated area and had only superficial contacts with neighbors. Later, Mrs. Newcomb became the despair of the teachers (one of whom we interviewed) because of her frequent intrusions into the classroom and her unreasonable demands to secure a proper education for her children and adequate recognition of their abilities. She considered both children to be unusually gifted. They certainly possessed talent—Jack's mechanized and repetitive playing of the piano gave evidence of much practice and some former brilliance. Although Mr. Newcomb was a successful man to whom Mrs. Newcomb was devoted in her fashion, she clearly conveyed to Jack that she had little esteem for her husband as a man and that she had much higher aspirations for her son. Despite her anxieties about her children's well-being, but perhaps partly because of them, she sent them to preparatory schools. Jack managed to get along, although he socialized very poorly and concentrated on his music until he became flagrantly psychotic during his first year in college shortly after being in an auto accident in which a classmate was killed. His sister, who had long been accident prone, then became severely upset, secured psychotherapeutic help, and broke completely with her mother.

When we turn to Mrs. Newcomb's developmental history, the shades roll up to reveal the psychopathology of an earlier generation. Despite the gaps and the potential unreliability in Mr. and Mrs. Newcomb's reconstructions, the evidence seems clear that the trend toward eccentricity and irrationality goes back at least to Mrs. Newcomb's parents. Her father was a man of great erudition who made brilliant starts on several careers but became a dilettante who achieved little. He displayed a rigidity and imperviousness that was characteristic of both Mrs. Newcomb and her son. He antagonized all of his children by seeking to direct and dominate their lives and by his penurious treatment of them. Mrs. Newcomb expressed open hatred of her mother whom she described as a woman who considered herself a great beauty, spending many hours each day admiring and beautifying herself. Her mother had come from a very wealthy family and let her children know that her wealth and beauty had been wasted in an unsatisfactory marriage. She neglected the household, hated housework, never prepared more than one meal a day, and paid little attention to her children. Mrs. Newcomb had grown up feeling unwanted because she was a girl. She became particularly embittered because her father refused to spend his wife's money to provide her with a college education, despite his emphasis upon the overriding importance of education. He saw no reason for a girl to attend college. He forbade any of his three daughters' boy friends to enter the home, and actually chased several out of it. Mr. Newcomb was the only suitor whom he had permitted to visit.

Dr. Margaret Singer interpreted Mrs. Newcomb's projective tests completely blindly. She confirmed the clinical appraisal, emphasizing the hypochondriacal, neurasthenic, obsessive, and highly intrusive trends, and the relative absence of ego boundaries. Quoting the personality description obtained from the tests would be redundant, but Dr. Singer's analysis of Mrs. Newcomb's thought processes is particularly significant.

She is an extreme blurrer of meanings, blurring in many ways and at many different levels. She gives a response and then soon comments that the blot no longer looks the way it did. She comments, "I don't see anything that looks like anything," and, at various times, says that there is little or no meaning to be found. Her content is very vague and when questioned about a vague response, she shifts, becomes more indefinite, and is impotent to account for her impression. When asked which Rorschach card she liked best, she "didn't see anything to like about any of them—this is the least questionable but I don't say I like it." When asked which she liked best, she commented, "This one is kind of humorous." The response forced the examiner to ask whether that meant she liked it or did not like it, to which Mrs. Newcomb replied, "I don't have any feelings one way or another about it." She takes a negativistic viewpoint and kills off meanings by saying that she feels nothing. She keeps conveying that meaning is hardly worth seeking because one cannot find anything likable or clear; and, furthermore, she will not try. She will not talk directly about anything. One might predict that this is a pervasive style of interacting with others, characteristic of her behavior in general. At the same time that she blurs meaningfulness, she creates an aura of being a nice, sweet person. Her references to people concern children, nice things, pretty little things; yet she also takes a carping outlook that makes others feel low, guilty, dejected, and hopelessly morassed by her. She is a person with low energy, with a limp indecisiveness, an unhappy neurotic life of a psychasthenic sort. She repeatedly creates the impression that the tester is to blame for her lack of clarity and her feelings of pointlessness. On her TAT responses, she is agonizingly contradictory, and when the tester inquires about an inconsistency, Mrs. Newcomb simply slaps down the examiner and further blurs meaning by stating that the picture does not make any sense. For example, she says that this is a young boy or a young woman and then talks about the boy. When the tester asks about the young woman, Mrs. Newcomb says, "The pose doesn't make sense in that case, it just looks like a child in distress and as if they haven't drawn it right." She repeatedly "recognizes" in others her own carping, unhappy, dissatisfied, displeased, and negativistic ways. In telling a story about a mother and her son, she says, "Things can be a mess if you don't have your own way." She can make any interaction seem nonsensical by claiming that it is illogical, but she never says what is logical. She destroys reality, but offers no reality to which she can adhere. She became extremely angry, diffuse, and attacking when a sexually toned picture was shown, but then talked about what an unhappy scene it was and how very upsetting; she ended by saying that her son would not tell a story to that card because she knew it would not make any sense to him either. References to her son indicated that she feels that she has him convinced that there is no reality where she says there is not to be any. Nothing about reality seems to please her or seems right, logical, or consistent. Sexuality is among her worst topics. People are both male and female at the same time.

The résumé of Mrs. Newcomb's behavioral patterns and the material from her projective tests convey the severity of her psychopathology, but it is difficult to classify her according to the usual terminology. Alanen (1958) has used the term "schizoid pattern of interpersonal relationship" and Delay et al. (1962) "psychotic character" to designate such mothers. She does not become disorganized because of her strange reality testing, the sterility of her relationships, and her fluid ego boundaries, but imposes her view of the world upon those few persons with whom she lives and whom she turns into extensions of herself. She maintains her own life and the family life within the narrow confines that she can tolerate and control in order to retain her equilibrium. Her own needs and those of her son are not clearly distinguished, and she expects him to feel and perceive as she does; she is intrusive into his life, but impervious to him as a discrete individual.

Turning to the parameters by which we are assessing capacities for motherhood, serious difficulties are apparent in each sphere. Mrs. Newcomb, despite her desire for children, was too fearful lest she harm her firstborn to provide proper nurturant care during his infancy, nor could she restrain her needs to control him as he grew older. Unable to set boundaries between herself and her son, he continued to respond to maternal needs and tensions as if they were his own. Yet, there are clear indications that she could never properly cathect her son, and instead consciously and constantly had to maintain an awareness of him. The family as a system did not achieve an organization requisite for directing the ego integration of its offspring, but the flaws were created by both parents. Although the Newcombs as spouses achieved reciprocal role relationships that were adequately satisfactory to both, the relationship was skewed. The family transactions followed the dictates, the peculiar and even bizarre dictates, of Mrs. Newcomb which were rarely, if ever, countered by her husband. Generation boundaries were broken because Mr. Newcomb filled the role of a child rather than of a husband within the confines of the home; and because Mrs. Newcomb displaced her husband by her son, gaining her major emotional gratifications from the children and making her husband subsidiary to them. Although Mrs. Newcomb expressed some ideas that she would have liked a husband to provide more guidance, there was ample evidence that she could not relinquish the direction of the family. The sex-linked roles of the parents obviously went askew because of the subsidiary role filled by the husband. In addition, Mrs. Newcomb's own confusions concerning sexual identity and her deep-seated lack of self-esteem as a woman created further complications for her children. Little need be said about Mrs. Newcomb's capacities to transmit instrumentally useful meanings to her children. She blurred meanings, denied the obvious, insisted upon her own deviant perceptions, and conveyed hopelessness of finding a meaningful view of life.

Mrs. Newcomb is an example of the type of mother of schizophrenic patients that has made the most profound impression upon psychiatrists. Two or three other mothers in the series showed a similar and equally deleterious configuration of traits. Mrs. Nebb, who has been depicted in greater detail in Chapter XIII, was even more eccentric and even more intrusive into the lives of her twin sons. She was flagrantly seductive in sleeping with them, bathing them, and administering enemas to them well into their adolescence; and she was overtly contemptuous of her husband. A severely phobic and hypochondriacal woman, her communications were seriously disturbed and her ideas bizarre. She had been raised in an isolated community, and seriously rejected by her eccentric mother. Mrs. Narab, an overtly schizophrenic woman, lived for her sons, in her sons, and through her sons—but the sons of her fantasy rather than the actual children. She conveyed a blurred perception of the frightening and hostile world of her delusions and hallucinations. In a sense, the study should be concerned with her mother. And, indeed, her mother was also an anxious, overly protective, intrusive, confused woman who grew up believing herself the younger sister of her mother—still another woman who had led a strangely confused life. Here evidence of serious pathology extends across four generations. Mrs. Schwartz might also be placed in this group of mothers because of her intrusive control of her sons and her marriage to a weak and chronically depressed man. She was a paranoid woman who believed that the family was persecuted, the telephone tapped, etc., but she ran the family business successfully and pushed her sons upward. However, she was not preoccupied with her schizophrenic youngest son because her thoughts, concerns, and indulgences focused upon her favorite eldest son who had become an embezzler. Although neglectful of the patient, she was also tactlessly overcontrolling and intrusive with him. She had emerged from a devastating childhood in Russia, orphaned at a very early age and raised without affection by her impoverished older siblings.

Mrs. Dolfuss was a very different type of woman who does not resemble the mothers under discussion, but the nurse-maid to whom she abdicated the maternal duties for the first eight years of her son's life was a highly intrusive, controlling person whose life seems to have been bound up in her charge. She permitted the boy little initiative, held grandiose ambitions for him, and was sexually seductive with him. The nurse, as did the mother, shared the delusion that Mr. Dolfuss was a reincarnation of an Asiatic divinity. Both parents took a formal, distant interest in their children but had little idea of just how they were being raised by the servants. The deviant milieu is presented in Chapter VIII.

Although one overtly schizophrenic mother of a schizophrenic daughter, Mrs. Thomas (who will be discussed later) was much like Mrs. Newcomb in some ways, no mother of a female patient in this series related as she did to both her husband and child. However, we have encountered such mothers of schizophrenic daughters outside of the series. For example, a woman who was a good author of local renown dominated the interviews held with both parents, scarcely permitting her husband to finish a sentence. She had very set ideas and impressed them upon her family. She insisted that her daughter was a genius who would emulate and surpass a world-famous novelist. Her own frustrated career would reach attainment through her daughter, not through her sons. She had little interest in her daughter as she was, or wished to be, and was oblivious to the girl's own aspirations. When a psychiatrist pointed out that Virginia Woolf, whom the daughter was to emulate, had committed suicide, the mother stated without hesitation that such creativity would be worth the price of a life of unhappiness and ultimate suicide.

The extreme form of mother who engulfed and intruded, unable to set boundaries between herself and the child, while treating her husband as a secondary figure, and who communicated in bizarre, blurred, and virtually psychotic ways, accounted for about half of the mothers of schizophrenic sons.

Only one of the mothers of the male patients had been overtly rejecting of her unwanted son and cold and aloof toward him. Mrs. Forel created a very different impression from Mrs. Newcomb. Mrs. Forel was an attractive woman with a very distant manner. As one psychiatrist stated, "The room seemed to chill when she entered." With great reluctance she came for a few interviews, but she remained extremely guarded. She was the only mother of a patient admitted to our hospital who had refused to visit her child. Mrs. Forel insisted, "It would upset him too much to have his mother see him in a mental institution." Most of the information about her was obtained from her three children whose accounts agreed and interdigitated. She assumed little responsibility for her adolescent son, expecting him to take care of himself.

Mrs. Forel had never paid much attention to her youngest son who was an unwelcome product of an attempted reconciliation with her husband. Her marriage had been a hostile encounter from its inception. Inordinately bound to her mother and two older sisters who directed much of her life, she stubbornly resisted her husband's attempts to draw her away from them. She treated her husband with contempt; paid little attention to his opinions and wishes; ridiculed his outbursts. She was a tease who enjoyed attracting men and making her husband jealous; but she was frigid, permitting occasional sexual relations until her daughter was born, after which she refused her husband for the twelve years prior to the patient's conception. Mrs. Forel capitulated when her husband finally threatened divorce unless she moved to a city where he was offered a good business opportunity, and unless she resumed the sexual relationship. When she soon became pregnant, Mrs. Forel became enraged and the marriage became even more conflictful. Several attempts to induce an abortion failed. She paid scant attention to her infant son, but his father and older siblings tried to compensate for her obvious rejection of him. Feeling lost separated from her sisters, Mrs. Forel began to drink heavily and to carry on numerous flirtations. Mrs. Forel treated her husband as an outsider and constantly derided him to the children. Mr. Forel, unable to gain direction of his family, gave vent to his frustrations in frequent childlike tantrums.

When the patient was six years old, Mrs. Forel was disfigured in an automobile accident for which Mr. Forel was responsible. She became depressed and remained secluded in her room for more than a year until her appearance was surgically restored. Guilt ridden, Mr. Forel catered to her wishes but only met with rebuffs. When he developed a malignancy several years later, Mrs. Forel avoided being near him lest she contract cancer from him. After her husband died, Mrs. Forel lived for a time with her married daughter, and then she moved in with her oldest sister, even though the sister refused to let the patient, then a young adolescent, into the house. He boarded in the neighborhood and his mother occasionally ate with him. Finally, faced with her sister's extreme hostility to her youngest son, she made a home for him by taking in female boarders with whom she formed intense friendships. Although usually distant and cold, Mrs. Forel, when intoxicated, became highly seductive with both of her sons, acting as if they were boy friends, embracing and kissing them so sensuously that they were afraid to remain in her proximity.

Although relatively little is known about Mrs. Forel's early development, her difficulties in relating to men fit her family background. Her mother, a teacher, was a "strong" woman who dominated the family, and there is evidence that the pattern of female dominance went back to the patient's maternal great-grandmother. Mrs. Forel's sisters had even more pronounced difficulties in regard to men. The oldest constantly proclaimed her antipathy for men, derogated them, and sought to dominate them. She asserted that she might marry when she became old in order to have a man around who would be subservient to her. The second sister had never gone out with a man, though she was a pretty woman. Mrs. Forel's attitudes toward men antedated her marriage: she liked to tell her children how she had made dates in adolescence simply to stand up the boy. Even without direct evidence, it seems apparent that there must have been something strange about a family that raised three daughters with such attitudes toward men.

Projective tests could not be given to Mrs. Forel, and we can say little about her style of communication as she was seen on but a few occasions very early in the study before we paid specific attention to the problem. She was a difficult woman, aloof from her husband and children, impervious to the feelings of others, highly narcissistic, frigid, and at least latently homosexual. Her poor integration and profound immaturity are evident from her lasting anaclitic involvement with her sisters and the extent of her alcoholism when separated from them. She appears to have defended her weaknesses by attacking others and by her imperviousness to their feelings. She was an extremely poor wife and scarcely anything of a mother to her younger son.

Although Mrs. Forel was very different from Mrs. Newcomb, some parallels are noteworthy. Their range of roles was extremely limited and, for the most part, they adhered to one characteristic pattern to which they forced family members to adjust. They could not set proper distance between themselves and others, or alter the distance in accord with the situation and the child's developmental needs: Mrs. Newcomb was overwhelmingly intrusive, and Mrs. Forel was coldly distant except when she was intoxicated at which time she became threateningly seductive to her sons. Neither could really share tasks with a husband, and both, in different ways, destroyed their husbands' worth as useful father figures.

It seems unnecessary to elaborate upon Mrs. Forel's deficiencies in being nurturant to her son and in guiding his development. Her shortcomings in filling the role of a parent, in forming a coalition with her husband, and in filling a feminine role created serious distortions of the family system. Confusions were created in the patient because his father filled the maternal role; because women came to be feared as hostile, nonsupportive, and castrating to men; because masculinity was derided and a cause for rejection by women. Mrs. Forel's breaching of generation boundaries by her physical seductiveness fostered incest panic in the patient during his adolescence. Although we could not examine her use of language and her ways of thinking, she conveyed a strange and culturally deviant view of the world and also a pervasive meaninglessness concerning many cardinal relationships.

Not all of the mothers of schizophrenic sons were as strange, disturbed, unempathic as the six who have been discussed. The remaining three showed capacities to relate to their children in more reasonable ways despite significant personality difficulties. They were all caught up in marriages to seriously disturbed men that preoccupied them, created a pervasive sense of despair, and contributed to the rigidity of their defenses. Their husbands were major factors in creating disturbed and confusing family environments.

Mrs. Newberg was an attractive and friendly woman who spoke clearly, and willingly discussed her problems in raising her children and her serious marital difficulties. She was not rigid, recognized her inadequacies, and sought help to modify her way of relating to her children. Her inordinate attachment to her older sisters, her anxious oversolicitude for her sons mixed with an aloofness, her need to find compensation for her marriage in her sons, her antagonisms toward her husband—all adversely influenced the development of her two sons who became psychotic. However, Mr. Newberg was a confused and confusing man who talked incessantly in a driven manner. In many ways Mr. Newberg resembled the poorly organized "psychotic characters" with poor ego boundaries and distorted meaning systems more commonly noted among mothers of schizophrenic patients. He was intensely rivalrous with his sons. It seems likely that the pathogenic trends in Mrs. Newberg's personality and ways of relating to her children reached serious proportions because of her husband's serious psychopathology, her efforts to counter his influences on the children, and because of the circular feedback of apprehension, mistrust, and defensive maneuvers between the couple.

If, however, we look beyond these hypothetical reasons for Mrs. Newberg's behavior, it is clear that her ways of relating to her husband and children were highly detrimental to her offspring. She was a very anxious mother who was afraid to absent herself from her children, even though her mother and two sisters with whom the children were very familiar lived in the same building. She left the children so rarely that when it became necessary for her to visit an obstetrician during her third pregnancy, the two children, then three and four years old, both suffered from severe anxiety. All her children suffered from serious anxiety upon entering school and verged upon having school phobia. Her indulgence of her younger son—her catering to his whims about food and his need to have her with him until he fell asleep at night—aroused jealousies in her older children. All three children had feeding and bowel-training problems, and suffered from enuresis. Despite her concern and indulgence, she was rather aloof in relating to them—an absence of spontaneous warmth rather than a coldness. She had very limited contacts other than with her sisters and their families and discouraged her sons from playing with children other than their cousins lest they become involved with bad companions. She held high hopes but not unrealistic aspirations for her sons. She came to depend very heavily upon her older son for emotional support and for compensation for her marital unhappiness. Quarrels between the parents were frequent, with Mrs. Newberg expressing her lack of confidence in her husband, her despair over his many eccentricities, and his lack of help in raising the children—concerns and complaints that were realistic. Her sisters, omnipresent figures, were even more open with their hostile and vituperative remarks about Mr. Newberg, freely expressing their feelings in the presence of his children. Mrs. Newberg believed that she remained with her husband only for the sake of the children; the marriage, however, was almost unique in the series in that both partners had, at times, gained very real satisfaction from their sexual relationship.

Mrs. Newberg had grown up in the unhappy and impoverished home of immigrant parents. As the youngest of four daughters, Mrs. Newberg had felt unwanted and a burden to her parents in their poverty. Her mother was an uneducated woman who considered herself a great beauty and felt cheated because her parents had broken up a romance with a man who later became very wealthy, a self-centered woman who paid relatively little attention to her children and constantly belittled her husband, who was a warmer and more considerate but passive and ineffectual person. Mrs. Newberg remained intensely attached to her oldest sister who had filled the role of mother to her, and she always became frightened at the threat of separation from her—a concern that created conflict with her husband and contributed to her oversensitivity to her children's separation fears. The sister, also unhappily married, shrewishly continued to dominate Mrs. Newberg's family life, belittling and antagonizing both Mrs. Newberg's husband and her own.

Mrs. Newberg despite her good looks had always considered herself an ugly duckling and was surprised by Mr. Newberg's ardent courtship. She had found Mr. Newberg, as a suitor, physically and sexually attractive, and considered him a self-assured "go-getter." Whatever her conscious and unconscious reasons for marrying him, she soon found that she had married a highly erratic, childishly dependent man who required constant bolstering of his self-esteem, and who was closely tied to his near-psychotic mother. Mrs. Newberg had good reasons to fear that he would give up his job to pursue some crack-pot scheme or, like his father, desert the family. Later, Mrs. Newberg feared that her sons would come to resemble their disturbed and unpredictable father, and clearly conveyed her dissatisfaction with her husband to them.

We have already noted that Mrs. Newberg was one of the few mothers who could think and talk clearly and rationally. Dr. Singer's blind analysis of the projective tests confirms both the clarity of the thought processes and Mrs. Newberg's relative detachment; but it also points up how her styles of thinking, perceiving, and of relating have a seriously detrimental impact upon her children.

The tests present a picture of a distant, detached woman who maintains a rigid barrier against any spontaneity or warmth and steadfastly conveys the feeling that she regards everything in life as a task, an unpleasant task. Her Rorschach indicates that she will appear a rational, sterile, nonintrospective person who sees the conventional meanings in a colorless, impersonal way. Her percepts are deadly accurate and will not give any clues about what she is like inside. She shows little if any warmth, and there will be almost no nuances in her feelings. She will have relatively little capacity for empathy and will not recognize the "inner person" in others at all.[1] To Mrs. Newberg, life is a task assigned and the world is an unpleasant place. She does not say that it is anything in particular but more of what it is not. She does not project but simply sees life as a task with an inevitable unhappy outcome. She expects unpleasantness, sarcasms, "thrusts" as she calls them, and is looking forward to only such unpleasantnesses. Thus while some parents of young schizophrenic patients have been termed unreal characters because they have a fixed pleasant version of life, this woman in her negative way fills a similar role because she expects an undeviatingly negative outcome. Power struggles are part of her world. However, these may be very covered over, because she has resigned herself to a fortified role in relation to an impersonal overpowering force against which struggle is useless. She seems to have severed relations with her affects. Again, it should be noted that in this family it is the father who was the blurrer of meanings—a person who beclouds everything with his nebulous, shifting thought processes. He is the epitome of vague ego boundaries in a man who reasons negatively.

[1]The investigators who knew Mrs. Newberg consider this an overstatement of a relatively accurate impression—perhaps created because Mrs. Newberg was requiring inordinately strong defenses at the time she was tested because of the psychoses of both of her sons.

In this brief portrayal of Mrs. Newberg we can again note serious impediments to a wholesome mother-child relationship: her overly anxious care of her children during early childhood, her difficulties in permitting them to gain a sense of autonomy and become separate from her, her need to gain a sense of fulfillment through her sons, her detachment, etc. In her role as a wife she could not shift the center of family authority from her sisters to her husband and she undermined the worth of her husband to the children, albeit because her husband's personality and behavior made it difficult to do otherwise. Although more aggressive and active, Mr. Newberg, like Mr. Newcomb and other fathers of schizophrenic sons, breached generation boundaries by behaving in many respects as a member of the childhood generation, by being rivalrous with his sons rather than by being an adjunct to his wife. Neither parent had become independent of his family of origin.

Mrs. Lamb came from a very different background and was married to a highly successful business executive, but her makeup and problems were essentially similar to Mrs. Newberg's. She, too, could perceive and communicate clearly but related in an aloof way that covered her disillusion and hopelessness. However, she tended to believe in spiritualism, and she had a sister with very eccentric ideas. Mr. Lamb was a seriously disturbed alcoholic who philandered openly to cover homosexual tendencies that he may have concealed from himself but not from his wife or son. He was extremely jealous of his son, and his outbursts constantly interfered with Mrs. Lamb's attempts to devote herself to her son as an infant and small child. She, too, was insecure as a mother, could not set limits, and her son had many serious childhood neurotic problems. Her efforts to support a positive image of Mr. Lamb who was a poor husband and a worse father confused her son, particularly as she clearly conveyed that she expected him to be an intellectual or an artist and not a crude man like his father. Mrs. Lamb had little esteem for herself as a woman and had shown a proclivity for sociopathic men other than her husband before her marriage. Her mother had been a militant feminist and her father a man who lived on his inherited wealth. In contrast to most other mothers in our series, Mrs. Lamb had been favored over her brother by their mother, but in a strange way. Her mother had sought to use her to demonstrate the superiority of women by pushing her to surpass her brilliant brother academically. Mrs. Lamb, however, displayed no feminist competition with men, but rather seemed to seek a masochistic subservience. The projective tests indicated aloofness, disillusion, and hopelessness about finding positive aspects in life—similar to Mrs. Newberg.

Mrs. Benjamin displayed characteristics that have already been noted, but in a different configuration. She was a seriously scattered woman who could be a profound blurrer of meanings. When anxious she would talk incessantly and ask countless questions without waiting for her respondent to answer any of them. However, when supported, she could converse meaningfully and with insight. Much of the time she seemed somewhat removed, caught up in her preoccupations and fantasies. She felt defeated and hopeless in her marriage to a very difficult man who sought to dominate the home and to blame her for his impotence—which left her feeling frustrated and disillusioned. Mrs. Benjamin was clearly very fond of her son, and she did not restrict his separation from her or his development of autonomy, nor did she instill grandiose hopes for his future. She had left his care for the first years of life largely to a nursemaid. Her relations to her son were marked by swings between preoccupied aloofness and an attentiveness that threatened by its seductive quality. Her interaction in the marriage filled with hostile recriminations was more akin to what transpired in many families with schizophrenic daughters in that she was the defeated member of the marital partnership. However, she also demolished her husband's worth as a model for their son. Here again it is important to note that Mr. Benjamin could, in a different way, confuse and obfuscate meaning as effectively as his wife. The complexities of this disturbed marriage and the confusing milieu created cannot be described here. Mrs. Benjamin also had a narcissistic, mixed-up, and near-psychotic mother who bemoaned how her career as an actress had been blighted by her marriage to an ineffectual man.

Certain characteristics appeared in all of the mothers of schizophrenic sons, including Mrs. Forel who differed most markedly from the others. They all had difficulty in achieving proper distance in relating to the child—in investing the child properly. They varied between extremely intrusive oversolicitude and overt disinterest—but even the oversolicitude reflected a difficulty in relating to the child as a separate individual. Each of these women related to her husband in a way that conveyed that he was incompetent as a husband, diminishing or demolishing his worth as an object for a son's identification, and thus formed a model of a woman who is nonsupportive and even dangerous to males. All of the mothers—abetted by their husbands—conveyed a confused system of meanings and distorted ways of perceiving and thinking. The two mothers who could think clearly contributed a sense of hopelessness about finding anything meaningful.

The four or five mothers who were either psychotic or near-psychotic clearly could not establish boundaries between themselves and the child. They treated the sons as extensions of themselves who would realize the mothers' frustrated ambitions and bring meaning to their lives. These mothers, in many respects, related to an imaginary child and implicitly threatened to reject the child who did not objectify the fiction. They needed and used a son to compensate for their own sense of emptiness and worthlessness as a woman, having married passive men who could not complete their lives and who would not intrude into their symbiotic relationship with a son. Indeed, for them males are but adjuncts to a woman's life, useful in giving them the penis they do not have as women or the child they cannot have without a man.

Mothers of Schizophrenic Daughters

When we examine the mothers of schizophrenic daughters, some very marked differences from the mothers of schizophrenic sons as well as some profound similarities become apparent. Although most of these mothers were protective and frequently extremely intrusive, there was, as Alanen (1958) has pointed out, an inimical quality to the protectiveness. Further, with one notable exception, they were not the controlling figure who set the pattern for the family but the devalued and defeated member in a schismatic marriage, considered to be inadequate wives and mothers by their difficult and often paranoid husbands. Although the mothers of schizophrenic daughters are more alike than are the mothers of schizophrenic sons, they are more difficult to describe because of their rather indefinite personality organization and their nebulous and confusing ways of communicating.

Some of the critical similarities to and differences from the mothers of schizophrenic sons can be noted in Mrs. Grau, a woman whom we describe in some detail in Chapter VI. She was an unusually vague, rambling, and scattered person who could talk a great deal and leave the listener puzzled as to whether she had said anything. Her remarks were filled with platitudes, clichés and "pseudomutual" statements that attempted to give a thin sugar-coating to the bitter leaven of her marriage. She created the erroneous impression of being feeble-minded. We could understand why her husband could become enraged when he tried to settle an issue with her. Her psychotic daughter said that her own thinking and speech had become vague after she decided to copy her mother's style of talking to avoid her mother's unbearable intrusiveness into just what she did when out of the home.

Mrs. Grau had very much wanted a child despite her husband's opposition to having children, but she was extremely insecure as a mother. In her uncertainty she had rigidly adhered to rules prescribed in books at a time when rigid, early habit training was advocated. She had been controlling and restricting, and often punitive when her older daughter who, very docile when small, became alienated from her mother and fractious by the time she entered adolescence. Unable to gain direction by sensitivity to the child's needs, Mrs. Grau became anxious and sought control by keeping her within close range in an effort to know everything the child did. She sought to be a devoted mother, but gained little pleasure or sense of fulfillment from the anxiety-provoking task. Throughout the patient's formative years, Mrs. Grau was disheartened to despair by her conflict with her husband that focused upon the child's religious upbringing but extended into every cranny of their lives. She was a woman who depended upon authority for direction, but she could not accept the authority of her husband when he forbade raising the children in the Catholic faith and constantly derided all Catholics.

Mrs. Grau never gave up her struggle for her daughter's religious salvation, and to make the girl an ally in the unending struggle with her rigid and determined husband. She used circumventions which further increased her paranoid husband's distrust and defamation of her. She virtually eliminated herself as an object for the girl's identifications by her intrusive but uncomprehending ways, while her worth as a wife and mother was demolished by her husband's constant attacks upon her.

As with everything else about Mrs. Grau, the picture of her own family background remained rather vague. We do not know much about her mother except that she was a devout Irish-American Catholic, and that Mrs. Grau felt that she received little attention from her. The father was a harsh and domineering German, but because she was her father's favorite, Mrs. Grau did not have as difficult a time with him as did her mother and brothers. Mrs. Grau married a man who resembled her father in many ways, but gained little support or affection from a man who was even more set and

dominating than her father. The intense and enduring conflict between them in which the patient was caught is discussed in Chapter VI.

In studying Mrs. Grau's projective tests, Dr. Singer noted:

Her responses and remarks create a picture of a nebulous, vague,
and evasive woman who scarcely ever gives a direct reply to what
she is asked. She diverts from the testing situation and brings in
extraneous material. At first one gains an impression that she did
not really give any responses to the test at all. Only after one
searches through her evasions does one note that she has given a
few partial, fragmented responses in ways that create the impression that she had really said nothing. She is circular, putting virtually everything in the form of a question, thus failing to convey
that she had found any meaning at all. The way in which she
manages her world is by darting her attention about and giving
partial responses in question form. Absolutely meaningless circu-
larity is treated as a reasonable communication. To cite an example:
she saw a sad girl on one TAT card. Eventually the tester asked
what the girl might have done, to which Mrs. Grau replied, "It
looks like she is probably broken up over what she was crying
about." Such double talk actually conveys no sensible meaning even
though it sounds as if it might. The general mood tone is one of
aversion. She does not expect to like things very well. In effect, she
says that people are not going to be interested in what is going on;
they are not going to be able to stand one another; and it would
be best for them not to be together. Yet, at the same time, she
appends pseudomutual themes here and there, just enough to create a *non sequitur* effect to her responses and interactions. She conveys two messages: the stronger and more frequent message is that
she has many aversions to interacting with people and that she
expects most interactions to turn out unpleasantly; but she also
inserts some platitudes about how nicely things will turn out some-
day.

Mrs. Grau had little confidence in her ability to care for
the child and followed a rigid unempathic pattern and had
even less confidence that the child could care for herself as
she grew older. Her concerns for the girl's moral welfare in
adolescence led to intrusiveness that conveyed an impression
of complete distrust. The marital schism together with the
mother's behavior virtually destroyed the mother's worth as

a model for the girl to follow into adulthood, and turned the child into an object for the parents' competition as well as the scapegoat for their unhappiness. Both parents inculcated a distrust of people including the other parent. The mother's constant blurring of meanings had a direct effect upon the patient's style of communicating and thinking, but the father contributed by his paranoid distortions.

The situation in the Reading family was strikingly similar to that of the Grau family. The birth of the patient, the older daughter, precipitated an enduring conflict in which she served as a pawn and scapegoat. Mrs. Reading, somewhat stronger and more direct than Mrs. Grau, was constantly attacked and derogated by her paranoid husband in a home that became increasingly chaotic. She was a seriously obsessive women who sought to supervise and control her daughters in an extreme manner. Whatever capacities Mrs. Reading may have had as a mother were dissipated in her struggles to maintain herself in the marriage. Mrs. Reading is distinctive in one respect. She is the only mother among the seventeen in the series who spoke warmly of her parental home. She felt that her parents had been strict but kindly, and she had been very close to her four sisters.

Mrs. Thomas resembled the most disturbed mothers of schizophrenic sons in being unable to tolerate separation from her sick daughter and in her conviction that no one other than herself could or would take care of her daughter. She, too, could not clearly differentiate her needs and feelings from those of the patient. Mrs. Thomas was schizophrenic, a wealthy woman who appeared dilapidated and who spoke in an almost incomprehensible manner. Her remarks were peripheral to what she sought to convey. After considerable experience in talking with Mrs. Thomas, the interviewer recognized that she only hinted at her intent, lest she antagonize someone upon whom her daughter's care depended. She had reason for such concern as her intrusiveness had alienated doctors and nurses; and her husband had long disregarded her desires and opinions and openly showed his contempt and repugnance for her. She correctly recognized that her paranoid husband was just as disturbed as she, but that few outside of the immediate family recognized his paranoid tendencies because of his great prestige in the academic world. Her authority and worth as a model to her four daughters had been destroyed not only because of her dilapidation, but also by her husband's calculated conniving to use her wealth and social prestige. When Mrs. Thomas felt that someone sought to understand her and was willing to listen to her, she demonstrated considerable good sense and judgment. As her daughter had already been ill for many years when taken into the study, it was difficult to re-create the child-rearing patterns, particularly as they had been carried out primarily by a constantly changing array of governesses. Although a devoted mother, Mrs. Thomas was inept and extremely anxious, seeking to improve her daughters' care by changing governesses and later by shifting the schools they attended. Despite her obvious psychotic incapacitation, Mr. Thomas left her in charge while he found a position that kept him away from home for long periods. Mrs. Thomas, as Mrs. Newcomb, devoted her efforts and much of her thoughts to her sick child and had difficulty in tolerating separation from her.

Mrs. Thomas, an only child whose mother had died at her birth, was raised by governesses and by a father who moved her to various parts of the world while paying little attention to her. She married a self-made man who found her wealth and social position highly useful and who had previously been engaged to another psychotic woman.

At least four of the five remaining mothers were markedly aloof and virtually disinterested in the daughter who became schizophrenic. Mrs. Ubanque was almost consistently rejecting, having little use for her second daughter whom she obviously disliked, calling her a "nasty little stinker" and insisting that her hebephrenic daughter was not ill but simply acting up through spite. In referring back to different periods in the girl's life, she had no hesitancy in making such comments as, "She was exasperating to live with; . . . everyone [her husband] spoiled her—she wanted to be queen." Her husband claimed that his wife had been envious of the patient's delicate physique and dainty appearance, resenting the attention he gave her.

The negative attitude seems to have pervaded Mrs. Ubanque's relationship to the patient since she had been conceived. Although Mrs. Ubanque had been delighted at giving birth to an older daughter after several miscarriages, she had become very upset and cried for days when she found herself pregnant again only five months later. She was further disappointed in having another girl and remained depressed for some months after the delivery. An obsessive housekeeper, Mrs. Ubanque, too, raised her children according to the books, following a rigid, clock-watching routine with them. A drooling baby on a clean rug was repugnant to her. When the patient was small, Mrs. Ubanque spent little time with her, encouraging the child to play by herself with her dolls and not annoy her mother. The patient remained a bed wetter and head roller to the age of seven, behavior that provoked angry punitive reactions from her mother. According to the patient, her mother had particular concerns about masturbation and would frequently smell her hands to find out if she had been "touching herself." During a remission, the patient complained bitterly about the mother's absence of interest and understanding, and her refusal ever to listen and respond to her pleas for help with her problems.

Mrs. Ubanque's talk was as scattered, inconsistent, and almost as nebulous as Mrs. Grau's. Mrs. Ubanque was even less empathic and seemed uninterested in trying to understand her daughter. She impressed us as being the most impervious mother in the study. She had little difficulty in changing reality to fit her needs, unable or unwilling to hear what she was told. At a time when any untrained observer could see that the patient was out of contact and in a desperate condition, Mrs. Ubanque insisted that her daughter was well enough to be taken home; the real reason was that the family had run out of funds. Soon after the patient emerged from her seriously disorganized state, an attendant who accompanied the patient on a drive with her parents reported that Mrs. Ubanque spent most of the time admonishing her daughter for past trivial misbehavior. She attributed her daughter's difficulties to misbehavior, to the mistakes of teachers, to the influence of college roommates who had talked to her about sex, and blocked discussion of her relationship with the patient.

Although Mrs. Ubanque spoke of her childhood as having been "normal" and of her parents' happiness before her father died, she had a rather tragic background. Her father had been an obsessive man, a slave to rigid routine, "who kept everything to himself." She thought that she had been his favorite and recalled how he would read to her each night precisely from 7:00 to 7:45. He committed suicide when she was six. Mr. Ubanque described his mother-in-law as a difficult, domineering, and highly emotional woman. Mrs. Ubanque said that she had been brought up fairly liberally, but also told how her mother had watched over her like a hawk during her adolescence. She admits that her mother was closer to her older brother who helped support the family after the father's death. The brother developed epilepsy in his adolescence and drowned when he was twenty-one.

Mrs. Ubanque had married the first man who had shown an interest in her, and she looked forward to marriage in childishly romantic terms. She had little interest in sex, "Mr. Ubanque felt cheated early in marriage because when I was bighearted it was twice a week, otherwise once." When the couple were interviewed together, Mrs. Ubanque clearly dominated the situation, ignoring or interrupting her husband whenever he entered the conversation. He seemed to accept this as part of his lot, taking a passive position in these sessions. Although both parents stated that they had been happy together, the patient spoke of many quarrels and of her father's infidelities. Her older sister intimated that many difficulties existed within the family, but would not elaborate and soon removed herself to a distant city, refusing to visit the patient or come for further interviews.

Mrs. Nussbaum could be severely rejecting of her daughter but, in contrast to Mrs. Ubanque, was extremely guilty and disturbed about her own attitude. When her daughter became disturbed, Mrs. Nussbaum tried to devote herself to making amends. Mrs. Nussbaum was upset by the birth as she and her husband had become embroiled in a serious and enduring conflict a few months earlier. Mrs. Nussbaum, incapacitated by an injury during the first year of the child's life and probably depressed, left the care of the child to a nursemaid. She never gained any pleasure or satisfaction from her daughter who soon developed behavioral problems which increased her impatience and irritability with the child. Mrs. Nussbaum suffered from periods of depression with marked irritability and may have verged upon psychosis, but at the time of the study had benefited from several years of intensive psychotherapy. Although she was still a difficult woman, she was, according to her husband, much less so than formerly. Mr. Nussbaum lavished seductive attention upon the girl, seeking the admiration and affection he could not gain from his wife, and the affection between father and daughter increased Mrs. Nussbaum's resentment of her. Her husband purposefully fostered his wife's jealousy not only by his seductive attention to their daughter but also by pretending that he was having affairs. The patient became a focal point in their dissension and a scapegoat for much of their conflict, but the schism had antedated her birth. When the girl first went to boarding school in adolescence, Mrs. Nussbaum sent her off with the remark, "I hope you come home in a coffin." Later, she suggested dual suicide. Still, when the patient became overtly disturbed, Mrs. Nussbaum devoted herself completely to her daughter's care, rarely leaving her. She had been a much more satisfactory mother to her son who had been born before the marital conflict had started and in whom she invested a great deal. Mrs. Nussbaum had felt unwanted as a girl having been raised in a large family by a mother who openly and frequently expressed her preference for her sons and who had a low opinion of women in general.

Mrs. Robb knew that she had been a poor mother to her two daughters, both of whom became schizophrenic. She had not been hostile or overtly rejecting but tended to be apathetic toward them. She had left them in the charge of nursemaids, although she took care of the son who was born between them. She knew that she had gained more pleasure from the boy. She became increasingly preoccupied with her husband's infidelities and her own vengeful involvements with other men. Her own insecurities as a wife and mother were heightened by her husband's disparagement of her efforts, and by his insistence that she follow the advice of a young woman teacher whom he had brought to live in the home and to whom he paid more attention than to his wife. The complexities of the Robbs' marital situation will not be reviewed here, but the discrepancies between the public image of the successful and understanding man and his behavior at home, and between the sedate mother and her extramarital involvements, created a confusing environment for the children. Mrs. Robb also had difficulties because of her own family background. Her family had moved a great deal because of her father's diplomatic career. Her mother had been an ardent feminist who left Mrs. Robb to the care of governesses. The father, of whom she had been so proud during her childhood, suffered a deteriorating organic psychosis when she was adolescent and had behaved in a way that had made her deeply ashamed of him—a circumstance that had affected her life profoundly.

Mrs. Frei was an inadequate mother to both her daughters in a basically schismatic marriage, but both spouses masked the schism from each other and themselves. The older daughter suffered from ulcerative colitis and the younger became schizophrenic. The younger daughter's upbringing, her bizarre eating habits in particular, became a focus of contention between the parents.

Mrs. Frei was the neglected youngest of nine children, and while intelligent enough to learn four languages in childhood, had only very sketchy formal education, which stopped altogether after her father's accidental death when she was fourteen. She then lived with married siblings, apparently moving from one to the other without having a definitive home where she belonged. Like other mothers in our series, she tried to overcome her uncertainty about mothering her firstborn by rigid adherence to schedules and books, and turned over the care of both daughters to servants as soon as financially feasible. While she was more flexible in tending to her second child, she was handicapped during the child's infancy by a breast abscess and probably was depressed. She often became angry enough to hit the baby with a towel. Mrs. Frei showed other characteristics already described with regard to the other mothers of schizophrenic girls, so that they need be mentioned but briefly. She was distant and aloof and concerned herself with the mechanical aspects of her daughter's problems rather than dealing with her needs. She tended to blame her husband for the patient's illness, and yet maintained that they got along well together, and she blamed the patient for "doing this to her." At the same time she overidentified and refused herself pleasure and gratification as long as her daughter did such "bad" things as starving herself. (The patient weighed seventy pounds on admission.) Mrs. Frei was indeed impervious to her own feelings as well as to those of others. On the Object Sorting Test, she as well as her husband showed thought disorder, reflected in abnormal scores. Both parents were pervasively concrete and fragmented, tending to ramble on and on about the separate objects, unable to conceptualize the group as a whole. While both have some tendency to change the function of the objects in an arbitrary manner and to confabulate, building up unrealistic stories around them, Mr. Frei showed more arbitrary and confabulated responses than did his wife. However, she demonstrated looseness of concept boundaries and tremendous stress on orality, giving the impression of being engaged in a desperate struggle to survive.

The seven mothers of schizophrenic daughters who have been discussed were all rather vague and poorly organized women, deficient in self-esteem as women and caught up in unhappy schismatic marriages in which they were the defeated and devalued partner. They gained little satisfaction from their daughters, and though some were intrusive and overcontrolling, there was an aloof, hostile, or an overtly rejecting quality to the relationship. However, the remaining mother, Mrs. Lerner, though also unable to cathect her daughter properly, was a very different type of woman, and her presence in the series prevents the formulation of a consistent picture of all of these mothers of schizophrenic daughters and of their life situations.

A satisfactory understanding of Mrs. Lerner and her family presented inordinate difficulties because of thorough falsification of the history. However, the misrepresentations were fundamental to her personality, and a manifestation of her profound need to maintain an image of herself as a successful, self-sacrificing mother who had made an eminently satisfactory marriage. The need to mask reality had permeated her life and the lives of the other family members requiring them to lead a life of pretense, and had forced the patient to deny her perceptions of the obvious, including what her parents were like and how she felt toward them.

The picture, as originally presented, was of an exceptionally well-knit and harmonious family life blighted by the illness of the highly gifted but extremely sensitive daughter. Their financial resources had become limited because Mr. Lerner, an eminent attorney, had suffered a stroke a year before the daughter's hospitalization. Mrs. Lerner now supported the family by pursuing her profession instead of working part time as she had previously. The patient had presented some special problems in child rearing, because she had very early displayed an unusual artistic gift—a talent that had been associated with insanity in several relatives. Mrs. Lerner had been caught between wishing to redirect the child into more usual feminine pursuits and the feelings of obligation to help her develop her endowment.

In reality, Mr. Lerner's success had ended twelve years earlier with the suicide of his partner when the patient was eight years old. His practice had declined rapidly, but the Lerners maintained the image of the eminently successful legal scholar to the world and to their children—his office expenses being paid out of his wife's inheritance and earnings. The stroke had actually lightened the burden by providing face-saving grounds for his retirement. The marital roles had been reversed many years earlier, with Mr. Lerner doing most of the shopping and cooking while his wife pursued a career that had become essential to her self-esteem as well as the support of the family. In a similar vein, the daughter's illness had to be carefully concealed lest it injure the mother's professional reputation and diminish her earnings. It gradually became apparent that Mrs. Lerner could not acknowledge having married a man who was a failure or having raised a daughter who had become mentally ill. As the patient improved and sought to discuss the family circumstances or to indicate faults in her parents, her mother regularly cut off such "misperceptions" and, with her husband's support, turned the discussion to the difficulties the patient had displayed since her birth.

We do not like to fall back on *post hoc* reasoning in evaluating a mother's maternal capacities, but the patient had presented severe feeding problems and suffered from extreme separation anxiety that mounted to a school phobia on entering kindergarten. Mrs. Lerner had been preoccupied with her older son's rheumatic fever during the patient's first two years of life and had left her largely to the care of nursemaids. When the girl had been sent to camp at the age of twelve to help her overcome her separation anxiety, she wrote letters home that were filled with delusions of persecution which would have led much less educated mothers to take the child home and place her in treatment, but Mrs. Lerner steeled herself and kept herself from even visiting her daughter.

Mrs. Lerner had grown up feeling unwanted and superfluous as the youngest of a series of daughters with a younger brother upon whom the family hopes rested. Although she admired her father and identified with him in many ways. She considered him a rigid and dominating man, and she had a marked antipathy for her mother for reasons that never became very clear. She had shown little interest in men until she fell in love with her husband who appeared to be a mature and competent man who loved and needed her. She felt that for the first time in her life she was accepted and wanted as a woman. Actually, he was a rather rigid but kindly man who had little interest in children and needed to be admired as an important figure by a woman. In contrast to her liberalism, he was a rigidly conservative reactionary. He readily ceded the control of the family affairs to his wife, and eventually the support of the family as well.

The clarity of Mrs. Lerner's conversation covered distortions created by her need to maintain her self-esteem and to combat despair by seeing things as she required them to be. But her projective tests resemble those of Mrs. Newberg and Mrs. Lamb.

She seemed to take the TAT pictures as a grim reality and the persons she described were overcontrolled. The world she perceived was a cheerless place in which one makes one's own bed and stays in it. Everything seemed matter of fact, detached, overcontrolled, dispassionate. People are sad and heartbroken but stolid and defiant, manage to cope somehow. Children are sad but detached, running from fears into a fantasy world. On her Rorschach, in striking contrast to the TAT, there are many fantasy responses in which she seeks to empathize with various childlike situations and has fun in her fantasying. There was a blatant, "pseudomutual" Pollyanna quality to her ideas. While an extremely bright woman, she has a very dreary outlook about all social interactions as they are but a Pollyannalike fantasy life about how things might be.

These few comments from Dr. Singer's interpretations of Mrs. Lerner's tests appear to reflect the dichotomy in her life in which she sacrifices herself, struggles, and carries on; basically she finds the situation hopeless, but she must maintain a front to convince herself and others that things have really turned out well.

Something had gone very much amiss in the relationship between Mrs. Lerner and her daughter from the earliest days. Perhaps specific difficulties engendered by the daughter's endowment created an unfavorable feedback, but very tangible difficulties in the mother's management soon arose. The disturbances in the family organization seriously affected the girl's development, notably because of the marked reversal of gender-linked roles in the parents in which the father carried out many of the wifely tasks. In the process, the patient had somehow never been taught many rudimentary skills about dressing, shopping, housekeeping, etc., but had learned that things were not the way they seemed to be, that facts could and must be altered to suit needs, and that openness would lead to rejection. Such difficulties also affected her career, for she had to maintain a shell of excellence that prevented learning certain rudiments of her craft, believing that as a genius she was supposed to know without study many things that require arduous effort and specific education.

These mothers of schizophrenic daughters all led difficult and unenviable lives, caught up in extremely unsatisfactory marriages. In contrast to many of the mothers of schizophrenic sons, they were, with one exception, the defeated and derogated partner in highly conflictful marriages. All had felt neglected or unwanted as girls in their parental homes, and they had sought paternal figures as husbands but managed to marry men who further undermined their self-esteem as women and increased their insecurities as mothers. They had difficulty in forming warm and close relationships and seem to have had particular difficulty in cathecting a daughter properly—not gaining any sense of fulfillment and gratification from a female child. They could be oversolicitous and even intrusive, but sought to control without warmth and closeness and often with an inimical quality to the relationship. All of these mothers conveyed a sense of defeat in life and hopelessness about being a woman. As has been amply illustrated, they were, with one exception, rather amorphous, nebulous persons and concomitantly profound blurrers or fragmenters of meanings and of meaningfulness. One aspect of the problem requires mention, though it cannot be documented from this study. In a series of female schizophrenic patients treated analytically, it became apparent that the homosexual tendencies of their mothers had confused the mother-child relationship: the mothers needed to maintain distance from their daughters, but sometimes showed a highly eroticized interest in the girls' bodies (Chapter XI).

DISCUSSION

Although a large proportion of these mothers of schizophrenic patients are much alike in certain essentials, no personality description will encompass all of them. However, certain highly characteristic patterns recur frequently, and an appreciation of these differing configurations can further our understanding of the etiology of schizophrenia and remove some of the confusions created by an expectation of finding a single specific type of mother. Dividing the series according to the sex of the patient enables more pertinent description and categorization, for there are significant differences between the mothers of male and female patients and also more clear-cut similarities within such groupings. We have carefully considered the possibility that such grouping reflects different ways with which women with essentially similar personalities respond to male and female children, rather than differences between these mothers. However, some of these mothers clearly formed more satisfactory relationships with children of the opposite sex from the patient, and as the mothers of male patients relate differently to their husbands than do the mothers of female patients, we believe that the personalities of the parents and the family configurations of male and female patients tend to be different, creating more serious developmental problems for the children of the sex of the schizophrenic child (see Chapters IX and XII).

The most striking type of mother is the strange, near-psychotic or even overtly schizophrenic woman who has been termed "schizophrenogenic." Although a description sounds extreme, it pales before the reality. However, such mothers are in a minority. About half of the mothers of the male patients in the series, but only an occasional mother of a female patient, fits the description that follows. However, some very important traits of these women are also found in other mothers of schizophrenic patients.

This type of mother seeks compensation for her dissatisfactions with life and the burdens of being a woman by finding completion through a son. She expects little from men whom she considers as weak figures dependent upon their wives or mothers. She may have married primarily to have a son and consciously or unconsciously selected a weak man who will remain an adjunct to her. She has a narrow range of ways of relating and effectively delimits the family pattern to conform with her needs, and she distorts her perceptions and masks what is untenable to maintain her emotional equilibrium. She manages to be impervious to the needs and wishes of other family members if they do not fit her preconceptions of how things should be. As her psychotic or very strange concepts remain unchallenged by the husband, they create reality within the family. Her communications are vague, fragmented, stereotyped, but they are spoken as if meaningful, creating perplexity in the listener. The husband's worth as a father figure to a son is demolished by her control of him, or because of his gross inadequacies.

She may have very much wanted the baby and fantasied how her child would fulfill her dreams by his greatness. The tangible reality of a child who needs her care is another matter; and she is uncertain and insecure despite her controlling attitudes. Obsessive oversolicitude commonly masks the mother's anxiety or meager responsivity to the actual child. She continues to relate to the child of her fantasies and lacks empathy and awareness of the child's needs. She envisions and seeks to establish a very special relatedness between herself and her son through which her dormant and frustrated potentialities will flow into her offspring. Lacking adequate ego boundaries, she fails particularly in setting boundaries between herself and the child and has difficulty in differentiating her own needs from those of the child. She commonly projects her own insecurities onto the child and becomes overprotective of him. Her feelings of unity with the child, her need for him, and her protectiveness, as well as her controlling attitudes toward males, hinder the child in differentiating and from gradually achieving a sense of autonomy. Parental figures and directives cannot be properly internalized as a superego and remain predominantly derived from the mother. The mother's use of a son in place of her husband as the major source of emotional gratification, which frequently includes highly eroticized and seductive behavior, confuses the oedipal transition. When the engulfing behavior provokes antagonisms in her son or her eroticized care makes him seek to withdraw from her, she may take refuge behind such platitudes as "a child always shows some anger to the person he loves most." Nevertheless, she suffers from periods of incapacitating anxiety or depression during which the burden of filling her emptiness or allaying her concerns falls heavily upon the son.

Four of the mothers of male patients were different types of persons. Two were somewhat aloof women who were not engulfing and intrusive and could communicate and think clearly and rationally, but they were uncertain, anxious, and overprotective with sons whom they needed as sources of emotional gratification, particularly because their husbands were very disturbed and difficult. Their disappointments with their marriages and their basic hopelessness about finding anything meaningful in life may have placed this insoluble burden upon their sons of bringing satisfaction to them. Another mother was more like the defeated and rather amorphous mothers of schizophrenic daughters, but she was fond of her son. She does not seem to have been intrusive and overcontrolling, but she was quite seductive at times, and her repetitive talk could blur meaning and provoke despair. The one mother who was clearly overtly rejecting of a son had none of the overcontrolling qualities or confusions between her needs and feelings and those of her son. But, she, too, had little regard for men, sought to control her husband and demolished his worth, and upon occasion was frighteningly sexually seductive with her sons.

We might note that all of these mothers because of their own personalities and needs, or because of their unfortunate marriages, became dangerous figures to males. They were engulfing, castrating, or chronically dissatisfied with their husbands. The husbands, in turn, were either destroyed or destroyed themselves as effective models for the son to emulate, and were not a source of the son's ego ideal or superego directives.

The mothers of schizophrenic daughters form a more homogeneous grouping. Characteristically, the mother is caught up in a very unhappy and conflictful marriage in which her low self-esteem as a woman is debased further by her husband's deprecation of her. She married a man who needs to defend his own image as a man, and requires the admiration or adulation of a woman but can give little of the paternal support that his wife needs, unconsciously envying the woman's role. The mother is disillusioned about her marriage, filled with hostility toward her husband, and preoccupied with her dilemma. Many are more amorphous than the mothers of the schizophrenic sons, tending to be colorless. A nebulous quality makes her difficult to know and to describe. She is deficient in feminine warmth and affectionate qualities. Her communications reflect her personality, having an illusive, scattered content, and conveying distance in interpersonal relationships. She had felt unwanted as a girl, has a low estimate of women and womanhood, and has grave difficulties in cathecting a daughter. While she may be oversolicitous and overprotective of her daughter, she is aloof from her and an inimical quality shows through the overprotection. The disappointment in having a daughter may be apparent. The mother of the female patient may also have difficulty in differentiating the daughter from herself, but the consequences are different than in the case of a schizophrenic son; her low self-esteem as a woman is transferred to the daughter, and feelings of emptiness in being a female impedes the relatedness to the daughter. We might say that her alienation from her feminine role contributes to an alienation from the daughter. She provides a poor identification model of a woman, wife, and mother for the girl to follow into womanhood, and her husband makes it clear to the daughter that anyone like the mother cannot gain his affection and esteem. Unlike some mothers of schizophrenic sons, she does not have set ideas of what the girl should become. She is more likely to seek to make the daughter an ally in the conflict with her husband, or to find in the dependency of the child a reason to continue her marriage or even a reason to continue living. She conveys a sense of defeat and hopelessness about the lot of being a woman, and perhaps about life in general. In the conflict with her husband, and in her efforts to survive in the struggle, she seeks to alienate her daughter from her father. The girl is apt to be caught in the schism and spends her energies in trying to bridge the gap, or to maintain the mother she needs, or forms divergent ways of relating to two irreconcilable parents—and her own development and integration suffers.

The portrait of the mother of a schizophrenic daughter is an unhappy one of a life of frustration and despair. Only two of the seven mothers in the study differed from it, and only one markedly. One was so impervious to the feelings of others that she suffered less, but her marriage was poor and her life sterile, though she may have managed to avoid recognizing reasons for dissatisfaction. The other was an extremely capable woman who could gain satisfaction from a career, and was the dominant figure in the marriage, willing to shield her husband from the impact of his failure. However, she, too, had difficulties in relating to a daughter, and her masking of reality required the entire family to share the pretense and helped distort the family structure.

Whereas personality traits and patterns common to all of the mothers could not be found, and even such categorizations that have been made are abstractions and are more or less arbitrary, the survey indicates that all of the mothers failed seriously in carrying out their cardinal maternal functions. We have directed attention to four interrelated sets of maternal functions necessary for providing the proper milieu, security, directives, and adaptive techniques to the child if he is to develop into a reasonably well-integrated and self-sufficient individual: the ability to provide nurturance and relate appropriately in accord with the child's changing needs and capacities; the mother's functions as a wife in forming and maintaining a family system with the structural requisites for properly channeling and directing the child's personality structure; the capacities to convey the basic adaptive techniques of the culture, particularly its meaning systems; and to serve for both an object of identification and a primary love object for the child. The marked incapacities of the mothers in all of these areas have been noted and illustrated.

Marked deficiencies and aberrations in the mother-child relationship existed during the child's infancy in all cases—though in some adequate nurturance may have been provided by substitutes. Either apprehensive oversolicitude or impoverished investment of the child affected the child's security and started a feedback that affected the mother. Difficulties may have been even more serious when the child began to show initiative and to differentiate from the mother. Although some mothers may have related to the child reasonably well during one developmental phase, few could shift to relate appropriately as the child matured. Such problems were not confined to infancy or early childhood but continued into and throughout the child's adolescence.

The hypothesis has often been raised that the mothers could not relate properly to the child who becomes schizophrenic because of some inherent deficiencies in the child—a situation that appears to occur with certain autistic children. The evidence does not support the hypothesis, though it may apply in a few cases. Notable difficulties in early infancy were reported in only a few patients; nursemaids took care of a number of these children; serious difficulties in the mother's capacities as a mother in other areas and as a wife were evident. It is more in accord with the evidence to postulate a feedback of disharmony in the mother-child relationship created by a combination of the mother's own difficulties, those of her husband, and the serious problems of the marriage.

The dynamic organization of all of these families was seriously disturbed by the marital schism or skew (Chapter V), the failure to maintain generation boundaries, and by failures of the parents to maintain their sex-linked roles, as we discuss in other chapters.

The father is involved as well as the mother, and it is difficult to assign responsibility for such failures. The controlling and dominating wife must have a husband who can be dominated, and some such fathers might be considered to force their wives to assume instrumental leadership of the family. However, as we have indicated, some mothers of schizophrenic sons needed to have husbands fill only adjunctive roles, and also breached generation boundaries by displacing the husband with the son. Most of the remaining mothers could not be supportive of their husbands as husbands or fathers; at the most two, or possibly three, of these seventeen women were adequate sexual partners; and all, in one way or another, undermined the worth of their husbands—though many of these husbands made it difficult for their wives to be supportive.

The deficiencies of all but a few of these women in transmitting and inculcating valid meaning systems are noted in Chapter VII. The communications of some are distorted psychotically, and in others by a need to adhere to preconceptions of the way things must be to maintain their own precarious equilibrium, disregarding reality testing when necessary. The re-examination of the protocols of their projective tests by Dr. Singer revealed even more profound and pervasive difficulties. They blur meanings or fragment them, deny their own perceptions, confuse by inserting extraneous material, perseverate a few ideas or perceptions even when clearly inappropriate, etc. There is often an inconsistency between verbal and nonverbal communications. The few mothers who can communicate clearly also conveyed a hopelessness and even a despair about finding anything meaningful in life. The "double-bind" of Bateson et al. (1956) is but one aspect of a more pervasive communication disturbance which requires considerable study.

Here again, it is necessary to emphasize that many of the fathers also contributed to the problem—and in some instances their thinking was far more disturbed than the mothers'. It is clear that the failure to inculcate properly the linguistic meanings of the culture and useful ways of categorizing experiences can prevent the acquisition of other essential techniques and also create serious impediments to adequate ego functioning.

The study serves to emphasize the inadequacies of these women as mothers. Too commonly the psychiatrist who encounters them as mothers of his patients views them and treats them as willfully malevolent or rejecting. Our attention has been forcefully directed to the deficiencies in the mother's own development. Hill (1955) had noted the frequency with which mothers of schizophrenic patients had themselves lacked adequate maternal care, and Alanen (1958) documented the embittered feelings such mothers had about their childhoods and their frequent hostility toward their own mothers. Even though the study was not designed to examine the developmental histories of the mothers and fathers, sufficient information is available for most mothers to indicate clearly that the trend toward social and emotional aberration had originated at least one generation earlier. Only one of the seventeen mothers spoke in positive terms about her family of origin, and animosities toward their own mothers were striking, particularly among the mothers of schizophrenic daughters. The frequency with which the mother's mother was a self-centered, narcissistic woman who felt that her beauty or talent was wasted in her marriage is noteworthy. The mothering that these mothers had received in childhood had been very faulty, suggesting that a woman who has not received adequate mothering herself will have difficulties in being an empathic mother. Their deficiencies in a sense of their worth as women, and even of the worth of femininity, appear to reflect the attitudes of the parents of these mothers toward daughters. Such deficiencies in self-esteem influenced the choice of husbands and left many particularly vulnerable to their husbands' disparagements.

In some instances, the mother's instability may have been due to the traumatic circumstances of her childhood as in the case of Mrs. Schwartz who was orphaned at an early age and raised by older siblings and dependent upon the meagre charity of poor neighbors and relations, and of Mrs. Thomas whose mother died at her birth. In others, as Mrs. Nebb and Mrs. Narab, the disturbances can be traced back for two or more generations. As the fathers of the patients had equally difficult backgrounds, the data suggest that the schizophrenic patient is the offspring of families that have become increasingly deviant in their child-rearing techniques and communication until societal norms and directives were no longer transmitted adequately. We would suggest, however, that because women become schizophrenic at a somewhat later age than men, and because they can remain sheltered longer, more women than men who are disorganized will marry, and that mothers may play a greater part in the production of schizophrenic children for such reasons as well as because of their greater influence upon the child.

The survey of these mothers of schizophrenic patients reveals their serious inadequacies in functioning as mothers.

Although they may seem to be particularly strange and difficult women as a group, the study of Delay et al. (1957, 1960, 1962) of French families containing a schizophrenic child which includes many lower-class families describes mothers who are at least as disturbed and some who are extremely bizarre. The evidence does not bear out the suggestion that the mother has difficulty in mothering the child who becomes schizophrenic because of some inherent unresponsivity or hypersensitivity in the infant. The mothers' problems transcend the relationship to the child and usually clearly antedated his birth. These mothers are not only difficult persons but unhappy and unstable, and we have sought to convey some impression of the continuity and increment of such personality problems across generations.

Mothers of persons with problems other than schizophrenia may show similar characteristics, but perhaps not in the same severity or in all four areas. However, as will be evident from the other chapters in this book, influences other than the mother contribute to family environments that are conducive to the genesis of schizophrenic conditions.

POSTSCRIPT

It should be noted that in contrast to one important study (Kety et al., 1968), but in accord with others, we found that three or approximately seventeen percent of the seventeen mothers were overtly schizophrenic, though none had been hospitalized, and several others (Nebb, Ubanque, and Grau) were not simply borderline, but very bizarre, and perhaps should be termed "psychotic personalities." In addition, Mrs. Dolfuss shared her husband's delusion that he was the reincarnation of a deity; and Mrs. Nussbaum may have gone through a psychotic episode prior to our study. On the other hand, four mothers—Robb, Lerner, Newberg, and Lamb—seemed to have been fairly well-integrated women, though all tended to be aloof and had grave difficulties because of their husbands' psychopathology. We could imagine that these four women might have been fairly competent mothers had they married supportive and better-integrated husbands. However, all of the mothers were depressed or greatly preoccupied with other matters following the birth of the child who became schizophrenic. In Chapter XI we discuss the homosexual tendencies of some mothers of schizophrenic daughters, a problem that requires consideration, but which we could not assess properly in this study. The mothers' difficulties in establishing boundaries between themselves and their children, which we noted in many instances, should probably have been emphasized more strongly. The relationship to difficulties in forming boundaries on the one hand, and being properly empathic on the other, will be related to the mother's egocentricities in Chapter XIX. As will become apparent in the next chapter, although none of the fathers was clearly schizophrenic (with the possible exception of Mr. Dolfuss), several were paranoid and some were very strange men.

Because our relations with the mothers were, in general, closer than with the fathers, it is more certain that the origins of their personality disturbances go back one or more generations, and that the choice of their husbands could be related to the pathology in their parents' marriages.

IV

The Fathers

(1955)

The article on the fathers of the patients was the first publication of our study because almost all papers concerned with the psychogenesis of schizophrenic disorders had focused on the mothers. We were struck by the deleterious influences of the fathers in all of these families, and the serious psychopathology of most of the fathers. Although a few investigators had commented on either the inefficacy or the domineering and rejecting characteristics of fathers of schizophrenics, this was the first careful study of fathers of schizophrenic patients.

As the first publication of our family studies, we introduced it by commenting why we considered the current psychoanalytic theories concerning the etiology of schizophrenia to be inadequate, and we now find that these reasons would also apply almost as well to the theories of borderline and narcissistic personalities of Kernberg (1975) and Kohut (1971) that are popular at present. We indicate why our findings were leading us into the broader concept of how all of these families failed to provide a proper milieu for the integrated development of the offspring who became schizophrenic, how it related to the psychopathology of the parents, usually both parents rather than the mother alone, and to the relationships between the spouses.

The paper presents some of our concepts of the father's role in a

Theodore Lidz, Alice R. Cornelison, Stephen Fleck, and Dorothy Terry: The Intrafamilial Environment of the Schizophrenic Patient: I. The Father. *Psychiatry*, Vol. 20, 1957, pp. 329-342. Copyright © 1957, The William Alanson White Psychiatric Foundation, Inc. This paper was presented in November 1955 to the Joint Meeting of the Washington Psychiatric Society, the Washington Psychoanalytic Society, and the Medical Society of St. Elizabeth's Hospital, Washington, D.C.

family and his functions in the personality development of sons and daughters respectively. The chapter also notes the importance of the oedipal transition to the child's security of gender identity as well as "ego identity," and the father's role in helping a son overcome his initial identification with his mother, as well as his oedipal attachment to her.

As part of our intensive study, we here present an initial compilation of material concerning fathers. We are not studying such fathers apart from their interaction with the remaining members of the families, or from their role as partners in marriages in which the wives are often, if not usually, very difficult women who also have serious neurotic or psychotic needs that tend to disrupt the marriage and the family life. We are here focusing upon the father because so much attention has been focused on the mother, with little recognition of the difficulties frequently imposed upon her and the children by the father, and because, in order to understand these marriages, which are predominantly unsuccessful and often torn by intrafamilial schism, we must understand the husband as well as the wife.

In the orientation that permeates our work, there is no incrimination of the parent, such as often develops from receiving the story from the patient's point of view. One rapidly realizes that these parents are struggling with their own problems and defenses and, with very rare exceptions, have striven to do their best for their children within their abilities and the limits placed by their own emotional difficulties. Too often the psychiatrist forgets his psychiatric understandings when dealing with parents and expects them to have been able to be different from what they were, or to change through reading a book or just because he tells them to behave differently. They, too, are as much bound to their unconscious conflicts as the patients and could not have been other than they were.

THE SCHIZOPHRENIC AND HIS FAMILY

Our focus has been on the entire period of maturation, seeking to grasp the complex interplay of forces that may prevent the patient from achieving an individual identity or an integrated self at the end of adolescence or early in adult life, very much as Erikson (1956) has been focusing on ego diffusion at the end of adolescence. The emphasis is upon the inability to find a "role" in life, a way into the future, a way of relating meaningfully to persons in and out of the family. The cause is not sought in a particular developmental period, nor in a single family relationship or traumatic experience, but rather in the confluence of factors that hem in the patient and prevent movement, *perhaps even successful regressive movement.* Of course, it is considered that in some instances the earliest mother-child relationships may have been so unsatisfactory that the ego was bound to founder, or that after a close mother-infant relationship the mother would not permit any independent movement of the child because of her anxieties, and so forth; but we conceive of the possibility that, even later in the process of maturation, reality factors, including parental attitudes and intrafamilial schisms, can warp or block further development so that the child or adolescent loses his way. It might be said—to return to the earlier frame of reference—that we are, in part, seeking causes for the withdrawal from reality in the nature of the reality in which the patient lived, not out of neglect of problems of ego strength and weakness, but rather because we believe that the ego is formed in relation to and in interaction with the "reality" in which the patient grows up, through reciprocal interaction with the people who surround and nurture him.

According to early analytic theories, the massive narcissistic regression of the schizophrenic indicates serious fixation at the early oral phase. The ties to reality are weak because of the libidinal impoverishment of the ego due to the early fixation of the libido, and, when objects are relinquished, regression to the earliest developmental stages follows. A major reason for such hypothetical frames of reference follows the reasoning of Abraham (1908, 1916), that schizophrenia, as the most profound disorganization of the ego, indicates the most profound regression. The symptoms indicative of later developmental stages are considered clear evidence of restitutive attempts to restore object relationships.[1]

This outline is, of course, only a condensed approximation of one of several related hypotheses; but if it is correct, the need to concentrate on the earliest period is obvious. Efforts to study the later family relationships may seem unwarranted, and the space left for consideration of the role of fathers is very narrow, although not entirely absent. However, a hypothesis serves only to direct investigations, and if it fosters neglect of facts it must be altered or discarded. At the moment, it seems pertinent to examine the understanding of some facets of the hypothesis. If one accepts the concept of early oral fixation in schizophrenia, one has not of necessity arrived at a concept of etiology. One can say that early infantile deprivation is necessary to the occurrence of the illness, but one must remember that an Anlage is not a cause. Patients with other entities, such as certain antisocial personalities and psychosomatic illnesses, have yielded clearer evidence of seriously disturbed mother-infant relationships than have schizophrenics. The specificity of illness may depend upon additional, later causative factors. Indeed, the paucity of evidence from case material of a qualitative or quantitative

---

[1]A review of psychoanalytic concepts of schizophrenia can be found in Brody and Redlich *Psychotherapy with Schizophrenics* (1952), and a brief review of psychoanalytic theories of the psychopathology in Freeman et al., *Chronic Schizophrenia* (1958).

Psychoanalytic ego psychology has broadened the understanding of schizophrenia, but many of its contributions concern suppositions about the psychic apparatus. Hartmann (1953) conjectures that deficiencies in primary autonomous factors in the ego contribute to the vulnerability of defense, of neutralization, and perhaps still other ego functions. Though recognizing the importance of early object relations, he leaves open the relative importance of various innate and environmental factors. Federn's (1952) contributions concerning ego boundaries helped clarify the phenomenology and the nature of the patient's problems. Fairbairn's (1944) studies of the endopsychic structure consider the nature of the internalized objects to a greater extent than Melanie Klein's theories, but they are also concerned primarily with the mother.

difference in the early deprivation of schizophrenic patients as presented in the literature is most striking. Hajdu-Gimes (1940) is among the few writers who present fairly clear evidence, and she invokes two other major factors—the cold, sadistic character of the mother and the passivity of the father—as etiological essentials. Further, there are other ways of regarding the extent of the regression in schizophrenia. L. B. Hill (1955) who has had extensive experience with schizophrenics and their mothers, believes, somewhat paradoxically, that the mother-infant relationship was usually satisfactory, despite his devastating description of the mothers. He adheres to the view that the intense fixation results from undue or untimely indulgence, impeding advance to the next developmental phase in which the child suffers deprivation, and that regression occurs to a pretraumatic period in the effort to regain gratification. There is good evidence in at least some cases that the mother badly wanted the schizophrenic child and was reasonably capable at mothering the infant. Severe and unqualified rejection, such as propounded by Rosen (1953), is probably not productive of schizophrenia.

What requires emphasis, however, is that the stage to which regression occurs need not indicate the period of deprivation, or even the level of the fixation. Leaving aside Freud's analogy to the dammed river breaking through the banks at a weak point upstream (Freud, 1911), and using instead his analogy to a migrant people's constructing fortified points to which they can retreat (Freud, 1916-1917), one can recognize that, in panic, an army can run past all shelters and fortifications until it reaches the ships from which it disembarked—or at least so went one campaign—even as the patient seeks the shelter of the womb.

Of course, the army may be overcome in battle because it has left too many behind to garrison the outposts or fortifications; that is, fixations may deprive the patient of libido to invest in the advance; but the defeat can also derive from split objectives, overwhelming opposition, difficult and uncharted terrain, dissension in the forces, defects in training, lack of grasp of reality by the generals—a very pertinent factor, we believe, in both military maneuvers and child rearing—or failures in the supporting troops. It is possible to continue the analogy, but what we wish to emphasize is that one cannot focus prematurely on a single explanation for all of the catastrophic defeats in living that are termed schizophrenia. The need to withdraw from reality can, and probably does, involve factors other than the early weakening of the infant who must find his way to achieve an independent and integrated identity.

The concept of regression as an entire explanation seems to contain a major defect. The primary schizophrenic maneuver, or at least *a* primary maneuver, is withdrawal and, although regression is a withdrawal maneuver, it is an attempt to find security in the dependency of infancy or childhood. The schizophrenic usually withdraws from reality and from object relations. The withdrawal of the schizophrenic is a "distance" maneuver and is often singularly ineffective in gaining for the patient the closeness attained by regressive efforts. The classic onset is a withdrawal from the love objects he desperately needs, with consequent feelings of catastrophe and annihilation. The regression, in itself, is of a delusional nature in the schizophrenic and is, by itself, an insufficient explanation.

There are further reasons to be cautious about accepting the concept of fixation at an early oral level as an adequate hypothesis. The belief that the schizophrenic regresses to this level is not clearly confirmed by observation. The critical symptomatology focuses on later developmental stages: the eluding of the painful confines of reality by reversion to a time when a private fantasy world did not conflict with reality; the escape from the demands of masculinity by a feminine identification with the mother; the striking revival of the oedipal conflict; the manipulation of symbols to personal needs, and the concreteness of meanings. All focus on the early oedipal and immediately preoedipal periods when the child must reluctantly come to terms with the inevitable force of the reality principle, the primacy of parental authority, the formation of sexual identity, and problems pertaining to the adaptation to extrafamilial influences. It is the narcissism of the schizophrenic rather than the level of regression that is the most forceful reason for considering the earlier level of fixation, for the cardinal defects mentioned are scarcely restitutive. There is ample narcissism in the early oedipal child. One should add that the earlier consideration of catatonia as a regression to an early infantile, helpless state also does not hold up, for the catatonic is immobile and mute because in his omnipotent, narcissistic state any movement or word can change the fate of his needed love objects or of the world. He is protecting himself against the catastrophe which follows upon his hate and withdrawal of cathexis from his love objects.

THE FATHERS

The fathers in the families under consideration were found to be very important, albeit often extremely disturbing, members of their families, whose presence and influence cannot be neglected. We would like to make room—theoretical room—for the consideration of the potentiality that the father requires scrutiny in the effort to understand schizophrenia and the schizophrenic patient.

The reasons for the predominant interest in the mother and the early mother-child relationship in schizophrenia derive principally from two considerations. Psychiatrists have not been able to avoid mothers of schizophrenic patients, and the obvious eccentric and paralogical characteristics of some of these mothers make a lasting impression upon the psychiatrists whom they harass, who tend to generalize from them to all mothers of schizophrenic patients. This does not appear clearly justified on the basis of our intensive studies, however. The dominant analytic theories concerning the etiology of schizophrenia have also warranted the close scrutiny of the mother-child relationship during the first year or two of life.

The father, however, also plays an essential role in the development of the child, and the child who grows up with a grossly maladjusted father or father image will undoubtedly have serious difficulties in maturing properly. The father's place in the developmental process of the child is, of course, extremely involved, and his deficiencies can impede or prevent the child's progress in many ways at all stages of development. Perhaps in the most general terms one can follow Zelditch (1955) and Parsons and Bales (1955) in pointing out that the father is the leader of the family in adaptive-instrumental roles, as against the integrative-expressive primacy of the mother, and, therefore, a "weak, ineffectual" father is more significant than a "weak, ineffectual" mother, whereas a "cold, unyielding" mother is more of a problem than a "cold, unyielding" father. It is usually the father in middle- or upper-class families who represents the family to the extrafamilial world, establishes the family position in society, and forms the major source of the family's prestige, pride, and self-esteem. Perhaps more than the mother, his friendly or suspicious attitudes toward outsiders cultivate the group attitudes of the family to the environment. To the child, he is the first intruder into the child's feelings of unity with the mother, and the child should develop a sense of identification with the father—one of mutuality as against the rest of the world. The mother's ability to mother and to be secure in mothering cannot be divorced from the support she gains from the father and his ability to share her with the child. Fathers who resented or could not endure the intrusion of the child and became rivals of the child or of the mother are common in our study. The child's appraisal of the worth of the mother as a love object and as a secure, sheltering figure also involves the father, through the father's esteem for her or enmity toward her. To a daughter, the father should be a suitable early love object, so that she can seek to gain the love of a man by growing into a woman like the mother—a course that can be impeded if the mother is despised or unwanted by the father, as well as if the mother forms an impossible model for identification.

A crucial event of the oedipal phase for children of both sexes is the achievement of sexual identity as a male or female. The boy has the difficult task of overcoming the primary identification with the mother, and the ambivalent fear and hostility directed toward the father, to enable identification with his father and thereby feel lovable to women in his male role. If the father is realistically jealous and hostile to the boy, if he is a weak figure, completely subservient to the mother, or if he is unacceptable to the mother, who constantly derogates him, then the assumption of a workable male role can be extremely difficult for the boy. It will be noted that few of the fathers in our study presented masculine images for their sons to incorporate that were even vaguely satisfactory. Whereas the girl need not shift her sexual identification, she must come to terms with her castration feelings and the worth of her sex. She has, however, a potential model in the home and can remain relatively passive after her emergence from the family, provided the mother as a mothering figure is appreciated. The boy, however, cannot grow in the image of the mother. A father figure, albeit simply the ideal of a father figure, which he can follow in his emotional development is essential—a father who is a representative of the outside world and who can get along in it without being overwhelmed; and a father who can show the way in relating in a masculine way to the mother, to guide the boy in the difficult turn-about from being a child dependent on a mother to becoming a man who can permit a woman to be dependent upon him. For a son to find his way in life—into a career role as well as a marital role—the covert as well as the actual support of an acceptable father is important. It may well be easier for a son to grow up without a father than to grow up with a father whom the mother cannot tolerate, or who is too aloof or grandiose to serve as a figure for identification. Too often schizophrenic patients must exclude such fathers and continue a mutuality with the mothers.

We have not sought to cover all of the needs for a satisfactory father figure in the family, but have only sought to emphasize the vital role which the father fills in the development of children. We should like to add one further consideration which has many ramifications, but may best be summed up by saying that the family structure and the proper development of children require that there not be confusion of the generations between parents and children. For the child's normal development, he must know that he cannot take one parent's place with the other, and that while he may identify with a parent, he does not become a parent figure in the familial home. The father who competes as a son of his wife, or remains a passive child who is displaced in the wife's affections by his child, or, on the opposite side, seeks to substitute a daughter or even a son for his wife, threatens this necessary division between generations that offers the child security against incestuous and castration anxieties, for his attitudes rather realistically foster one or the other fear. Parsons and Bales (1955) emphasize such considerations in slightly different terms.

Fathers have not been altogether neglected in the study of schizophrenic patients. Lidz and Lidz (Chapter II) indicated in their survey of fifty families that ". . . the paternal influences are noxious as frequently as are the maternal . . . study of some cases leaves the impression that had there been a stable father . . . the patient would not have been so seriously affected by the mother's difficulties." The ineffectiveness of the father in the paternal role, his passivity or weakness, his aloofness from the patient, have been noted by Gerard and Siegel (1950), Hajdu-Gimes (1940), Ellison and Hamilton (1949) and Frazee (1953). The last three investigators noted that a fair proportion of the fathers were cruel and rejecting, or domineering and sadistic, and commented on the unfortunate combination of cruel fathers and overprotective mothers. Reichard and Tillman (1950) describe a schizophrenogenic type of father who is domineering, sadistic, and overtly rejecting. They pertinently note that these fathers are basically weak and ineffectual and that their jealousy of the children and rivalry for the mothers' attention prevent the mothers from giving the children adequate care and attention. This formulation appears to us to be highly pertinent, although more of a composite of outstanding traits than a description suited to any one father.

There are fourteen fathers whom we have now studied and understand reasonably thoroughly.[2] None filled his paternal role effectively, although several were ineffectual primarily because of their passivity rather than because of positive deleterious traits. In the following pages, we shall discuss these fathers in terms of five groups, which we believe are useful for demonstrating the types of tangible problems created for the mothers and children concerned and also for purposes of broad theoretical conceptualization. The groups are not to be regarded as clear-cut and mutually exclusive; they are, rather, five somewhat overlapping patterns which seem to be of significance, practically and theoretically.

The first group, comprising fathers of some female patients, is made up of men who are in constant, severe conflict with their wives, undercutting their authority with the children and derogating their worth as persons, while seeking to win the daughters to their own side of the controversy. They rigidly and unrealistically expect that their wives will docilely conform to their own peculiar ways of regarding the world and of raising children, probably wishing for wives who would agree constantly with them and build up their self-esteem. Disappointed in their wives, they would like to mold their daughters to fill their needs. They are paranoid in their distrust of people, and when their unreasonable demands force the wives to subterfuge, their mistrust is heightened.

The conflict antedates the birth of the children, who simply become the focal point in the struggle between the parents. Although these fathers have tyrannical tempers and are habitually cruel in their attitudes, if not physically, to their wives, they are not necessarily strict with their daughters. Rather,

---

[2]*See postscript to the chapter for comments concerning the three fathers studied after this article was written.*

they are constantly in opposition to their wives' expectations for the children. The wooing of the daughters is designed primarily to gain their allegiance, although it may also be sexually seductive.

The father is highly inconsistent, and the children, who seek to satisfy him, are confused by his demands, for the behavior he requires of them depends upon his neurotic or psychotic needs. Furthermore, the children are disillusioned by his basic though unconscious dishonesty, which seems to derive from his projection of his own wishes onto his wife or daughter.

In our experience, it is the daughter who sides with the father and seeks his love who becomes psychotic. She seeks to differentiate herself from the mother, rather than to follow the mother in her development; but the father's demands are too inconsistent and unrealistic to allow her to establish a satisfactory relationship with him. Moreover, the father's hostility to the mother is crippling to the daughter, for the daughter needs the mother in order to develop a secure feeling of feminine identity.

The Grau's marriage has always been seriously disturbed; almost from the beginning Mr. Grau would frequently become violently infuriated with his poorly organized wife, and spells of gloomy depression would punctuate his chronic irritability. He has always believed his way of doing things to be right, and his wife's failure to comply with his set notions has been unbearable to him. They married several years after his graduation from college, where he had been ill at ease, unrealistically feeling handicapped and unwanted because of his rural background. He had never dated a girl before his brief courtship, and he married without concern over the fact that his wife was a devout Catholic, agreeing to raise the children as Catholics.

Soon after marriage, he informed Mrs. Grau that the children's religion would not create a problem because they would not have any children. Although he made the religious difference the reason for not wanting children, his wife believes that he could not tolerate having her pay attention to a child. Continuous conflict began with the first pregnancy. He accused his wife of conceiving to prevent the marriage from breaking up, although he had assumed responsibility for the contraceptive practice. His refusal to let the children be baptized Catholic began a conflict which continues to the present time.

As long as the children can remember, there have been incessant strife and threats of separation; Mr. Grau's instability and outbursts have kept the home in a state of chronic tension. This became more pronounced when he became ill during the patient's ninth year. He was invalided for the next eight years, stubbornly refusing a necessary operation. His disposition worsened as he became physically dependent upon his wife, and his leadership and authority were impaired, further diminishing his effectiveness as a father. His illness also caused considerable economic insecurity for the family.

He always not only has been constantly critical of his wife and oblivious to her feelings, but has pointedly sought to hurt her. Thus, perhaps jealous of her devotion to the Church, he blames Catholicism for all her faults and for the wrongdoings of any Catholic miscreant of whom he reads in the paper. The younger daughter, who is not the patient, has espoused Catholicism, but she keeps it secret from her father, for she is certain that he would turn against her as violently as he has turned against his wife. However, religion, while a focal issue, has not been the only cause of strife; for instance, Mr. Grau constantly belittles anyone without a college education, derogating his wife because she attended only a two-year junior college. He has always made it clear to his daughters that he hates and scorns his wife, at the same time letting the patient feel that she is more important to him than his wife. However, he has been inconsistent with the daughters, being overly permissive but also harsh, critical, and cynical. In general, he is lax concerning their supervision and their dating, but he forbade their dating before the age of sixteen and he objects violently if they go with a boy who is a Catholic or who does not have a college education. His unfeeling and thoughtlessly cruel remarks to his schizophrenic daughter, even though she has always been his favorite, reflect his disappointment in her and in his own life.

Although Mr. Grau is fairly successful in his career, he is suspicious of his superior and his coworkers. He has also inculcated in his daughters a suspiciousness of outsiders and a feeling that one lives in a basically inimical world. His own suspiciousness is reinforced by his bigotry against his wife's religion, but more specifically by his distrust of her. Mrs. Grau, who has always been very insecure and rigid in raising the children, has met constant opposition from her husband in her efforts to raise the children according to the only pattern she knows—that of devout Catholicism—and her worth and authority have been constantly undermined. While she has also undercut Mr. Grau's authority with the children, this has been primarily because of her own struggle to retain her children's loyalty. The fact that Mr. Grau has turned to his older daughter to fill the emptiness left by the mother has involved confusion of the father-daughter roles.

The second grouping concerns the fathers of some of the male patients, whose hostility turns toward the offspring rather than the wife. These men are rivals with their sons for the mothers' attention and affection, behaving like jealous older siblings who must outshine the patient. They are extremely self-centered and eager for prestige, sometimes resenting their children as impediments to their success and hence to the admiration due them. They advertise their successes to their sons, at the same time belittling the boys' efforts and sabotaging their self-confidence. These fathers do not participate in raising the children, but interfere with their wives' efforts to be mothering. Their effectiveness as fathers is further diminished by absence from the home or withdrawal—in some instances, apparently because they cannot endure the attention the wife must give to the son.

The wives are torn between the jealous demands placed

upon them, and either the husbands or the sons, or both, feel the deprivation of their attention. The father's behavior is sometimes such that the children feel ashamed of him. The son, recognizing the father's inadequacies as a husband, seeks to fill the gap in his mother's life, which, however, increases his fear of the jealous father.

The inconsistent behavior, the temper outbursts, and the personality disturbances of these fathers create great tension in the home, just as in the case of the fathers of the girls who have been described. Some of the mothers in this predicament have given the impression that they could have been reasonably satisfactory mothers had the fathers not resented and opposed their efforts.

Mr. Lamb is a forceful and successful businessman. At the time he met his wife he was feeling dejected and disgraced because he had been dropped from college for cheating on exams. Nevertheless, he was considered to be a glamorous figure. For a year prior to the marriage, they lived together in a Bohemian atmosphere, and their relationship seems to have been happiest during this period. Difficulties began with their marriage, for Mr. Lamb tended to separate sex from marriage and found it hard to feel sexually aroused by a woman who was his wife. Thus early in the marriage he began to drink and consort with other women. Nevertheless, he expected to be his wife's sole concern. When a son, the patient, was born seven years after the marriage, Mr. Lamb showed a great deal of jealousy of the infant, objecting to any interference with their social life because of the child, and engaging in violent outbursts whenever his wife could not pay immediate attention to his own wishes.

During the following years he became increasingly irritable and demanding of his wife's attention, and also more alcoholic and promiscuous. Mrs. Lamb, striving to satisfy his need for companionship and at the same time to care for the son, found the situation intolerable; thus when an opportunity arose for him to take a promising traveling position which would keep him away from home except for occasional weekends, she agreed, feeling that this was the only way in which the marriage could continue.

Mr. Lamb, who had been an outstanding athlete in his youth, found no common interests with his son, who shared his mother's intellectual and artistic interests. However, it became clear that although the father was disappointed in not having a manly son, he could not have tolerated one; for instance, instead of coaching or encouraging his son in athletic endeavors, he criticized his son's efforts and lost his temper over them. It developed that he had, as a boy, squelched the efforts of his own younger brothers in the same way. At the same time, he belittled the interests or achievements of the son in other fields, and mocked at his effeminate traits and artistic inclinations.

Even though Mr. Lamb was now away from home most of the time, his brief sojourns with his family were always unpleasant. He was usually partly or completely intoxicated, and he sought to take his wife away from the children.

During the patient's adolescence, Mr. Lamb's affairs with a woman in the neighborhood created considerable scandal. His wife considered getting a divorce and told the patient that he might have to assume more responsibility for the family if she did so. At the same time, the patient's efforts at masculine achievement, made in a desperate effort to gain recognition from his father, were continuously belittled by Mr. Lamb.

Despite the disturbances throughout their marriage, a definite attachment and fondness has persisted between the spouses, and Mr. Lamb has been eminently successful in his job.

This case illustrates how a father can intervene in and seriously affect the mother-child relationship from the early months of the child's life. There was no possibility that Mrs. Lamb could care for the child with equanimity. Most striking among the noxious influences were the father's constant derogation of the son and his failure to offer any support to him.

Although neither parent overtly discredited the other to the children, the father's extramarital affairs, which were obvious to the adolescent son, indirectly devalued the mother. The mother, along with trying to meet the father's needs for attention, tried also to bolster his prestige with the children. Such efforts, however, presented an inconsistent and contradictory image of the father to the children, for the father's defects as a husband and his weaknesses as a man were apparent to them. Similarly, a perplexing discrepancy was presented by the father as they knew him and his reputation as a strong man among his business associates. Thus he was not a reasonable figure for identification for the son; the boy could not follow the pattern of a father who caused intense unhappiness whenever he was at home. The mother's efforts to make up for the father's deficiencies led to overindulgence and inconsistency, which weakened the son and increased the father's jealousy.

Other fathers in this group tend to be paranoid, suspicious of the motives of others and grandiose in their notions of their abilities, and to have distorted concepts of causal relationships.

There may well be a relationship between the two types of fathers who have been presented. Both types are unable to tolerate lack of admiration or the failure of their wives to center their lives about them. Of the cases presented, one father was paranoid and the other alcoholic, and both required bolstering of their masculinity. The fathers of daughters turn against the mothers and seek to gain the daughters' support and admiration. The fathers of sons become rivals of the sons, but some of them lose their wives' esteem in the process.

A third group of fathers presents a somewhat different problem, or perhaps one which is not fundamentally different, but simply brings into sharper focus a characteristic of many of the fathers in our study by presenting it in exaggerated form. These are fathers whose exalted concepts of themselves contain features of paranoid grandiosity, even though they have realistic abilities and achievements. The mothers and the children, and sometimes people outside the family, may share the fathers' estimation of themselves, being impressed with the importance of their positions and of the people with whom they associate. These fathers are aloof from the children and physically distant, conveying the impression that their offspring cannot reach their stature, and giving little or no support to their sons, in particular. The mothers are needed as adulatory admirers, and their attention to their fatherlike husbands may result in lack of attention to the children; or, conversely, they too may feel their husbands' distance and seek to complete their lives by attaching a child to them. In either case, a son becomes too weak to emulate his father and is apt to become a sham shell, assuming his more bizarre characteristics.

Mr. Dolfuss was a European-born manufacturer and inventor, whose grandfather had been a prominent statesman, but whose father had been an alcoholic. He married an emigré member of the nobility, and they settled in a Boston suburb, living in the rigid and formal tradition of European landed gentry. This unrealistic life in terms of their environment isolated them from the community, where they felt rejected as enemy aliens. The household was organized so as not to disturb the father, the children being raised by a seductive governess and permitted to see their parents at specific times in a formal relationship. The father studied Eastern mysticism with a close friend and felt that this set him apart as a select, superior being. The mother, and, to an even greater extent, the governess idolized him and considered him a sort of demigod, catering to his whims and hypochondriacal needs and accepting his beliefs implicitly. When the father died, the family believed that he still lived in a sense, but had been removed for more important tasks elsewhere in the universe.

This family, upon casual observation, seemed to be very superior, but actually the children were being raised in a paralogical atmosphere divergent from the culture in which they were living. While this is an extreme example, it is not the only instance of a father who is so positive and dominant that the mother and even the children go along with his beliefs in a sort of *folie en famille*.

As we have suggested earlier, the grandiose type of father, which we have illustrated by the case of Mr. Dolfuss, cannot be clearly separated from our other groupings. While these characteristics emerge most predominantly in our upper-class families—using class in a strict, sociological sense—they are clearly present in ten of the fourteen fathers, although somewhat obscured by the lower social status of the families in some cases, or by the fact that the fathers' evaluations of themselves, in other instances, receive less emphasis because they are unsupported or openly opposed by their wives and associates.

To discuss this particular tendency further, as it appears in varying forms in the greater number of our cases, the fathers exhibit an almost insatiable need, which has the quality of an addiction, for narcissistic satisfactions in the form of adulation from others. They expect to be the foci of their wives' attention and admiration, but, even if this is forthcoming, they require other sources of supply. Thus, Mr. Lamb required admiration as an athlete, and his extramarital relations were with women who flattered him and made him feel that he was outstanding. Another father had become a livestock auctioneer as a compromise between his interests in acting and farming. A physician turned from his home and built up a following of admiring women patients, listening to their personal problems and being unduly available to them at all hours of the night. Even though these men are assertive and often domineering, their fundamental lack of self-esteem and their insecurity in their masculinity are apparent. One such father, a man who has achieved unusual prestige, explained his intolerable marriage by saying that at the time he married he "had felt only half a man and would not expect to find a wife who was more than half a woman." Few wives can consistently supply the admiration that is needed. Furthermore, many of these wives require a man who can help them overcome their own narcissistic cravings, and clashes soon ensue. Whether the persistent need for admiration in these husbands was very marked before marriage or whether, in some instances, it was heightened into a serious problem by the wives' undermining or attacking of their masculine self-esteem, is a question which may be answered eventually by further scrutiny of the husband-wife interaction.

At any rate, the offspring, particularly the son, is in a difficult position, for if he is really successful, he may threaten the father's need to be the shining light in the home. The child may recognize that much of the father's greatness exists only in his own self-evaluation and self-deceit; this contributes to the child's faulty and corrupt superego formation and distrust of others. Wedge and Fry (1955) have called attention to the predicament of college students whose parents are unusually successful, but the difficulty is considerably more pronounced when the father's greatness is unreal and his weaknesses as a father and husband are apparent.

We shall now focus upon a group of fathers who have failed in life and become virtual nonentities in the home, scarcely participating in the responsibility for the children. The children are left virtually fatherless. Some of these fathers had earlier seemed infallible, but collapsed when their efforts to maintain their prestige collapsed, while others slowly faded, striving at the same time to retain their self-esteem by projecting the blame. Some had been unable to cope with their wives' coldness and exclusion. Thus these fathers have become rather pathetic figures, without prestige in the family and, at times, treated with disdain by their wives. The children are apt to be caught up in the fathers' failures and the social decline of the family.

Mr. Lerner had, before the business depression, been an outstanding and scholarly attorney who provided extremely well, if not lavishly, for his family. He considered himself to be superior, and much of his conversation was about his very prominent associates. His wife regarded him as a fatherly figure who admired her but who also had an intense need for her. While he was kindly toward his children, he was never an effective father, for he was always an aloof man who related to his wife to the exclusion of the children. He was only passively appreciative of his unusually gifted daughter, the patient, although she was the center of the larger family's attention.

When his partner committed suicide during the depression, Mr. Lerner was unable to gain new clients, since he was primarily a scholarly brief writer, and he withdrew into obsessive studies that shut him off from the plight which now faced his family, as well as from outside contacts. The entire burden of support of the family fell upon his wife, who went to work, and the economic status of the family declined severely in ways which were very apparent to the children—for instance, while they had always been encouraged to be proud, they now found themselves wearing hand-me-downs from relatives. Yet both the husband and wife pretended within the family and to his associates that he was still a busy and important man, and the wife helped support this pretense by maintaining his office. She dared not press him to any practical steps for earning money to support the family for fear that he might become overtly psychotic or commit suicide. Yet to the children, the failure of the father whom they had been taught to regard as a great man was apparent, and the very fact that it was hidden and made mysterious by the mother made it all the more frightening.

One of the problems of the patient was her difficulty in choosing between marriage and the chance of success in a career, and this conflict appeared to be heightened by the disgrace of the father's failure and the burdens of the mother's role.

While some of the types described so far are overlapping and have been differentiated largely to illustrate the varieties of difficulties that arise, the next and final grouping appears to be quite distinct.

These men are very passive and demand little for themselves, acting the part of lesser siblings in the family, and accepting their wives as grown-up authorities. They are not masculine figures to their wives, who seem to have married them because they did not wish to be dominated by a man. While they offer their wives passive support, implementing their decisions and wishes, they are unable to assert needs of their own or to express any ideas concerning the raising of the children.

To the children, these fathers are pleasant, even mothering figures, but they offer weak models to their sons. Moreover, they fail to counter the eccentric and bizarre patterns of child rearing which tend to be established by their wives—perhaps the most pathogenic feature of these families, and a situation which the sons come to resent, feeling that the father has abandoned them to the mother's whims. These fathers accept without apparent resentment the fact that the sons are their wives' primary concerns, and do not impede their sons' growth into the passive role which seems to fill the mothers' needs. The wives, who have little respect for their husbands, anticipate that the sons will live out the lives which are closed to them as women. It is interesting to note that the two most striking examples of such passive fathers were themselves adopted children.

There is very little of a definite nature to say about Mr. Newcomb other than that he is a good breadwinner and a competent accountant, and that he is very meek. In his visits to the hospital where his son was under treatment, for a long time he scarcely said anything to the personnel except what his wife wished him to convey; he served primarily as an apologetic mouthpiece for her. It was not that she was inarticulate, but that she could not repeat the same unanswerable questions or the same set ideas concerning the etiology of her son's illness often enough to overcome her belief that no one listened to her. However, after a time Mr. Newcomb began to speak securely and sensibly, mildly blaming himself for never having taken a stand against his wife. He had never

intervened in the relative social isolation which Mrs. Newcomb imposed upon the children nor contradicted her bizarre ideas. After the son became ill, he accepted his wife's
dictum that their lives must be devoted to the son's recovery,
for "we have no life while he is ill," and for many years Mr.
Newcomb scrimped and saved to maintain the son in private
hospitals despite very pessimistic prognoses.

Mrs. Newcomb had married him after the death of her
fiancé of five years' standing. She had not been aware that
Mr. Newcomb was courting her, simply considering him a
young man who went along with her group. When he proposed, she was taken aback and blurted out, "But how old
are you?" However, he apparently had an unusual asset as
a suitor, for in one of her most insightful· statements Mrs.
Newcomb said, "He didn't get as annoyed with my talk as
most men." The hospital personnel who have listened at
length to Mrs. Newcomb agree that it takes an unusual man
to live with her.

Mr. Newcomb is a conscientious and pleasant man and is
a "good" father in the sense that he does his best for his son.
It is essential to realize that his wife forms the paradigm of
a "schizophrenogenic mother" in her impervious solicitude
for her son and her bizarre reasoning and ways of rearing
children. However, in a sense Mr. Newcomb is not a father,
for he has permitted his wife to try to be both mother and
father, and completely to dominate him and the home, while
he has found refuge and solace in his work. He has not been
a satisfactory masculine figure to his wife, even though a
satisfactory husband to her. The son has never received protection or support from him in his efforts to grow into a man,
and both the son and the daughter—who once verged on a
schizophrenic break—have gained from him an unrealistic
image of a man.

A more striking illustration is afforded by the father of
schizophrenic twin sons. While the father was a competent
man at work, he went along with his wife's bizarre use of the
twins as obvious phalluses, building up fantastic expectations

of their greatness and refusing to accept the reality of their semidelinquent behavior. The pattern of this family was so extraordinary that it cannot be presented in abbreviated form, but suffice it to say that the father was excluded from his wife's room, was banned from using the family toilet because he was "dirty," and was generally treated with contempt and disrespect by his wife and sons (see Chapter XIII).

These fathers cannot be considered apart from their wives, because the wives, who follow closely the descriptions of domineering mothers of schizophrenic patients frequently found in the literature, are virtually schizophrenic themselves. In the case of the mother of the twins, her narcissistic injury—rather clearly related to castration—dominated the scene, and the father was a pawn in maintaining her restitutive maneuvers.

There are other implications in the material presented that the narcissistic needs of one and often both parents are deleterious to the formation of a family that can foster the child's growth into a mature and independent person. However, it is premature to focus upon specific dynamics. The primary purpose of this paper has been to call attention to the deficiencies of the fathers of these patients, which often impeded the mothers' efforts to be mothering. The fathers presented poor models and offered little support to the children and, quite aside from the mothers' deficiencies, went a long way toward creating a family environment which was distorted and rent by schisms between the parents over the fathers' bizarre ideas about the raising of the children. However, it must be repeated that although few, if any, of these fathers functioned effectively as parents, we do not believe that such fathers are specific to the families of schizophrenic children. Indeed, we know that they are not. We are, as we emphasized earlier, concerned at present with the integrative and disintegrative forces in these homes and the constructive and destructive models and patterns afforded the children. The father contributes but part of the family environment; he is only one of the parents. The difficulties of the mothers of schizophrenic patients have been presented in the preceding chapter, as well as by others.

Still, lest it seem that this series of fathers does not differ very much from the usual assortment in the population, let us consider them not as individuals but as a group. We will simply focus on their propensity for paralogical reasoning, which was also amply fostered by many of the mothers. Five of the fourteen were clearly paranoid, particularly in their distrust of outsiders. Another, although not definitely paranoid, had a grandiose concept of himself and rigid and bigoted ideas, and finally withdrew in unrealistic fashion. One father's obsessive needs were rationalized in a fashion that seemed both dishonest and perplexing to his family, who were expected to act in accordance with his incomprehensible ideas. Another father, who was eccentric and chronically depressed, was treated as a handyman around the home. Three fathers went along with their wives' distorted thinking, and, for practical purposes, shared it. Of the remaining, two were alcoholics and one was overtly seductive of his daughter.

COMMENT

We have been concerned largely with the role of the father in the family environment in which the patient grows up and have not gone very far in offering specific characterizations of such fathers. Indeed, we feel that efforts to specify a type of father, or necessary characteristics of fathers of schizophrenic patients, might be misleading, for we are not seeking the cause of schizophrenia in the fathers' characteristics. We have, however, noted certain characteristics which seem to occur frequently. It has been noted that the fathers are frequently insecure in their masculinity and need admiration and undue attention to bolster their masculine self-esteem. A goodly proportion are paranoid or given to paralogical or irrational behavior that dominates or seriously affects the attitudes of the entire family. One characteristic which we have not emphasized in this paper, that quality which seems to us to epitomize best the mother of the schizophrenic—imperviousness to the feelings and needs of others—also applies to a number of the fathers. We have attempted to indicate how the father can interfere with the mother's ability to be mothering, even in the first months of a child's life; how he can foster a confusion between the roles of the two generations in the home, and how, by his own insecurity as a husband and father, he can fail to provide the necessary object of masculine identification to a son and can interfere with a daughter's identity as a woman. The fathers, as are so many of the mothers, are so caught up in their own problems that they can rarely satisfactorily fill the essentials of a paternal role.

POSTSCRIPT

The paper was written when only fourteen of the seventeen families had been taken into the study, and work with most of the fourteen was still in progress. The three additional fathers, all fathers of schizophrenic daughters, did not lead to any need for revisions, aside from a greater emphasis on their role in confusing the intrafamilial communication. Mr. Thomas was a lecturer and writer, a highly narcissistic man who needed the prominence he gained by organizing various "causes" and supporting churches and universities with his schizophrenic wife's inherited fortune (Chapter III), but he had little empathy for his wife and neglected his family, managing to pursue activities that kept him away from home most of the time. Mr. Robb, an eminent professor of education, virtually destroyed his wife's ability to be a mother by bringing in teachers to care for the children; by his promiscuity, including an attempt to foist "wife swapping" on his wife, much against her puritanical upbringing; and by being seductive with his daughters, taking them into his bed when they were upset, even during their adolescence. We do not know a great deal about Mr. Frei, but he was very vague and scattered, and his projective tests indicate that he was very schizoid, if not a borderline psychotic.

The sketch of Mr. Lamb does not adequately convey the difficulties he created. As he is now dead, a bit more can be added. His wife was aware that homosexual tendencies, probably latent, had attracted him to professional athletics, and she eventually confided that he had contracted syphilis, which greatly impaired their marital relationship. His son's recovery seemed to relate to Mr. Lamb's death, just as the clinical recovery of Mr. Lerner's daughter may well have been related to his death, even though she had by then been schizophrenic for many years. In contrast, the psychosis of Mr. Dolfuss's son became manifest soon after his death when the son not only felt that he had to assume the responsibilities of the "man of the family"; but like his father, believe that he had become a reincarnation of an Asiatic divinity, and later the Messiah.

The survey of the fathers in the paper does not emphasize two rather common problems: their incestuous and homosexual tendencies, which are considered in Chapter X.

Further material about all of these fathers will be found in other chapters of the book.

V

Marital Schism and Marital Skew

(1956)

Herein we broached a concept that became increasingly important as our studies progressed and gained broad usage among persons who studied or treated families of schizophrenic patients. It had become apparent that many of the natal families of schizophrenics were split by long-standing and serious conflict between the parents, each of whom sought to gain the loyalty of the children who felt rejected by one parent if they sided with the other, or even if they did not side with that parent. However, we soon became aware that families in which there was no apparent conflict between parents could be extremely deleterious to the offspring because one rather passive parent failed to counter the dominant parent's strange and even bizarre ways of rearing children and structuring the family.

We did not wish to imply that the families of schizophrenic patients were always either clearly schismatic or clearly skewed, but originally were seeking to show how some families that seemed harmonious could prevent the integrated development of an offspring and distort intrafamilial communications and relationships. Some families were something of an admixture of schism and skew; and an occasional family, such as the Forels, shifted from being schismatic to skewed because of events that changed the family configuration. As the study progressed, it became apparent that skewed families were predominantly those with schizophrenic sons and schismatic families were

Theodore Lidz, Alice R. Cornelison, Stephen Fleck, and Dorothy Terry: The Intrafamilial Environment of Schizophrenic Patients: II. Marital Schism and Marital Skew. *American Journal of Psychiatry*, Vol. 114, 1957, pp. 241-248. Copyright © 1957, The American Psychiatric Association. This paper was presented at the 1956 meeting of the American Orthopsychiatric Association.

more frequently those with schizophrenic daughters. The difference in the sex of the children affected in the two types of families led us to consider more closely than previously the differences in the developmental tasks and intrafamilial relationships of boys and girls. We also came to recognize that despite the notable differences in the two types of families, they had some underlying common characteristics that predisposed offspring to becoming schizophrenic.

Wynne and his coworkers (1958) reached a closely related division of the families of schizophrenics, which they termed "pseudomutual" and "pseudohostile." Their pseudomutual families are essentially the same as our skewed families, and although their pseudohostile families closely resemble our schismatic families, we do not believe there is anything "pseudo" about the hostility between these spouses.

It seems important to emphasize that neither "schism" nor "skew" by themselves give rise to schizophrenia in families for, as will become apparent in subsequent chapters, many other factors enter into the picture, as we shall seek to summarize in Chapter XIX.

We wish to report briefly on another fragment of the work in progress, namely, on the defects in the marital relations of parents of schizophrenic patients. The topic is selected because, like the psychopathology of the fathers and mothers, the marital difficulties stand out in bold relief; and also because these marital problems are basic to the study of the intrafamilial milieu. The potential relationship of these parental difficulties to the maldevelopment of the children will have to remain largely implicit in this paper.

We must emphasize as strongly as possible that we do not seek to establish a direct etiological relationship between marital discord between parents and the appearance of schizophrenia in an offspring. It is obvious that bad marriages do not, in themselves, produce schizophrenic children, but it is unlikely that they do not have some relevance to the problem of schizophrenia.

The deficiencies in the relationships between parents of schizophrenic patients have been noted and studied by relatively few investigators. Lidz and Lidz (Chapter II) called

attention to the frequency of broken homes, markedly unstable parents, and unusual patterns of child rearing, and
found that at least 61 per cent of thirty-three patients had
come from homes marked by strife. Tietze (1949) reported
that thirteen of twenty-five mothers of schizophrenic patients
said that their marriages were very unhappy, but that the
statements by nine that their marriages were "perfect" did
not stand up under investigation, for the marriages were
strained and far from happy. Frazee (1953) found that fourteen of twenty-three parental couples were in severe conflict
and none was "normal" or had "only moderate conflict,"
whereas thirteen of the control parental couples were near
normal or showed only moderate conflict. None of the parents of schizophrenic patients revealed any degree of marital
stability, whereas well over one-half of the control group
manifested only moderate conflict or had made a good marital adjustment. Gerard and Siegel (1950) found open discord
between 87 per cent of the parents of seventy-one male schizophrenics as against 13 per cent in the controls. Reichard
and Tillman (1950) cite the unhappy marriages of the parents
of schizophrenics and analyze the sources of discord in terms
of parental personalities. Of interest, too, is Murphy's report
(1952) of the family environment of two adopted children
who became schizophrenic, in which the marital relationship
was filled with hostility and mutual recrimination between
two seriously disturbed parents. Many individual case reports
emphasize or mention the bad marital relationship between
the parents.

In our efforts to study and describe marital relationships,
it has become apparent—as it has to others—that one cannot
adequately describe a family or even a marriage in terms of
the personalities of each member alone. A family is a group
and requires description in terms of group dynamics and the
interaction among its members. We are indebted to Parsons
and Bales and their coworkers (1955), to J. Spiegel and F.
Kluckhohn (1954), Nathan Ackerman (1954a), Reuben Hill
and his coworkers (1953), Bradley Buell and the Community

Research Associates (1953), and others for their efforts to analyze marital and family interrelationships. We are still searching for suitable frames of reference, but the deficiencies of descriptive method should not blur the basic consideration—that the parental relations are highly disturbed in all of our cases.

The requisites for successful marriages are unfortunately far from clear, but some essentials are emerging. A couple must find reciprocal interrelating roles with each other and in their respective roles with their children. Absence of such role reciprocity means making constant decisions, self-consciousness, and tension. As Spiegel (1957) has pointed out, role reciprocity requires common understanding and acceptance of each other's roles, goals, and motivations, and a reasonable sharing of cultural value orientation. Mutual trust and effective communication between partners are important requisites especially supporting the spouse's role and self-esteem during periods of loss of confidence. We have been particularly impressed by the need to maintain boundaries between generations: that is, not to confuse or blur distinctions between parents and children. Spouses cannot remain primarily in a dependent position to their parents to the exclusion of an interdependent marital relationship; nor can one behave primarily as the other's child; nor as a rival with one's own children for the spouse's attention, nor reject a parental role completely. The need for both parents to form sources of primary love relationships for children and objects for stable identification will not be entered upon here, as we are concerned primarily with marital interaction.

It seems helpful to follow the lead of Parsons and Bales (1955) and consider the father's role in the family as primarily "adaptive-instrumental" and the mother's as "integrative-expressive." In broad terms, which may differ somewhat from Parsons', the father supports the family, establishes its position with respect to other families, determines prestige, and the social patterns of interaction with other groups. The mother's basic functions pertain to intrafamilial interactions;

tensions and their regulation; supplying the nurturant needs, both tangible and affectional. Each parent, in addition to filling his own role, must support the role of the other through his or her prestige, power, and emotional value to other family members.

The marriages of these parents of schizophrenics are beset by a wide variety of problems and ways of adjusting to them. However, the fourteen marriages can be placed in two general groupings, which, of course, tend to overlap in places. Eight of the fourteen couples have lived in a state of severe chronic disequilibrium and discord, which we are calling marital schism. This paper will focus primarily upon these eight couples. The other six couples have achieved some state of relative equilibrium, in which the continuation of the marriage was not constantly threatened; and the marital relationship could yield some gratification of needs to one or both partners. However, the achievement of parental satisfaction or the sacrifices of one parent to maintain marital harmony resulted in a distorted family environment for the children.

MARITAL SCHISM

In the eight families in which the state of disequilibrium designated as marital schism existed, both spouses were caught up in their own personality difficulties, which were aggravated to the point of desperation by the marital relationship. There was chronic failure to achieve complementarity of purpose or role reciprocity. Neither gained support of emotional needs from the other; one sought to coerce the other to conform to his or her expectations or standards, but was met by open or covert defiance. These marriages are replete with recurrent threats of separation, which are not overcome by efforts at re-equilibration, but through postponement of coming to grips with the conflict or through emotional withdrawal from each other—but without hope or prospect of improvement or ever finding any gratification in the marriage. Communication consists primarily of coercive efforts and defiance, or of efforts to mask the defiance to avoid fighting. There is little or no sharing of problems or satisfactions. Each spouse pursues his needs or objectives, largely ignoring the needs of the other, infuriating the partner and increasing ill-will and suspiciousness. A particularly malignant feature in these marriages is the chronic "undercutting" of the worth of one partner to the children by the other. The tendency to compete for the children's loyalty and affection is prominent; at times to gain a substitute to replace the affection missing from the spouse, but at times perhaps simply to hurt and spite the marital partner. Absence of any positive satisfaction from the marital relationship (excluding the children) is striking, though strong dependency needs may be gratified in a masochistic fashion in a few instances. Mutual distrust of motivations is the rule and varies only in the degree to which realistic causes for mistrust extend into the paranoid.

In seven of these eight families, the husband retains little prestige in the home and with the children, either because of his own behavior or his wife's attitudes toward him. He becomes an outsider or a secondary figure who cannot assert his instrumental leadership, and when he strives to dominate in tyrannical fashion, he eventually forces the family to conspire to circumvent him. His instrumental role is basically limited to financial support, which he may have originally considered as a husband's basic function, or he is relegated to this position. The ineffectual role of the father applies equally to five of the six marriages in the other group in which marked schism is not present.

The wives will be considered only in respect to their wifely functions, excluding the complex maternal relationships which also cause marital discord because eccentric, cold, rigid, or overindulgent attitudes toward the children antagonized the husband. All distrusted their husbands and had no confidence in them. They were openly defiant in major areas of interaction and rather habitually disregarded or circumvented their husbands' demands. They were emotionally cold and distant and, with one or two exceptions, sexually aloof. They competed for the attention and affection of the children and tried to instill their value systems, which differed from those of their husbands.

Communication in these marriages is greatly impeded by mutual withdrawal and by masking of motives from one another, but is further hindered because four wives show seriously scattered thinking and four husbands show paranoid thinking and rigidity. The imperviousness to the feelings of others, characteristic of many parents of schizophrenics, also creates communicative difficulties.

It seems of interest that in five of the eight marriages, the focus of the partners' loyalties remained in their parental homes, preventing the formation of a nuclear family in which the center of gravity rests in the home. The grandparents or the parental siblings often carried out much of the expressive and instrumental roles rather than the marital partners. The cardinal emotional attachment and dependency of one or both partners remained fixed to a parental figure and could not be transferred to the spouse.

The eight families can be grouped into three categories, according to the groupings of the Community Research Associates in their "Classification of Disorganized Families," which describes ten combinations of masculine and feminine personalities which are potentially hazardous to successful marital and family relationships (Buell, 1953).[1]

Four marriages seem best described as "Man-dominated Competitive Axes." The husband strives to assert his male dominance to a pathological degree, rather clearly in reaction to his feminine dependent strivings. He needs an admiring wife who supports insatiable narcissistic needs and complies with his rigid expectations, and is angered when she reacts with defiance and disregard. Indeed, her inadequacies as a wife or mother may well produce exasperated frustration.

---

[1]The classification used to find common ground with other members of a panel has not been used by us again, as it added little to the understanding of the families.

He distrusts her increasingly and undercuts her prestige with the children. The wives are disappointed and disillusioned in the father figure they married who cannot grasp their needs, and, if they are overwhelmed by force, they manage to gain their ends through circumvention. The husbands are rigid paranoiacs or obsessives, and the wives are poorly organized obsessives or schizophrenics. The marriages are marked by chronic severe mistrust without (except in the least serious instance) any semblance of affection. The family is split into two factions by the conflict and mutual undercutting. Although both members are fighting, it is the husband's moral brutality, his disregard and contempt for the wife whom he tries to force into compliance that dominates the picture.

Mr. Reading, a forceful and successful but paranoically suspicious man, sought to control his wife's behavior from the start of the marriage. He was infuriated and disillusioned when she joined a church group against his orders to remain aloof from any organizations. He was dependent upon his mother, who lived in the home for many years; he followed her advice in household matters in opposition to his wife's, whom he considered incompetent to furnish the house. Marked strife began with the birth of the elder of two daughters, for he was clearly jealous of the attention the wife paid the child. He disapproved of everything she did in raising the child, often with good reason, but he competed rather than supported. Mrs. Reading was obviously overprotective of the children, whereas her husband wished to inure them to the hard knocks of life. Violent scenes, filled with Mr. Reading's dire threats and some actual violence, were commonplace. The marriage further disintegrated into a hostile battleground after Mrs. Reading discovered that her husband was having an affair, which she reported to her mother-in-law to gain an ally her husband feared. Mr. Reading never forgave his wife for this betrayal and, apparently to spite her, sold their home in the best section of the city to move into a two-family house in an undesirable neighborhood. Thus, he struck a foul blow at Mrs. Reading's major preoccupations—her social aspirations and her insistence that her daughters associate with only "proper" companions. The family, previously split into two groups, now united against Mr. Reading and refused to eat meals with him. The difficulties engendered by the wife's indecisive obsessiveness and the husband's paranoid trends cannot be depicted here. Both partners used interviews primarily to incriminate the other and persuade the interviewer to judge in their favor against the spouse.

The second group of two families may be categorized as "Woman-dominated Competitive Axes," according to the "Classification of Disorganized Families." The outstanding common feature is the wife's exclusion of the passive and masochistic husband from leadership and decision making. She derogates him in word and deed and is emotionally cold and distant to him. Her attention is focused on her narcissistic needs for completion and admiration. These wives are extremely castrating and their husbands are vulnerable. The husband withdraws from the relationship in an effort to preserve some integrity when defeated in the struggle, and may find solace in alcohol. The husband's function in the family is restricted to providing a living or, if willing, to supporting the wife in her domination of the family. The wife does not fill an expressive, supportive role to her husband and her expressive functions with the children are seriously distorted.

Both Mr. and Mrs. Forel were closely tied to their parental families. Mrs. Forel, the youngest of three sisters, was very dependent upon her eldest sister, a masculine aggressive woman with open contempt for men, who tended to dominate the Forel household. Mrs. Forel refused to live at any distance from her family and spent two months each year with them away from her husband. She was an extremely cold, narcissistic woman and a "tease," who flirted constantly but denied her husband sexual relations. Mr. Forel was a passive man who sought to assert a pseudo domination of his family when his men friends were about. He formed fawning attachments to men, which increased his wife's contempt for him. He was excluded increasingly from the family circle, his opinions disregarded; and felt like an outsider who was barely tolerated. He was closely attached to his mother, whom he helped to support. Mr. Forel finally took steps to separate unless his wife would detach herself from her sisters. She capitulated but became pregnant in the process of reconciliation. She was ashamed and concealed the pregnancy, and then took it out on her husband. Separated from her sisters, she began to drink heavily and carried on open flirtations, or perhaps affairs, neglecting her baby. The discord heightened. After Mrs. Forel was seriously disfigured in an accident for which her husband was responsible, she became depressed and withdrew into seclusion until plastic surgery restored her appearance. Mr. Forel then tried to make amends through becoming a weak and spineless husband who mothered the youngest neglected child. However, he soon developed cancer and his wife displayed a physical abhorrence for him, fearing that she might catch the disease. She refused to nurse him during his terminal illness.

The remaining two marriages may be classified as "Dual Immature Dependency Axes." Mutual withdrawal of the spouses and dependency on members of the parental families were outstanding. It is difficult to say which spouse dominated the marriage, though both tried and at the same time resented not having a strong figure who would provide leadership. Resentment of the mates' attachments to their families was prominent. The inability to gain mutual gratification of needs and support led to mounting disregard of the other and increasing emptiness of both lives. These marriages were replete with threats of separation by both members, but each tended to go his or her own way, undermining the other to the children by deeds and attitudes more than by words. Despite the long duration of both marriages, they remained tentative, as if both partners were awaiting and contemplating release.

The Nussbaums' dissension had started shortly after their

marriage twenty-five years ago. Mr. Nussbaum had been largely supported by his elder brother, whom he regarded as a father. Mrs. Nussbaum's father had suicided following business reverses, which her family blamed upon his affiliation with Mr. Nussbaum's brother. Mrs. Nussbaum appeared to side with her family in their accusation of her husband's brother. Mr. Nussbaum considered her attitude to show utter disloyalty as it furnished the finishing blow to his feelings of being excluded by her close-knit family. There was little or no discussion of the matter, but they drew apart. Mrs. Nussbaum was very sensitive lest her husband dominate her, and stood her ground with the help of a violent temper. She refused to accompany him on social engagements essential to his career and antagonized his friends. Mr. Nussbaum felt unloved and unwanted and constantly deprecated. He stayed away from home much of the time, and fostered the impression that he was having affairs, either to spite his wife or to mask his impotence, or both. Weeks would pass when the couple would not speak to each other. The wife found solace in her relationship to her son, and the husband in his seductive attachment to his daughter, our patient.

Although the Newbergs had been in violent disagreement and there had been repeated threats of separation, some elements of goodwill toward each other could be uncovered. Mr. Newberg is a very disturbed man, pushing numerous impractical schemes that are often grandiose; talking incessantly in a loud voice; seeking to dominate but with faulty judgment and, although a steady and hardworking provider, he had frightened his wife for years lest he leave his job and launch upon one of his impracticable schemes. He spent little time with his family, partly because of his attachment to his mother and partly because of his wife's attachment to her sisters, which forced the family to live in a home two hours from his job. Mr. Newberg resented his wife's attachment to her three sisters and mother, and her domination by one sister who constantly disparaged him to his wife and children.

Mrs. Newberg claimed that she remained dependent upon her sisters because her husband provided her neither emotional support nor help in raising the children. She considered him impossible to live with because of his demands, his thoughtlessness, and the constant confusion he produced in the home. She remained with him only because she felt the children needed a father but found she had to treat him as a child, humoring him to avoid strife. They blame each other's families for interfering and discourage and disparage each other's interests. The situation reached a crisis when Mr. Newberg wished to move to the West Coast because his mother and brother were moving there. He threatened to leave his wife if she would not move and she threatened to leave him if he tried to force the move. Both had intense needs which the other could not begin to satisfy. Although Mr. Newberg had strong paranoid trends and Mrs. Newberg had difficulties in being close, and the hostility was marked, this family offered the best chance of any for some reconciliatory movement, because both showed potential ability to recognize the other's needs as well as their own difficulties.

The portrayals of these marriages are little more than symbolic fragments of the wealth of material collected. Still, they indicate the virtual absence of complementarity in each marriage. Husband and wife do not support each other's needs, and the marital interaction increases the emotional problems of both, deprives the spouses of any sense of fulfillment in life, and deteriorates into a hostile encounter in which both are losers. Instead of any reciprocal give and take, there is demand and defiance leading to schism between partners that divides the entire family, leaving the children torn between conflicting attachments and loyalties.

MARITAL SKEW

In six of the fourteen marriages, this type of schism did not exist, although the family life was distorted by a skew in the marital relationship. In all, the rather serious psychopathology of one marital partner dominated the home. In some, the dissatisfaction and unhappiness of one spouse is apparent to the other and to the children, but husband and wife manage to complement or support each other sufficiently to permit a degree of harmony. In the others, the distorted ideation of one partner was accepted or shared by the other, creating an atmosphere of *folie à deux*, or even of *folie en famille* when the entire family shared the aberrant conceptualizations.

In all of these families, one partner who was extremely dependent or masochistic had married a spouse who had appeared to be a strong and protecting parental figure. The dependent partner would go along with or even support the weaknesses or psychopathological distortions of the parental partner because dependency or masochistic needs were met. In contrast to the marriages with overt schism, one partner could gratify rather than combat a spouse's narcissistic needs. It may be significant that no member of these six marriages had intense emotional bonds to the parental family, and it is possible that absence of such alternative sources of gratification tended to hold these spouses together. A striking feature in all cases was the psychopathology of the partner who appeared to be dominant, creating an abnormal environment which, being accepted by the "healthier" spouse, may have seemed to be a normal environment to the children. Considerable "masking" of potential sources of conflict occurred, creating an unreal atmosphere in which what was said and admitted differed from what was actually felt and done.

We shall cite examples in cursory fashion, primarily to illustrate that even though these marriages provided some gratification to the marital partners, the family milieu was as distorted and disturbed as in the case of the schismatic marriages.

The Schwartz family was completely dominated by a paranoid mother who supported the family. Her husband had left her on one occasion, unable to tolerate her demands, but had returned long before the patient, the youngest son, had been born. Soon thereafter the father suffered a nervous breakdown, after which he lived as a sort of handyman around the house and worked as a menial helper in the wife's business. The wife was extremely ambitious for her four sons, pushing them and dominating their lives, as well as making it clear that they must not become like their father. She was paranoically fearful of outsiders, believing that their telephone was tapped and that the family was physically endangered because they were Jewish. A severe schism actually existed despite the peace between the marital couple. The mother was intensely protective of her oldest son, a gambler and embezzler, who consumed all of her attention as well as much of the family income. A chronic ambivalent conflict existed between them that tended to exclude the husband and the other sons. The husband did not intervene, but merely told his sons that the trouble in the family existed because they did not obey their mother as he did.

Here the father had abdicated and the mother was a paranoid instrumental leader, while the father supplied no masculine image with whom the younger sons could identify.

Illustrative of the *folie à deux* and the *folie en famille* group, the Dolfuss family lived like European landed gentry in a New England suburb, isolated from their neighbors. The family life was centered in the needs and opinions of Mr. Dolfuss, a successful but paranoically grandiose inventor. The children were raised by a seductive nursemaid of whom the cold and distant mother was intensely jealous. However, Mrs. Dolfuss devoted her life to her husband, catering to his whims, and keeping the children out of his way. Mr. Dolfuss' major interest was an oriental religious sect. He believed that he and a friend were among the few select souls who would achieve a particular type of salvation. Both Mrs. Dolfuss and the nursemaid virtually deified him. They and the children shared his beliefs as well as his grandiose notion of himself, living in what we termed a *folie en famille*. Here, the children were largely excluded from the lives of the parents, the model of the father was an unrealistic one for the son, and the intellectual and emotional environment was estranged from that of the larger culture into which they had to emerge.

In all of these six families, the fathers were particularly ineffectual, assuming little responsibility for family leadership other than earning a livelihood. They were either weak, ineffectual men who went along with wives who were schizophrenic or at least questionably so, or they were disturbed men who could maintain an outward form of capability and strength because of the support of a masochistic wife. In all instances, the psychopathology that pervaded the home was masked or treated as normal.

The analysis of the pathological environment in these last six cases, and of the effects upon the children, cannot be gone into here, but we trust we have shown that we have not simply discarded less disturbed family environments in choosing to focus this paper upon the eight marriages in which overt schism between the partners existed.[2] In considering the eight schismatic marriages we do not seek, as emphasized previously, to relate directly the appearance of schizophrenia in an offspring to the marital disorganization. There are many other factors in the family environment which we are studying that affect the children, but they all bear some relationship to the personalities of the parents and the atmosphere created by their interaction. We are only seeking to describe bit by bit what this family environment is, until we can assemble the fragments into a meaningful description of the whole. We are still occupied with the grossest factors, for unless we start with what appears fairly obvious, these factors may be overlooked during our preoccupation with subtleties. In this presentation, we have paid minimal attention to the individual personalities of the parents in order to concentrate upon problems created by their interaction.

[2]The Newcomb, Lerner, and Lamb families, described in other papers in this volume, are other examples of skewed families. The Nebb family also had schismatic elements.

Discussion

We find a number of features in these marriages that are theoretically adverse to the "normal" developmental process of a child. In these families each parent constantly denigrates and undercuts the other, making it clear to the children that each does not respect or value, but rather dislikes or hates, the other. Each parent more or less openly expresses fears that a child will resemble the other, and a child's resemblance to one parent is a source of concern or rejection by the other parent. One or both parents seek to win the child away from the other. The boundary between the generations is violated. A child may feel the burden of being expected or required to complete the life of one or both parents; and this creates a block to growth into an independent individual. A child may be used and needed as a replacement for the spouse. There is excellent opportunity for intensification of the oedipal rivalry rather than for its resolution. The child can insert himself as a wedge between the parents, becoming inordinately adept at widening the breach and becoming caught in the incestuous concern that the parent can be seduced or might seduce, as well as in the guilt over hostile-destructive impulses toward the other parent. A parent of the same sex with whom the child should identify during latency and adolescence, who is not an acceptable love object to the other parent but is hated and despised, cannot provide a model through which a child can achieve mature identity. Potential homosexual trends, which play a large role in schizophrenia, are opened. Many other serious impediments are placed in the way of the child's achievement of a stable identification with a parental figure, a requisite to the formation of a stable ego identity by the end of adolescence. In addition, children of a rejected marriage are likely to feel rejected themselves. Caught in the anxiety that a needed parental love object can be lost through separation of the parents, the children may devote much energy toward balancing the precarious marriage. The stronger the incestuous tendencies, the greater the need for protection by the presence of both parents.

When one or both parents have paralogic and scattered ways of thinking and behaving, the difficulties are further heightened.

POSTSCRIPT

We now find that in this early paper, we did not emphasize or properly illustrate skewed families. More typical than either of the families cited were the Newcomb and Nebb families in which the mothers sought completion from their sons, but because of their own needs and egocentric orientations were impervious to their sons' needs as separate individuals though they were extremely intrusive into their lives. The husbands were very passive men who went along with and even supported their wives' ways of raising their children. These families are discussed in some detail elsewhere in the book.

The three cases that had not been studied when the paper was written were all seriously disturbed. The Robb family, that had two schizophrenic daughters, was schismatic, though the mother sought to resist rather than fight her husband's domination. The Thomas family could not be designated as clearly schismatic because Mr. Thomas was rarely at home, and his overtly schizophrenic wife buried her deep resentment of his neglect and contempt of her in her psychosis, and left the rearing of the children to maids. The Frei family, who had an anorexic schizophrenic daughter and another daughter with ulcerative colitis, is not readily classified as both parents were very insecure and disturbed but tended to be skewed in that the passive father did not counter his wife's oversolicitous and anxious intrusiveness into the daughters' lives.

VI

Parental Personalities and Family Interaction

(1957)

In the preceding chapter, we noted and illustrated that although most of the families in our series were disrupted by overt conflict between incompatible parents, the remaining families were also seriously distorted or disturbed even though there might be no overt conflict between the marital couple. Here we turn to the study of the family in terms of the dynamics of a small group which must meet certain requisites dictated by both biological and cultural considerations if it is to provide an adequate setting for the development of its offspring. We focus on how the personalities of the parents can prevent the formation of an adequate family structure, the provision of proper nurturance, meaningful communications, and the transmission of fundamental instrumental techniques to the children. We use a schismatic marriage to illustrate various problems that arise for parents as well as children when a couple is unable to form a parental coalition, and enter upon the need for psychiatric study of family transactions rather than focusing simply upon either individuals or on the interaction between two persons. The topic is considered in greater detail in a book about the family's functions in human adaptation (Lidz, 1963a) and in articles on the family as a system (Fleck, 1980) and also is amplified in other chapters in this volume.

Theodore Lidz, Stephen Fleck, Alice R. Cornelison, and Dorothy Terry: The Intrafamilial Environment of the Schizophrenic Patient: IV. Parental Personalities and Family Interaction. *American Journal of Orthopsychiatry*, Vol. 28, 1958, pp. 764-776. Copyright © 1958, American Orthopsychiatric Association, Inc. This paper was presented at the 1957 annual meeting of the American Orthopsychiatric Association.

The family's subtle task of transmitting acquisitions of its culture essential to the new generation and of shaping personality has been largely implicit, guided by custom and pedagogic and religious precepts. Only in recent years have scientific attempts been made to analyze this process in which so many factors have been taken for granted that they have not been scrutinized. As with many other human functions that transpire almost automatically, study of the pathological helps focus attention upon essential functions and processes.[1]

The study of the family has been approached in very many ways. The approaches may be said to vary from the sociological, concerned primarily with the effects of the structure of society upon the structure of the family and vice versa, and then upon the functioning of the persons involved, to psychological approaches focusing primarily upon the effects of personalities upon one another and upon the family organization. Our studies have certainly rested heavily upon a variety of certain sociological orientations. We have found it useful, following Parsons and Bales (1955), to consider the family in terms of small group dynamics. The nuclear family is a true group; all members are interdependent, the actions of any member affecting all, and because the family provides a protecting shelter for its members both within and against the society in which it exists. Still the family differs from all other small groups in that its organization follows a number of imperatives that must be taken into account. One approach to family interaction is to study how each family or any given type of family seeks to fulfill these imperatives in comparison with other families, and the effects upon the personalities involved. The most categorical of these imperatives derive from the biological structure of man born either male or female helplessly dependent and requiring prolonged nurturance and protection, with a set of basic drives and needs, but developing into a self-sufficient person by assimilation

---

[1]See, for example, Ackerman (1954a); Bott (1955); Dicks (1953); Foote and Cottrell (1955); Group for the Advancement of Psychiatry (1954); Handel and Hess (1956); Hill (1954); Jackson (1957a); Jensen (1952); Kluckhohn (1952); Locke et al. (1955); Spiegel (1954, 1957).

from the persons who rear him the instrumentalities of the culture in which he happens to be born. Other imperatives are implicitly set by the culture to ensure that each generation will be able to live in and transmit the culture.

We can but touch upon the nature of our thinking in this area to designate how it can lend coherence to the diffuse material gathered in a family study. The family contains two categories of members according to generation, and two categories according to sex. The parents raised in two differing families seek to find a permanent union by finding reciprocally interrelating roles and a shared set of values for living with each other and for raising children. The children, however, in contrast to members of any other small group, receive their primary training in group interaction within the family. The child learns largely through interaction in this group how to emerge and live in other groups, including how to start one of his own as a parental figure. He is trained to belong and yet to leave. The functions of the two generations differ; for example, parents can be dependent on each other, and children must be dependent upon parents, yet limitations must be set on parental dependency upon immature children. Or, as another example, sex taboos exist between all family members except the parents, for whom sex relations are more or less obligatory.

Similar analysis can be made of the division according to sex. The female role, linked to child rearing and mothering, is more confined to the home, permits a more sheltered and dependent life for the woman, and promotes her greater dependence upon the emotional relatedness of family members. The total care required by the newborn dictates that the father provide subsistence and protection for the family, and that he assume a more instrumental role, forcing him to emerge more from the family into society. The mother must possess skills, patterns, and emotional ability to care for children, with graded patterns for abrogation of total care commensurate with the children's increasing abilities and with instilling confidence in them. The long dependency of the child causes a blending of parent-child and sexual love, which must, however, become differentiated. As the family is a mutually protective group, some undefined degree of primacy must be given by all members to the needs of the family group and by the family as a whole over the needs of outsiders.

The requisites within the family to provide for the gradual socialization of the child cannot be reviewed here. We shall simply mention that parents must provide models of identification for children of both sexes which can be incorporated smoothly only if the models are not conflicting and mutually exclusive. Each parent's worth as a primary love object depends not only upon that parent, but also upon the spouse's esteem for that parent. Also, a parent's own self-esteem helps build the child's ego strength. If parental personalities or the interpersonal processes within the family are too aberrant, children may be able to live within the family, but will become perplexed when they emerge from it and may be unable to socialize harmoniously.

In some families, such as those we have studied, gross failures in carrying out essential functions like the few enumerated are apparent. Even within this framework a great many variant approaches to a study can be undertaken. Here, we shall pursue the effects of parental personalities on the family interaction. It seems apparent that whatever the approach, parental personalities and their interaction will provide a uniqueness to each nuclear family, influencing its structure and functioning, and the children's personalities. However, families cannot be understood through the study of individual personalities alone, but only through the interrelatedness of these persons. Their behavior evokes reaction and counterreaction, and creates an environmental atmosphere which exists over and above the influence of individuals. We wish to emphasize particularly that the personality of each parent contains resultants of his own parental family interaction and the societal culture in which he was raised, so that a study of parental personalities implicitly or explicitly includes consideration of many basic sociological factors. In a strongly antitraditional society with rapid changes in mores, as in contemporary middle-class United States, where the nuclear family tends to be isolated from collateral kinship systems, the influence of parents upon family interaction is unusually strong. Neither the structural pattern of the family nor parental and children's roles are as clearly defined as in more static societies, and there is a dearth of paternal and maternal figures to provide security and models along with the actual parents. Here the two parents come together from two differing families, having had a relatively narrow experience with family life and parenthood, largely confined to their own parental families. The actual pattern of the family, the harmony of the home, the security afforded the children, the skills and knowledge to be imparted, etc., all depend upon what the parents bring with them, including their value systems, and the interaction between these personalities.

The families that we have studied are all disturbed. However, this does not interfere with the intent of this paper, but rather may simplify the task because of the exaggerations involved, which permit us to note specific types of failure in essential areas of family interaction. In Chapter V we divided the disturbed marriages we were studying into two general types: marriages marked by severe marital schism that split the family into two opposing camps, and "skewed" marriages in which serious strife was avoided because the dominant parent's seriously distorted ideas were accepted by a more normal but very dependent spouse, giving rise to a deviant and paralogic family environment. Here we wish simply to present a single family and some of our efforts at analyzing its structure and interaction by starting with the personalities of the couple who married.

We have selected the Grau family for presentation because the pathology was not too extreme and because the parents came from sufficiently divergent backgrounds to illustrate some areas of interest with reasonable clarity. It is an upper-middle-class suburban family, relatively aloof from kin. The family, when the study was started four years ago, consisted of the father, fifty-two; the mother, fifty; Nancy, a twenty-one-year-old schizophrenic daughter; and Ellen, a college girl of eighteen. The marriage was troubled from the start because both parents were strange, showing many psychotic features both in our contact with them and on projective tests.

Let us first look at the persons who married twenty-five years ago. At twenty-six, Mr. Grau had never dated a girl before meeting his wife. He was a shy chemist who even then viewed the world with a jaundiced eye, and was given to depressive moods. He came from a Dakota farm family of German Evangelical origin. His father, a relatively wealthy man, must have been rigid and somewhat paranoid. We know, for example, that his wife was not permitted to leave the farm to shop in town more than once or twice a year. Born in Germany, she was better educated than most farm wives of her generation. Our patient's father had little use for his numerous siblings, except for one sister Ellen, and retained little contact with his married sisters and one bachelor brother, all of whom settled on farms near the family home. Mr. Grau had always been aloof and without close friends. He felt an outsider in high school because most of the others came from Scandinavian families, and in college because he was a "hick" even though it was a state college. He had difficulty finding himself after high school, and was permitted to go to college by his father only when he promised not to study agriculture, as his father had set prejudices against scientific farmers. After completing a year of graduate school, Mr. Grau accepted a position with a large chemical firm in upper New York state, and remained with it. Just how and why he married his wife remains obscure, because he talked as if he had been an unwary country boy who had been trapped. We know he could have escaped since she agreed to marry only after he had willingly given his written promise to raise their children as Catholics.

Mrs. Grau's father was a German Catholic and her mother a devout Irish Catholic. The father was a strict man, cruel to his wife and sons, but he favored his only daughter. According to Mr. Grau he was a tavern keeper, while Mrs. Grau said he was a restaurant owner—at any rate he ran a speakeasy at the time of the marriage. Mrs. Grau's mother managed to get along with her difficult husband. The bond between mother and daughter was very close. Mrs. Grau had an adequate social life before her marriage, and had just completed two years at a junior college. She had set ideas of right and wrong and adhered strictly to her Catholicism. For many years before our study started, at least, she had been vague and scattered in her talk, conveying the impression of being childish and feebleminded, but it soon became clear that her intelligence was not defective. Though perhaps attracted by a scientist from a well-to-do family, she certainly married a man who resembled her father in being stubborn, German, and set in his beliefs.

Trouble started almost immediately. Mr. Grau, insecure as a man, followed his father's pattern and expected his wife to obey and to mother him. He deeply resented her attachment to her church as an infidelity to him. He claimed that he had known few Catholics, and had not understood that Catholicism was a way of life as well as a religion. He was suspicious of his wife's fidelity without provocation, and he trailed her on occasion. He developed great contempt for her "stupidity." The arguments soon focused on religion, because Mr. Grau decided not to have children as a way out of his pledge to raise them as Catholics. Evidence indicates, however, that he could not tolerate having rivals for his wife's attention.

When Mrs. Grau became pregnant three years after they were married, Mr. Grau felt that his wife had trapped him, following her mother's advice to have a child to preserve the tottering marriage, although he had assumed responsibility for the contraception. Fighting raged constantly, and Mr. Grau struck his pregnant wife in the abdomen, a fact which she never forgot. Thereafter, the marriage became a hostile encounter, focusing on the daughter's religion. Mr. Grau refused to allow her to be baptized Catholic. Mrs. Grau felt betrayed and attacked by his assault on her religion. She considered leaving him but was advised by her priest to stay for the sake of the child. Mrs. Grau could not accept a situation that left her child living in sin. Her insecurities in raising the child were heightened because she could not rear her in the tradition in which she felt secure. In any event, she was very rigid with Nancy, following to the letter the strict schedules taught in her book, and she was apprehensive of any initiative the girl showed. Nancy became a docile, conforming child who never stood up for herself with her mother or playmates when small. Her birth had clearly separated the parents, rather than bringing them closer together. Three and a half years later Ellen was born—also unwanted by her father but welcomed by the mother. The birth did not arouse such violence, but the discord continued. The father, having gained his way with Nancy, expected his wife to follow his orders with Ellen. However, hopeless about ever gaining his consent, Mrs. Grau secretly had both children baptized, justifying herself because of her husband's broken promise. When, at some later date, Mr. Grau learned of her action, he became infuriated and grew increasingly distrustful of her.

Mrs. Grau, however, was much less restrictive in raising Ellen, having learned that raising a child required more than providing for physical needs according to schedule. Ellen soon showed herself to be more aggressive and less compliant than her sister.

Several attitudinal patterns were permanently established in this family. The father constantly displayed a peculiar paranoid attitude about Catholicism, blaming his troubles and many of the troubles of the world on the way Catholics raised their children. He could not tolerate the acceptance of a belief which conflicted with his own cynical suspiciousness of people's motives. He constantly deprecated his wife as a Catholic, contemptuously calling her a fisheater and still less complimentary terms, and never missed an opportunity to call attention to Catholic miscreants he read about in the newspaper. He had fixed ideas about education, derogating anyone without a college degree, and considered his wife in particular stupid, and her views worthless because she had attended only junior college. Mrs. Grau received no emotional support from her husband in raising the children. He constantly deprecated her to the children and she responded in kind. The family had almost no social life: the mother saw a few women friends, and the father stayed home in what seems to have been a disinterested and almost apathetic state. Communication had descended into irritable fights over trivia, always turning into conflicts over religion. Under stress, the mother became even more scattered than usual. As Nancy grew older, the father wooed her to win her to his side of the conflict.

This couple, who had hoped their needs would be met in the marriage, floundered in a hapless situation. Mr. Grau, whose insecure narcissism needed constant support through admiration, became jealous of the attention his wife gave the children and attacked her and her way of life. Mrs. Grau, who had been her father's favorite, married a man like her father, but found no fatherly support but only criticism from a husband who favored the children and rejected her. Mr. Grau, who tried, like his father, to insist upon his pseudo-masculine dominance, only provoked defiance. They were enemies but could not get along without each other. They could not avoid fights because Mr. Grau could not forego cynical comments, and Mrs. Grau, with remarkable tactlessness, did not know when to keep quiet. Afraid of her husband, she often pretended to agree but then did as she wished, further infuriating him. Talk of separation became common, but they stayed together "because of the children."

When Nancy was nine, the situation deteriorated further when Mr. Grau developed a chronic disease which incapacitated him for long periods, and forced dependence upon his wife. He was an irritable patient with a violent temper at home, and apparently preferred the hospital. When Nancy was fourteen and Ellen ten, Mr. Grau became completely invalided for three years because he refused an operation which would improve his condition. Mrs. Grau worked, and with liberal help from both grandfathers, the family managed without notable change in economic status. Mr. Grau could not take the pressing needs of the family into account and undergo the operation for their sake. Eventually he had to accept the operation, after which he was able to return to work though he continued to suffer considerable pain at times.

When, during her father's invalidism, Nancy entered adolescence, she changed markedly. Mrs. Grau had continued to be distrustful and extremely intrusive, wanting to know exactly what Nancy did whenever she was away from home. Nancy began to fight back, and unable to retain some privacy by maintaining silence, because her mother would nag and insist that she tell, she learned to talk but reveal nothing. She purposely became vague and confusing—in a sense all that she had to do was copy her mother's confused talk and her father's evasiveness. Her father would not permit her to date until she was sixteen—but then Nancy focused her attention on boys, dressing in a dramatic and inappropriate fashion that infuriated her mother and made her suspicious. If Nancy went out with a Catholic boy, her father was infuriated; if with a non-Catholic, her mother hounded her. Aside from his concern about the boy's religion and education, Mr. Grau showed a peculiar neglect concerning whom she dated, as if in collusion with Nancy to aggravate and worry her mother. Nancy went with some rather questionable characters, and Mrs. Grau would chase her about the house, insisting on hearing every detail of the evening, and slapped her when she would not tell. Fights between Nancy and Ellen would soon turn into fights between Nancy and her mother, with Mr. Grau on the sidelines making no effort to head off the battle.

Entering upon the genesis of Nancy's illness would require too much detail for this presentation. We wish only to note that by the time Nancy entered college she clearly sided with her father, insisting that her mother had deceived him in having her baptized and that she was a Protestant. She considered her father to be the perfect man, a judgment which made the hospital staff shudder, for he was a bitter, cynical, and verbally sadistic person who consciously sought to make his daughter cynical and suspicious. Nancy felt that completing college was essential, as her father could not respect her unless she gained her degree. She wished to become an interpreter, a meaningful and necessary occupation in this family. Hating her mother and seeking love from her father, she sought to become totally different from her mother.

Whereas Nancy always got caught between her parents and became the focus of their hostility to each other, Ellen managed differently. There had been notable differences in the way the two girls had been raised. Ellen had not been a source of conflict or a substitute conflict for the parents, nor had her mother restricted or nagged her as much as she had Nancy. Her father had become seriously incapacitated when Ellen was only five or six.

Ellen considered that she had profited greatly from seeing how her sister got into trouble, and sought to avoid repeating her errors. She patterned herself to be different from Nancy. She managed to pick the strengths of each parent, and warily and diplomatically placated both of them. She sought to gain their trust by being the type of daughter each wanted. Even when she was permitted to go out with boys at sixteen, she disclaimed any interest in boys, and concentrated on studies and athletics. Above all she gained her mother's approval and confidence by letting her know that she espoused Catholicism, a fact which through silent collusion they hid from Mr. Grau. As a Catholic she was not so restricted by her mother, and since she did not go out on dates, she avoided the Catholic boy vs. non-Catholic boy controversies. To all except the father it was clear that the family was divided into two camps: mother and Ellen as against father and Nancy. How well Ellen concealed her loyalty to her mother became apparent when Mr. Grau and Ellen were interviewed together, Mr. Grau acting as if Ellen were on his side and shared his contempt for her mother. Ellen considered such concealment essential, for if her father knew, for instance, that she had joined a Catholic society at college, he would hate her as much as he hated her mother. Ellen saw her mother's shortcomings, and considered that she had handled Nancy very badly; but she had few misconceptions about her father.

When Ellen went away to college she joined the Catholic society and started dating Catholic boys. Ellen chose strength, for Catholicism was her mother's strength and the only consistent guiding principle in the family. She also chose to study science, for her father's strength lay in his profession, and she also thus bought his interest and approval. Her father had sent her to a western college to lessen the chances of her meeting Catholics, but he could not observe what she did away from home. There are many such details, but the essence of her ways was shown in her choice of a husband. He was Catholic, and a chemical engineer. Her father's violent objections to his religion were dissipated in his interest in finding that his prospective son-in-law shared his professional interests. In a sense, Ellen was correcting the error her mother had made twenty-seven years before in marrying a non-Catholic, as if this had been the source of her unhappiness. Although Ellen was reasonably well adjusted, in fact, a master at tightrope walking, she paid a price, for both interviews and projective tests clearly indicated that this highly intelligent woman was seriously constricted, deprived of imagination and inner stimuli.

In leaving the description of the family at this point, we wish to comment that attention to these family problems proved rewarding therapeutically. Mrs. Grau came to believe that the constant conflict over religion was largely responsible for Nancy's illness. Knowing that her husband would never

give in, she did. She encouraged Nancy to become a Protestant, and her father to take her to church. Perhaps this
shift was made possible because she now knew that she had
been victorious with Ellen. Mr. Grau, pleased by his Pyrrhic
victory with Nancy, managed to restrain himself in his quarrels with his wife to some extent.

We have examined these twenty-seven years of family interaction, abstracted briefly here, according to a number of
systems of reference which have contributed to the understanding of the problems involved. Sociological approaches
which pay minimal attention to the individuals concerned
and their personal assets, idiosyncrasies, and problems do
not meet our needs. Still, consideration of family dynamics
must include the value systems and cultural usages that fuse
along with the parents to form the new family unit. We cannot
understand the functioning of a family, its assets and liabil-
ities, without grasp of its structure in relation to the society
in which it exists.

We are struggling to achieve a dynamic approach useful
for the study of the influence of the family upon its component members. We are not concerned with the problems
of each parent taken singly, or with why these two people
could not get along together; we are concerned with how the
behavior of each produces reaction and counterreaction in
the entire family, creating difficulties over and above those
arising from the shortcomings of individuals. Such understanding moves beyond the level of blame and recriminations.
We see both parents coming into the marriage carrying with
them entire systems of social and personal values, but also
with unfilled unconscious needs that they hoped would be
fulfilled in the marriage.

Like most people, the Graus came to marriage incomplete,
and with unresolved oedipal problems that helped dictate
the choice of a partner. They not only failed to achieve such
fulfillment, but in the marriage they could not even maintain
the ego defenses that they had managed to erect before mar-

riage. Needing and wanting more than they could give, they became insecure and vulnerable, and fell back upon new and more regressive defenses which further separated them. The advent of children created still more adult demands of the parents, which heightened the conflict and intensified their regressive needs. These children, then, were needed not just to fill normal parental desires for relationships with children, but even more to satisfy unconscious and regressive needs unsatisfied by the spouse. Such unconscious demands form serious impediments to the children's ego development, for they are in contact with and reacting to—and thereby are prone to introject—the immature narcissism of parents rather than adult models. Such children are also caught in a conflict, for responsivity to the needs of one parent means disloyalty to the other and provokes the latter's antagonism and rejection.

In this family, the husband, who was very insecure as a man, expected to set the pattern for the family and gain admiration and conformity from his wife. He considered her dependence upon the church and the priority she gave its rules and mores as disloyalty to him. His furious opposition to the church threatened to deprive Mrs. Grau of a major source of strength to her ego which she could not afford to relinquish. She could not replace her premarital dependence upon the church or supplement it with confidence in and dependence upon her husband, particularly when his anger and broken promises forced her to be distrustful and defensive. Of course, Mrs. Grau's seemingly naïve faith in her religion as well as her unintelligent overgeneralizations and clichés conflicted with her husband's paranoid cynicism and need for an intelligent and admiring wife in the image of his mother. We can assume that his need for attention and mothering, which led to his refusal to have children, and his temper outbursts and accusations when his wife was pregnant were related to inability to tolerate sibling rivalry in his childhood. The struggle between the parents could now be displaced onto a struggle over the children, and depersonalized in part by becoming a conflict over religion. The children were from the start caught up in this contest to gain their loyalty and affection away from the other parent.

In raising children, the mother followed her lifelong pattern, and fell back upon authority, rigidly adhering to the rules found in books. Her own needs for conformity were transferred to the child's behavior. Her insecurity as a mother had been further undermined by her being forbidden to follow a Catholic pattern as well as by her husband's biting devaluation of her efforts. Her capacities as a mother were diminished by her characteristic insensitivity to the needs and feelings of others, which permitted adherence to the set prescriptions of a book. The father remained aloof from Nancy when she was small, but later he seductively wooed her, seeking someone to give him the admiration and affection he could not gain from his wife. He could also use the child to hurt his wife, and his efforts to win the child increased Mrs. Grau's intrusiveness into Nancy's life lest she should fail to mold the child into her way of life. The father thus was breaking the necessary boundaries between the generations. Then his worth as a father figure and instrumental leader was further diminished by the chronic illness that made him pathetically dependent on his hated wife. The mother was forced to fill the instrumental role, but she was constantly being undercut and devalued. Her worth as a mother was not only weakened by her own imperviousness, but also by her castigating husband's derision and contempt. The father's value as a father was, of course, similarly being diminished by his own behavior as well as by the mother's disregard for his wishes.

In this family, the oedipal situation could not be worked through normally because of the parents' problems. Nancy's desire to be loved by her father meant that she must avoid identification with her mother and become unlike her. She could not follow her mother's model into womanhood. The mother's restrictiveness and rigid disciplining while the father was seductive led to accentuation of Nancy's choice of the father as a love object—a primary model of a love object that was distorted—an image of a castrated, hostile man, generally antagonistic to women. He trained Nancy to hate her mother and be suspicious of everyone. Nancy's turning to the father then increased her mother's feelings of inadequacy as a mother and made her even more intrusive and suspicious of Nancy. The efforts of each parent to win the girl away from the other opened the way for Nancy to separate her parents, which she continually did by fomenting dissension. Alliance with her father while he rejected her mother heightened Nancy's incestuous wishes and fears. When she became ill, her solution of her difficulties and those of the family lay in the fantasy that her mother and sister would go away to live, and leave her father to her. At the time she became psychotic, she feared leaving home lest she lose her father to her sister, just as she had lost her mother.

However, Ellen could manage the situation. As noted, her early training was different and her father was an invalid during her oedipal period. Ellen recognized her mother's shortcomings but did not accept her father's exaggerations of them. To Ellen, her mother was the potential source of security, and her father's affection was secondary. She could identify with her mother, follow her pattern, and imagine a more satisfactory outcome of a similar life if she married a Catholic husband. She became adept at mother's ability to dissemble to avoid father's wrath and still gain her own ends. From watching Nancy, she learned that it would be easier to handle her father than to oppose her mother. She gained stability by choosing her mother's religion and way of life, and in the process gained her mother's favor and room to live. She grew up to become an improved version of her mother. She bided her time, hiding her choice of religion, and avoided going with boys until she was free at college. She would not return home after college, and soon found a husband to provide a new home for her. We should note that Ellen's marriage finally established some degree of balance between the parents, for with Ellen in the fold of Catholicism, Mrs. Grau could relinquish the ancient struggle over Nancy's religious upbringing and cede her to her father.

Such consideration of the interpersonal dynamics of the family, even if greatly amplified, still omits an essential ingredient. The parental personalities also create a domestic atmosphere that affects everyone living in it. This family never formed a real entity which served as a protective shelter for its members. Indeed family members were more exposed to attack and required stronger ego defenses within the family than outside the family. A spirit of mistrust pervaded the home, and each person had to protect himself from derision and hurt. Feelings and motives were concealed, for open expression brought attack and rejection. Things were not done to please another, or through sensitivity to unspoken needs, but often to hurt or spite. The family failed to provide a place where one felt wanted despite failings. The parents' preoccupation with their own defenses left little room for sensitivity to the needs of others, causing them to be impervious to the emotional needs of their children. As the parents could not share the children, loving one person came to mean hating the others. There was intolerance of difference, blame for error, projection of one's own deficiencies onto other family members. The home seemed temporary, apt to dissolve from one day to the next, even though the parents were firmly tied by their dependency. Here, there was no hope of gaining happiness or satisfaction, but only effort to avoid the intolerable. There was little leadership, for the father's pseudo dominance was not so much leadership as intrusion into and sabotage of the mother's efforts. The conflicts, whatever their origins, could not be resolved, because of the failures in communication. Not only did each person hide his real feelings and intentions, but each parent had his own strange paralogic reasoning. The mother was vague or stereotyped and seriously scattered under stress, and the father rigid and paranoid. Then Nancy's vagueness, at first purposeful and later schizophrenic, added to the confusion.

It seems natural that the two girls shared nothing but were

wary rivals, jealously protecting their own interests. They, too, found ways of playing the family game, playing one person off against another, seeking allies, concealing real interest, and in the process heightening the discord between the parents.

This study of a family includes psychodynamic aspects as well as some basic sociological and biological considerations. The family is studied in terms of the dynamics of a small group which has certain structural requisites dictated by both biological and cultural imperatives. Individual families or categories of families can be compared in terms of how these requisites are met. The personalities of the parents serve as a focus for such study, for the parents carry into the marriage and the family that they form resultants of their own family origins, including ethnic, religious, and class mores, as well as conscious and unconscious attitudes toward marital and parental roles, and unresolved needs they hope will be met in the marriage. The fusion of two individuals provides a uniqueness to each family, which cannot be grasped by the study of individuals alone. It requires scrutiny of their interrelatedness; the reactions and counterreactions engender an atmosphere that in itself exerts an influence on all family members. Similarly, the model afforded by one parent as an object for identification and as a primary love object for a child cannot be considered simply in terms of a dyadic relationship. The differentiation of the intrafamilial forces impinging upon schizophrenic and nonschizophrenic siblings which was only incidental in this paper will be elaborated upon in Chapter XII.

Postscript

The brief description of the family with two daughters who were close in age illustrates how the children in a family can be affected very differently by the family transactions, a topic we consider more specifically in Chapter XII. We also wish to draw attention to the variety of factors that appear to have contributed to Nancy's schiz-

ophrenic thought disorder. She was chronically caught in a double-bind, though not so much by the divergent communication and meta-communications or the contradictory directives of one parent as originally described by Bateson et al. (1956), but by the opposing expectations and directives of both parents so that fulfilling the expectations of either parent meant rejection by the other—a situation later described by Weakland (1960). Nancy was also consciously taught to be paranoidally suspicious not only of "outsiders" but also to distrust her own mother. The amorphous and fragmented character of the mother's communications, later demonstrated to be typical of parents of schizophrenics by Wynne and Singer (1963a, 1963b; Singer and Wynne, 1965a, 1965b), was particularly pertinent because Nancy intentionally copied her mother's style of communicating as a defense, and later it became habitual or autonomous.

VII

The Transmission of Irrationality

(1957)

The paper is the first of a series (see Ciarlo 1967; Lidz et al., 1963; Rosman et al., 1964; Chapters XVI and XIX) that focus on the origins and nature of the aberrant thought and communication that form the essential attribute of schizophrenic disorders. The primary interest in this chapter lies in the irrationality, deception, and contradictions that pervaded the spoken and unspoken intrafamilial communication over the years. The children live in a "Procrustean environment in which events are distorted to fit the mold. The world as the child should come to perceive or feel it is denied. Their conceptualizations of the environment are neither instrumental in affording consistent understanding and mastery of events, feelings, or persons, nor in line with what persons in other families experience. . . . The acceptance of mutually contradictory experiences requires paralogical thinking. The environment affords training in irrationality."

The article was in press at the time Bateson and Jackson's important "double-bind" paper was published (Bateson et al., 1956). While it encompasses the double-bind concept that has been a major contribution to the understanding of the etiology of schizophrenic disorders, the chapter covers a variety of other intrafamilial influences that open the way for the schizophrenic offspring to fall into deviant, illogical, and delusional thinking. The article also touches upon the amorphous and fragmented thinking of the parents which

Theodore Lidz, Alice R. Cornelison, Dorothy Terry, and Stephen Fleck: Intrafamilial Environment of the Schizophrenic Patient: IV. The Transmission of Irrationality. *A.M.A. Archives of Neurology and Psychiatry*, Vol. 79, 1958, pp. 305-316. Copyright © 1958, American Medical Association.

Wynne and Singer have found to be characteristic of parents of schizophrenic patients, but not in the systematic and measurable way that these investigators evolved. Here, too, it will be noted that the problems extend far beyond the typical stylistic communicational problems that Wynne and Singer have emphasized.

One of the distinctive features of schizophrenia lies in the disturbed symbolic functioning—in the paralogic quality of the patient's thinking and communicating that alters his internal representation of reality. We are following the hypothesis that the schizophrenic patient escapes from an untenable world in which he is powerless to cope with insoluble conflicts by the device of imaginatively distorting his symbolization of reality. Such internalized maneuvers do not require action, or coming to terms with other persons, or altering their attitudes. The patient can regain the mastery that he once possessed in childhood, before his reality was firmly structured, and it could still give way before the power of his wishes. It can be an alluring way because it is self-contained. It is a bitter way because it is isolating.

The present study will focus on this critical characteristic of schizophrenia, and, therefore, must neglect many other aspects of the developmental forces active during the childhood and adolescence of schizophrenic patients, even though these other aspects can be separated from the forces distorting mentation only artificially.

The distortions of mentation, the core problem of schizophrenia, have been relatively neglected of late because of interest in "borderline cases" and in "pseudoneurotic schizophrenia" and in the similarities between the underlying psychopathology of certain psychosomatic conditions and that of schizophrenia. Patients suffering from these conditions are not clearly schizophrenic, because they remain sufficiently well integrated to permit a consensus between their thinking and that of others, and effective social communication remains possible. Such patients are potentially psychotic, and when their communication breaks down and becomes instrumentally ineffective, they are psychotic. Some never need this solution, but others may be unable to utilize it. It is possible for many persons to break under extreme conditions and achieve flight into irrationality, sacrificing reality to the demands of id impulses or to preserve some semblance of ego structure of self-esteem. A theory of schizophrenia must explain not only the patient's need to abandon reality testing but also his ability to do so. We must seek to understand why some persons can escape through withdrawal into unshared ways of experiencing the world around them more readily than others.

The thinking disorder in schizophrenia has been taken by some, and perhaps classically, to indicate dysfunction of the brain—dysfunction caused by lesions, deficiency, or metabolic disorder. The search for this brain dysfunction has been pursued for over 100 years. Each advance in physiology or neuroanatomy brings new hope; and each new form of physical therapy tantalizingly provokes prospects of leading to definitive knowledge of the malfunctioning of the brain. However, careful studies, and even casual observations, show that the thought disorder in schizophrenia differs markedly from any produced by a known organic deficit or a toxic disturbance of the brain. This is not the place to enter upon the nature of such differences.[1] Although it is true that schizophrenic patients tend to concretize, they are also obviously capable of high degrees of abstraction, and may tend to abstract all too readily. More pertinently, unless a patient is permitted to become dilapidated by social isolation, the irrationality either remains or becomes more or less circumscribed. A girl who writes violently invective letters filled with delusions to her parents will in the next minute write a letter

[1]*Since the publication of this paper, attention has been drawn to similarities between the delusions and hallucinations of patients suffering from amphetamine intoxications and those of schizophrenic patients. At a superficial level, amphetamine addicts usually talk freely of their hallucinations and delusions and expand upon them, whereas schizophrenic patients tend to be secretive about their delusions. In general, patients with drug reactions suffer from decrement in intellectual abilities whereas schizophrenic patients do not. However, it may be difficult to test some persons with either condition (Lidz et al., 1942; Lidz and Kahn, 1946).*

to a friend without a trace of delusional material, and then sits in her room and correctly composes inordinately complex music. No defect of thinking due to dysfunction of the brain permits such highly organized conceptualization.

There have been many approaches to the search for a genetic predisposition to schizophrenia. Our studies do not turn away from such consideration, but consider that a meaningful approach would focus upon a predisposition to symbolic distortion. Although our emphasis leads in another direction for theoretical reasons, which we shall seek to indicate briefly, we wish to point out that neither our theory nor our interpretations of data are of primary concern at present. We are attempting to present data derived from our study which we believe reliable and highly pertinent.

We consider that man is not naturally endowed with an inherent logic of causal relationships, but, rather, that the surroundings in which he is raised influence his ways of perceiving, thinking, and communicating. What makes "sense" at different periods of history and in different cultural settings (and, to a less extent, from one family to another) varies greatly. The Hindu way of regarding life in this world and life after death is irrational to us—and our way is just as meaningless and confused to the Hindu. Still, a trend toward a type of rationality exists in all cultures and in all groups. It is not that any of us has some particular ability to perceive reality as it is, for the actuality of reality—the *Ding an sich*—is never attainable by our senses. There is, however, a pragmatic meaning concerning what is fact—what is reality. It is measurable in terms of how our perceptions lead to effective action: if what we tell ourselves about events in the world around us leads to a degree of mastery over our environment and to workable interaction with the persons with whom we live. The effectiveness of reflective mentation is measured by how it helps the individual master his environment and achieve sufficient consensus with other persons to enable collaborative interaction. Communication, the outward manifestation of symbolic activity, measures the efficacy of mentation by the ·g1 : of consensus attained with others concerning wh.. 	erceive and what events mean. However, matters are not so simple. A large portion of mental activity is autistic rather than reflective; and autistic reverie is closer to primary-process thinking, and to a great extent in the service of the wish of instinctual drives. The permeation of reflective thought, by the autistic processes, provides a major key to the understanding of schizophrenic thinking. Then, too, schizophrenic regression can reintroduce elements of perceptions and thought processes of early childhood that interpenetrate with more mature reflective and autistic mentation. Further, not all shared ideas need be reasonable and effective for purposes of controlling the environment. Man's need for emotional security, while he lives in this world of contingency, leads to systematization of ideas that actually may run counter to experience. Such systems, based upon unproved and untestable axioms, can direct our perceptions and understanding. As they are culturally approved, they are termed "beliefs" rather than "delusions." They result in compartmentalization of experience into segments that are kept from conflicting and challenging one another. Adherence to an axiom into which the perception of experience must be fitted almost requires distortion of perception of the environment. The issue is raised because a similar situation may be found within the family. If a parent must protect his tenuous equilibrium by adhering to a rigidly held need or self-concept, and everything else must be subsidiary to this defense, distortions occur that affect the rest of the family.

The family is the primary teacher of social interaction and emotional reactivity. It teaches by means of its milieu and nonverbal communication more than by formal education. The child's sources of identification and self-esteem derive from the family and markedly influence the developing patterns of symbolic functioning. However, the child is also exposed to the parental interpretations of reality and the parents' ways of communicating. Parental interpretations may have limited instrumental utility when they primarily serve to maintain the parents' own precarious equilibrium. The topic is very complex, and this paper will deal only with some of the more obvious influences of parental instability upon the children's thought processes.

We shall pursue the hypothesis that the schizophrenic patient is more prone to withdraw through distortion of his symbolization of reality than other patients, because his foundation in reality testing is precarious, having been raised amidst irrationality and chronically exposed to intrafamilial communications that distort and deny what should be the obvious interpretation of the environment, including the recognition and understanding of impulses and the affective behavior of members of the family.

Primarily, we are seeking to describe these families and find common features among them, rather than compare them with other types of families. We are, so to speak, describing the terrain of a country we are exploring, not comparing it with the geography of other countries. We have been skeptical, holding aloof from accepting too readily many current and past theoretical formulations. In general, rather than focusing attention upon one phase of development or any single interpersonal relationship, we have been more interested in studying the forces that interfere with the emergence of a reasonably independent and integrated personality at the end of adolescence—the critical period in the development of schizophrenia, even if the onset is later in life.

We shall discuss in this chapter two closely interrelated aspects of the family environment—the rationality of the parents and the nature of the communication within the family.

PARENTAL IRRATIONALITY

We shall first consider the rationality of the parents in the grossest terms. The findings are unexpectedly striking, when compared with data from larger statistical studies (Kallmann, 1953; Pollock et al., 1939). However, the study reported in Chapter II by Terry and Rennie (1938) found comparable figures, though their data are difficult to evaluate clearly. None of the parents of our patients was ever hospitalized in a mental institution and thus probably would not have been indexed as psychotic in any broad epidemiological survey of psychoses in the parents of schizophrenic patients. Minimally, nine of the fifteen patients had at least one parent who could be called schizophrenic, or ambulatory schizophrenic, or clearly paranoid in behavior and attitudes. The finding is difficult to express explicitly, for the shading between what one terms schizophrenia and what bizarre behavior and ideation is arbitrary, and the line between psychosis and a paranoid outlook is equally fine. Although the proportion of families with more or less schizophrenic parents is very high, minimally 60 per cent of the families, it will become apparent that the cut-off point was quite arbitrary and other families could have been included. The classification is made difficult because of parents who maintain a reasonable degree of social presence and yet display seriously distorted thinking and motivation. Some of the mothers are seriously scattered and confused, particularly when anxious and under pressure. Fathers may be eminently successful but display behavior to their families that is pervaded and dominated by paranoid beliefs. Brief illustrations will clarify these statement.

We shall say little about the two mothers, Mrs. Narab and Mrs. Thomas, who were frankly schizophrenic except to say that despite delusions, hallucinations, and very confused reasoning they had continued to be the parent with the major responsibility for raising the children. The husband of one was somewhat grandiose, if not paranoid, and spent most of his time away from home, while the other couple was divorced. Although a third mother, Mrs. Schwartz, sounded frankly schizophrenic, she ran the family business after her husband had suffered a "nervous breakdown" (before the patient was born), after which he had become passive and subservient to her. She openly expressed beliefs that her telephone was tapped and that the neighbors might burn down the home.

There were two mothers, Mrs. Nebb and Mrs. Newcomb, who completely dominated the lives of their passive husbands and children. We consider these women typical "schizophrenogenic" mothers in needing and using their sons to complete their own frustrated lives. Their sons had to be geniuses, and any faults in them or anything that went wrong with their lives were consistently blamed on others—classmates, doctors, teachers, and society in general. They believed that only they understood their sons. We could never really understand these mothers, for their incessant talk was driven and mixed up, displaying unbelievable obtuseness to any ideas not their own. While we have hesitated to call these women schizophrenic, they are certainly not reality-oriented and are very close to being psychotic. Brief descriptions may convey the problem.

Two major private psychiatric hospitals had refused to keep Jack Newcomb, not because of his behavior but because they could not stand his mother's incessant interference. Such behavior had plagued the boy and his teachers throughout his school years. Mrs. Newcomb talked incessantly about some fixed idea of the cause of her son's illness. When her ideas were questioned, she counterattacked; and if forced to abandon a theme, she would relinquish it only temporarily, retreating to her next equally unreasonable idea. When the family had wished to build a home, she had exhausted four or five architects, and the house was never built. When the daughter eventually gave up attempting to inform her mother that she intended to get married and simply announced her engagement, Mrs. Newcomb steadfastly ignored the daughter's intent. While the girl was seeking an apartment, the mother would only talk about re-engaging her college room for the next academic year. The mother ignored the need to make plans for the wedding until the father, an unusually passive man, finally intervened shortly before the date that had been set for the wedding.

Mrs. Nebb's life was dominated by the idea that her twin sons were geniuses, whose development must not be hindered by setting any limits except in defense of her own extreme obsessiveness. Delinquent acts of the twins while they were still in grade school, such as breaking into and robbing a house and setting a barn on fire, were ignored and blamed upon other children. She insistently regarded a move from a mountain resort to the city, required because the twins were ostracized, and which disrupted her husband's business and social life, as a move to give her twins the superior education they required. Mrs. Nebb fell into violent rages because of trivia that interrupted her obsessive cleanliness but gave inordinate praise for acts that the twins knew were nonsense. The household under her domination was a crazy place, and description could not be attempted without provoking the charge of gross exaggeration. For example, both twins claim that for many years they thought that constipation meant disagreeing with mother. Whenever one of them would argue with her, she would say they were constipated and needed an enema; both boys were then placed prone on the bathroom floor naked while the mother, in her undergarments, inserted the nozzle in each boy, fostering a contest to see which could hold out longer—the loser having to dash down to the basement lavatory. The projective tests of these last two mothers were judged frankly schizophrenic.

Only one of the four or five fathers who were considered psychotic or paranoid was as disorganized as these mothers. Mr. Newberg, though a steady provider and a man with an ingenious turn of mind, was constantly engaged in working out one or another of his many inventions, which never materialized. He was vaguely suspicious and paranoid, fostering suspicion in his children; but it was his incessant talk, in which he jumped from one topic and one idea to another in driven fashion, that seemed most disturbing to the family. Like Mrs. Newcomb, he would hammer away at a fixed idea, and an hour with Mr. Newberg thoroughly exhausted either of the two interviewers who tried to cope with him. The other fathers were more capable and less disorganized but more fixed in their paranoid ways. Mr. Dolfuss was also an inventor, but a successful one, for a single ingenious invention had made the family wealthy. He spent much of his time steeped in the mysteries of an esoteric Asiatic cult, believing that he and a friend who shared these beliefs were among the few select who would achieve salvation in reincarnation. Whether he believed in his divinity or it was his wife who deified him is not clear, but this family lived in what we have termed *folie en famille*, which centered about the father and his esoteric beliefs, and according to a social pattern that was widely divergent from the society in which they actually lived. Mr. Grau and Mr. Reading may be mentioned together as being competent business men who expressed many paranoid beliefs which did not interfere appreciably with their business activities but seriously upset family life. Among other things, Mr. Grau was paranoically bitter against all Catholics, not an unusual situation, but here the paranoid bigotry focused upon his wife who was a devout Catholic. At times he feared going to work because he felt people were against him. His wife, who has not been counted as psychotic, probably as a matter of relativity, was an extremely immature, scattered woman. Mr. Reading was so suspicious that people were taking advantage of him that the hospital staff could not establish any relationship with him over a six-month period. His major concern at all interviews was to prove to the staff that his wife, who was actually a seriously obsessive woman, had been a malignant influence and had ruined his daughters, and also to make certain that the hospital was not lying, misrepresenting, or somehow taking advantage of him. Both men were hostile and contemptuous of women, and both had only daughters. The material offered here concerning these parents has been sparse, but we have abundant information which permits us to be certain that all nine have been virtually psychotic or markedly paranoid at least from the time of the patient's birth until the onset of illness. We are more interested in scrutinizing the situations in the remaining six families, in which the parents cannot be labeled so readily.

We can extract some generalizations from the study of these more disturbed parents which seem to apply to most, if not all, of the remaining six families, as well as to parents of many other schizophrenic patients. The struggles of these parents to preserve their own integration led them to limit their environment markedly by rigid preconceptions of the way things must be. The parents' precarious equilibrium will tumble if the environment cannot be delimited or if the parents must shift from the one rigid role they can manage. Mrs. Nebb must see herself as the mother of twin geniuses. We understand something of how this came about. She, too, was a twin, but the deformed ugly ducking of the family, who dreamed of the phallus that would turn her into a swan. The birth of twins was her triumph, and their accomplishments were her means of outshining her dominant twin sister. Mrs. Narab had written of how she had given birth to a genius, or perhaps a Messiah. She kept a diary of the child's development for fifteen years, presenting an idyllic picture of the home life, which we learned from the sons and husband had little resemblance to reality. In a somewhat different sense, Mrs. Grau, the rejected Catholic wife, could only raise her daughters as Catholics, for she could not live according to any pattern except the one established for her by the Church. Mr. Reading had to dominate his household and maintain his narcissistic esteem through admiration from all of the females around him—his mother, wife, and two daughters. The slightest challenge to his imperious and unreasonable demands provoked a storm of fury. These people must retain the necessary picture of themselves and their family. Some will fight to retain it; but others adhere to their conceptualization which reality cannot alter or a new situation modify. They perceive and act in terms of their needed preconceptions, which they relinquish only under extreme pressures, and then with all sorts of maneuvers to explain through projection or ignore through isolation. We should like to take an example from outside the series of fifteen families—from a case in which the sibling of a schizophrenic patient was in analysis. The father had left home when the children were very young to gain justice and revenge against a rival firm that had ruined his business by publicly accusing him falsely. Nothing mattered to him except to re-establish his power and prestige and gain revenge. He pursued his course for over fifteen years without even visiting his family, though always writing that he would return home the following week. He was markedly grandiose and paranoid, however just his cause. Still, his attitude was scarcely more pathological than the mother's. All through the years of separation, she insisted that nothing was wrong with the marriage, maintaining a shallow, euphoric attitude and telling her children that their concerns were groundless—the father was just attending to his business and would be back next week. Penelope was finally rewarded, but she could not unravel the fabric she had woven. Her son became schizophrenic within a month of her husband's return.

THE NATURE OF THE PARENTAL COMMUNICATION

The parents' delimitation of the environment, and their perception of events to suit their needs, result in a strange family atmosphere into which the children must fit themselves and suit this dominant need or feel unwanted. Often the children must obliterate their own needs to support the defenses of the parent whom they need. They live in a Procrustean environment, in which events are distorted to fit the mold. The world as the child should come to perceive or feel it is denied. Their conceptualizations of the environment are neither instrumental in affording consistent understanding and mastery of events, feelings, or persons, nor in line with what persons in other families experience. Facts are constantly being altered to suit emotionally determined needs. The acceptance of mutually contradictory experiences requires paralogical thinking. The environment affords training in irrationality.

The domination of a parent's behavior and attitude by

rigid defensive needs clarifies other traits often noted among these parents. "Impervious" is a word we find ourselves using frequently to connote a parent's inability to feel or hear the child's emotional needs. The parent may listen but does not seem to hear and, further, seems oblivious to unspoken communications. These parents cannot consider anything that does not fit in with their own self-protecting systems. Indeed, as Bowen and his coworkers (1957) have also noted, such parents may respond to the child only in terms of their own needs displaced to the child, thus building up an entire pattern of maladaptive interactions. Bateson et al. (1956) have recently studied a related aspect of parent-child interaction. The parent conveys the impression of being cold or rejecting, and, of course, may be, but imperviousness is not simply a consequence of rejection of the child, but more a rejection of anything that threatens the parent's equilibrium or self-image.

Some parents often talk in clichés conveying a false impression of limited intelligence. Clichés and stereotypes serve to simplify the environment to enable the parents to cope with it in terms of their set needs. Such parents not only label a child as "the selfish one" or "the quiet one" but actually perceive the child only in terms of the stereotype. The fixed notions of an etiology of the illness, which may drive the psychiatrist to the verge of desperation, is a related phenomenon.

"Masking," which also confuses communication, refers to the ability of one or both parents to conceal some very disturbing situation within the family and to act as if it did not exist. "Masking" usually contains a large degree of self-deception as well as an effort to conceal from others; but it involves a conscious negation, as well as unconscious denial. The parent, unable either to accept or to alter the situation, ignores it and acts as though the family were a harmonious and homogeneous body which filled the needs of its members. Although some degree of masking may exist in all families, in some of our families the masking of serious problems dominated the entire family interaction. Problems which family members will not or cannot recognize are unlikely to be resolved. Children who grow up in such homes are aware that something is not right. They may become deeply resentful that the more intact parent takes no action to protect them from the situation. The children are puzzled, but may also learn to mask or ignore the obvious. Their efforts to explain away the situation, or to accept or convey pretense of affection and devotion, which has no resonance or real meaning, distorts their value systems.

The following two cases illustrate rather extreme degrees of imperviousness in which the parents appear severely rejecting.

The Ubanques impressed the hospital and research staff as strange people, but they were one of the few couples in our series who may have been reasonably happily married. The younger of two daughters was severely hebephrenic. Mrs. Ubanque sought to blame the sex talk of the girl's college roommates. However, both parents could convince themselves to an amazing degree that the daughter was not really ill but merely being contrary and refusing to behave normally. This tendency increased as their financial means for retaining the girl in the hospital diminished, bearing little relationship to her condition. However, after some months of intensive therapy, the patient improved considerably. She repeatedly expressed her hopelessness that her parents would ever listen and understand her unhappiness over her school and social problems. As the patient could not be kept in the hospital for a long period and as the psychiatrist who was interviewing the parents found it impossible to get them to focus upon any meaningful problems that might be upsetting, a therapeutic experiment was undertaken with great trepidation.[2] The patient and the parents would meet together and, with the help of both psychiatrists, would try to

[2]*This may seem strange today, but the session was among the first, if not the first, conjoint therapy session ever conducted—and unfortunately, perhaps due to our inexperience, turned out badly.*

speak frankly to one another. The daughter carefully prepared in advance what she wished to convey, and we tried to prepare the parents to listen carefully and to reply meaningfully. The patient, to the surprise of her psychiatrist, freely poured out her feelings to her parents and in heart-rending fashion told them of her bewilderment and pleaded for their understanding and help. During the height of her daughter's pleas, Mrs. Ubanque offhandedly turned to one of the psychiatrists, tugged at the waist of her dress and blandly remarked, "My dress is getting tight. I suppose I should go on a diet." The mother had fallen back upon her habitual pattern of blocking out anything that would upset her bland equanimity. The next day the patient relapsed into incoherent and silly behavior.

Mrs. Forel, a cold and highly narcissistic woman, has been the only mother who did not wish to visit her offspring in the hospital. She said, "Wouldn't it upset Billy too much to have his mother see him in a place like this?" This clearly meant: I couldn't stand visiting my son in a mental hospital. Mrs. Forel's intense dependency upon and attachment to her older sister, a very masculine woman, had contributed greatly to ruining her marriage. The sister had developed an intense dislike for the patient when he was still a small boy. After her husband's death, Mrs. Forel lived with her sister, but her twelve-year-old son was not allowed in the house and had to live in a boarding house nearby. One Christmas eve the mother stood by while the sister turned Billy away from the home and from spending the evening with them. Later, when they were all going to visit relatives in a distant city, the sister refused to take Billy along, and the mother remained blandly in the car while they passed the boy trying to hitchhike in a snowstorm. Mrs. Forel's dependence upon her sister took precedence over her son's needs.[3]

Another type of imperviousness existed in the cases of the

[3]Literary and dramatic illustrations of many features of these families which we seek to convey can be found in Eugene O'Neill's *Long Day's Journey Into Night*, Tennessee Williams's *The Glass Menagerie*, and August Strindberg's *Easter* and *The Father*.

Narabs and the Nebbs. The mothers were solicitous enough, but the vision of the genius child who would complete and justify their lives made them oblivious to the actual needs, abilities, and deficiencies of their children. Mrs. Schwartz was so caught up in a struggle with her eldest, psychopathic son that she scarcely noted anything that occurred in the life of the youngest son, who eventually became schizophrenic, even though she was very controlling of much of his life.

"Masking" also distorts the communication within the family severely. Mr. Lerner had been an eminent attorney who supported his family at a lavish level and basked in the light of his legal prestige and his associations with prominent persons. After his partner, the contact man for the firm, committed suicide, his income fell off disastrously. Mr. Lerner was an obsessive brief writer and researcher who could neither gain clients nor plead cases. Gradually, he withdrew into his office, and into his study at home, spending his time making scholarly analyses of legal matters, which earned him almost nothing. The need to consider himself a great legal mind and a prominent person took precedence over the needs of his family. He could not admit his failure to himself or anyone else, and could not alter his ways. His wife, who, fortunately, was a competent woman, went to work and, with the help of her relatives, managed to support the family as well as her husband's law office. For over ten years she helped maintain the pretense to the world and to her children and even managed to keep herself from recognizing the resentment she felt toward a husband who let her shoulder the entire burden of the family. She had to maintain the myth of a successful marriage to a strong father figure. The children could not help but know that it was all fraudulent. The situation required consistent falsification, and all the communications between members of this household had a high degree of pretense concerning the feelings they felt obligated to express in order to maintain the facade. The daughter, as a patient, kept protesting the expense of her hospitalization to her father, though she was well aware that he had earned nothing since her early childhood.

Mr. and Mrs. Lamb both strove to mask a situation they could not hide successfully. Mr. Lamb, a successful business man and once an athlete of renown, needed to be the center of considerable adulation. Mr. Lamb could not tolerate the rivalry of his son and required the help of alcohol and numerous affairs to maintain his feelings of masculinity. To alleviate his anxiety and to prevent open conflict, he pretended that he was not an alcoholic and that he spent most of his time traveling in order to provide well. His wife also tried to maintain the pretense that they were happily married. Unable to consider separation seriously, she strove to blind herself to the seriousness of his alcoholism; his noxious influence on their son, whom he constantly belittled; and his extramarital affairs, which were highly embarrassing to the family.

Mrs. Lamb appeared to accept her husband's obnoxious behavior but sought to establish altogether different standards in her son, in whom she fostered aesthetic interests. A son, in such situations, gains confused concepts of what his mother cherishes in a man. The many other problems that beset this family are outside the immediate interests of this chapter; but we should note that the highly sensitive mother often became impervious to her son's needs because she had to center her attention on her husband and support his infantile needs.

Habitual masking may then be viewed as an irrational form of communication, but another feature that often affects the child's mental functioning is complete breakdown of communication between parents, especially when the child is caught between different value systems and attitudes which cannot be integrated. Mrs. Nussbaum resented the daughter who was born after she and her husband had become emotionally estranged, whereas Mr. Nussbaum sought from his daughter the affection he could not receive from his wife. The parents had quarreled before the patient's birth over their respective attachments to their families, attachments which took precedence over the marital relationship. Mrs.

Nussbaum's family had accused Mr. Nussbaum's oldest brother of ruining their father's business. When Mrs. Nussbaum had seemed to side with her family, her husband considered her disloyal and never forgave her. Indeed, they never spoke of the matter again, but never became reconciled and were openly hostile, though continuing to live together. Communication between them was largely vengeful and undermining. The father, for example, perhaps partly to punish his wife and partly to escape her vituperative temper, spent his evenings in his office reading, but, to conceal his own impotence, let his wife and family believe that he had a mistress with whom he spent much of his time. Many of the family quarrels centered on this nonexistent situation. In addition, the father's seductive use of the daughter to bolster his narcissism, while seeking to ignore his wife, further confused communication and meaning in this family.

We could properly place the Benjamins, the remaining family, in the large category of borderline parents, but their extrafamilial functioning remained reasonably intact. Mrs. Benjamin, particularly when anxious, spoke incessantly and said very little, and even less that was pertinent to the situation. She asked questions endlessly, but constantly interrupted with another question before anyone could answer her. This woman might be termed obsessive, but her obsessiveness was extremely scattered and disorganized when she was anxious. In contrast, her husband's ritualized obsessiveness led to behavior that often seemed highly irrational. He would go into rages if a toothpaste cap was not replaced, throw his wife's entire wardrobe on the floor because her clothes were in disorder, or her fur coat into the bathtub because she had left the coat lying on the bed. Although he frequently complained and worried about money, he could not keep from making unnecessary purchases. When seriously concerned about meeting the cost of his son's hospitalization, he bought a third car and could not understand why his wife was angered by his fine present for her, even though his purchase of a second car just a month before had precipitated a violent quarrel. Mr. Benjamin saw nothing hostile in the purchase. We wish to call attention to the irrational atmosphere produced in a family when the parents are obsessive-compulsive, particularly when the two obsessive patterns are in direct conflict. The covert, hostile, and symptomatic behavior of each parent challenges the defensive pattern of the other. Neither makes sense, but both parents find rationalizations for their own behavior which neither the spouse nor the children can really understand. Though Mrs. Benjamin, along with Mrs. Ubanque, Mrs. Forel, Mrs. Grau, and Mrs. Reading could not be considered overtly psychotic, they all were strange, disturbed persons. The defensive structure of all these women led to a type of behavior that created great difficulty in communication within the family because what they said was more in defense of their fragile equilibrium than a communication pertinent to the given situation.

Before ending this initial survey of the irrationality present in the family environment in which schizophrenic patients grow up, we wish to direct attention to the conscious training of children to a paranoid orientation that takes place in some families. Both Mr. Grau and Mr. Reading sought not only to make their daughters distrustful and suspicious toward their mothers but to share their own paranoid suspiciousness of almost everyone. In a different vein, the Dolfuss parents inculcated a system of religious belief that was aberrant and virtually delusional in the society in which the family lived.

COMMENT

The study of the irrationality and defective communication in these families presents a complex task. A fairly complete picture of each family would be required to bring out the many frustrating problems involved. Here, we have merely sought to convey an impression of the broad sweep of the distorting influences present in all of the families studied, which have also been apparent in most, if not all, of the families of the many other schizophrenic patients treated in the Yale Psychiatric Institute during the past several years. Other less obvious and subtler influences also require attention; these will be considered in subsequent chapters.

Although our studies encompass only fifteen families, they form a good random sampling of middle- and upper-class families with schizophrenic offspring. The marked disturbances in instrumental utility of communications that can readily be noted in all of these families cannot be ignored in the search for reasons why these patients may be prone to withdraw from a reality orientation when unable to cope with their serious interpersonal problems.

We are not pointing to such defects in communication and the presence of an irrational milieu as a cause of schizophrenia. We are concerned with multiple factors distorting personality development rather than seeking a "cause." Here we simply, but significantly, indicate that our patients were not raised in families that adhered to culturally accepted ideas of causality and meanings, or respected the instrumental utility of their ideas and communications, because one or both parents were forced to abandon rationality to defend their own precarious ego structure. We are, therefore, concerned here with factors that may differentiate the genesis of schizophrenia from the genesis of other psychopathological syndromes, in that persons who grow up in such families, having had their symbolic roots nourished by irrationality in the family, are less confined by the restrictions of the demands of reality when means of escape and withdrawal are required.

Of course, the presence of poorly organized or disorganized parents can just as well be taken as evidence of a genetic strain that transmits schizophrenia. Indeed, we have probably found more evidence of mental illness among parents and in other relatives than any study of the genetic factors of schizophrenia. At this time we are describing what exists in the family rather than explaining how it came about. According to our concepts of human development, such distortions of reasoning are more explicable through extrabiological transmission of family characteristics than through genetic endowment. However, we need not seek a solution with an "either-or," for, as with many other conditions, both genetic and environmental factors may well be involved.

POSTSCRIPT

Further and more detailed examples of the intrafamilial "irrationalities" will be found in other chapters, notably in Chapter XIII on identical twins and in Chapter VIII describing the Dolfuss family, even though the articles were written for a different purpose.

The material presented in this chapter has particular importance because it has guided us to a crucial aspect in our therapeutic orientation (Lidz, 1978; Lidz and Lidz, 1982; Chapters XVII and XIX); namely, to free patients from the need or obligation to perceive, feel and comprehend the world as the parents have mandated and come to trust their own perceptions and feelings.

A later, more comprehensive discussion of the origins and nature of schizophrenic thought disorders will be found in Chapters XVI and XIX; and a more thorough discussion of the role of language in human adaptation and integration in Chapter III of The Family and Human Adaptation (Lidz, 1963c). The contributions of Wynne and Singer to the relations between parental styles of thinking and schizophrenic thought disorders are of critical moment to the understanding of schizophrenic disorders. We also wish to call attention to the work of Blakar (1980) and his colleagues in Norway, which, as have several other studies, indicate that many schizophrenic patients, despite their psychoses, are often able to reason more coherently than their parents.

In his article "The Transmission of Irrationality Reconsidered," Stierlin (1978a) notes the significance of this contribution and discusses subsequent additions to the knowledge that the parents of schizophrenic patients have distorted ways of communicating and influencing their offspring.

VIII

The Understanding of Symptomatology through the Study of Family Interaction

(1957)

The following paper describes in some detail the parallels between a father who ran his family and household like a theocrat, if not a deity, and the patient's bizarre symptoms and behavior. It was one of the clearest examples we had encountered of learning "how to be psychotic."

We have found that some schizophrenic symptoms can be related in detail to individual behavior in the family through the process of imitation, parental tuition, and identification (Cameron and Magaret, 1951; Fleck, 1953; Fleck et al., 1957; Miller and Dollard, 1941; Chapter IV). In addition to the parental models, however, family interaction and deviant family organization also are reflected in the schizophrenic's personality and behavior. To illustrate this thesis in some detail, we have selected one patient and his family. This is a skewed family whose life was so bizarre and deviant from its social environment that we coined the phrase *folie en famille* to characterize such maladaptation. We shall first describe the patient's illness and his symptoms which, as will be seen, leave no room for doubt concerning diagnosis. The patient's behavior and personality organization reflect, often in cari-

Stephen Fleck, Daniel X. Freedman, Alice R. Cornelison, Theodore Lidz, and Dorothy Terry: The Family Environment of Schizophrenic Patients: V. The Understanding of Symptomatology Through the Study of Family Interaction. Presented at the May 1957 meeting of the American Psychiatric Association and published in the original edition.

cature, not only one parent's characteristics, but also show a combination of the parents' attitudes and their perception of each other.

THE PATIENT

Emil Dolfuss was twenty-six years old when he was transferred from another hospital to which he had been admitted for the second time following a serious suicidal attempt. At the time of admission to the Yale Psychiatric Institute, he conducted himself in a haughty and pompous manner, choosing his words and accent carefully. He spoke calmly of his suicidal attempt which, he explained, followed a quarrel with his mother. He answered most questions in vague generalities and stated that he was in the hospital because, "It's usually the case that one hopes to become more stable and achieve a more harmonious relationship to one's self and to one's family and others."

Overt psychotic behavior first appeared when Emil was twenty-one, although we later learned that shortly after his father's death when Emil was fourteen symptoms in the form of ideas of persecution had occurred. Although Emil was highly intelligent, his school record had been so poor that he could not gain admission to college and after a few years of aimless studying, he traveled alone to the Orient although his family recognized then that he was severely disturbed. While abroad, he developed ideas of saving the world, lived out religious delusions, and was returned to the United States by consular authorities after he persistently attempted to contact the President. Emil was then hospitalized for the first time for approximately eighteen months; he received insulin and electric shock treatments and psychotherapy. During this hospitalization he was catatonic and exhibited many rituals, most of which were derived from various Eastern religions or philosophies; and he would periodically refuse to eat meat. He declared his only sibling, Adele, a goddess, and knelt and prayed in front of her before speaking to her. For a period he became mute and refused to see his family.

Between hospitalizations, Emil maintained a marginal adjustment, changing occupations often, but gradually he again became preoccupied with Eastern religion and, at times, believed himself a God. He insisted on having such brilliant lights turned on constantly within and around his garage apartment that it disturbed the neighborhood. After the argument with his mother which concerned a religious trinket that belonged to a friend of his father, Emil offered an engagement ring to his sister's friend whom he knew but slightly, and ostensibly his suicidal attempt followed the rejection of his proposal.

In our hospital the patient's behavior gradually deteriorated. Because of his many pompous and unreasonable demands, he found himself increasingly isolated from other patients who resented in particular his attempts to enforce his belief that all rooms must be fully illuminated around the clock. These and other demands made it extremely difficult for the staff to maintain a harmonious and consistent attitude toward him, a factor which contributed to his behavioral incontinence. At first he was immaculately overdressed, as if he were at an exclusive English country club, but then his dress became increasingly slovenly, and he refused to shave or have his hair cut. Following a major crisis about the lights five months after admission, Emil became combative, remained mute for weeks, and refused to eat. He then demanded and ate enormous quantities of beef for a period, after which he put himself on a strictly vegetarian diet. From this time on, he also steadfastly refused to wear trousers. He would remain attired in shorts, a checkered waistcoat, and a heavy jacket even on very hot days; later he wore only shorts even in winter while insisting that his windows be open. He refused to sleep in bed throughout the remainder of his hospital stay and slept either standing up or in a chair. Emil was never without light in his room. Although he acted as if he had the right to command the staff to carry out his wishes, it was clear that the absence of light caused him to panic and become combative. He communicated with the staff by signs, charades, or in a foreign language. He refused to wash or to be bathed, and while quite oblivious to certain health hazards, he also propounded many faddish health theories and was deeply worried about insufficient food supply. He hoarded food, especially candy, fruits, and nuts in large quantities, and when his mother objected to these foods for health reasons, he accused her of stinginess.

Emil also became quite interested in Jewish customs and history (he had a Jewish therapist) and even wished to be circumcised, but in his behavior continued to adhere to the dicta of a mysterious Eastern religion. In observance of the latter, he counteracted gravity by never lying down, worshiped light, and avoided "animal excitation" by not eating meat.

A vignette of Emil's life in our hospital follows: a tall, bearded young man with hair to his shoulders, dressed only in shorts stands in a room stacked with magazines and fruit, or sits on the toilet in the adjacent bathroom reading the *Wall Street Journal*. The doors and windows are open; he motions to a passer-by in the hall to come into his room. There he forces a sticky fig into the visitor's hand and makes a request in sign language. When he is refused, he listens carefully, then shoves the visitor out and shoots him with mock gestures.

THE FAMILY

Mr. Dolfuss, of a wealthy middle-class background, was sent from Austria in early adulthood to conduct the American branch of the family business. Mrs. Dolfuss who came from an Austrian family of considerable renown also immigrated to this country as a young adult. After they married, they moved to the home near Boston which Mr. Dolfuss had established as a bachelor. He ran his well-appointed home in the manner of European nobility which set the family apart from the rest of the community. The formality of the household was unusual—the chauffeur wore white gloves even to shop for groceries, and all members of the household had to dress formally every afternoon to receive the master at the door. The children were permitted to be with their parents only during specific hours. When at home, Mr. Dolfuss spent much of his time in his bedroom, where he was not to be disturbed, and only his wife or the "Fräulein" was permitted to look after his needs. He was mortally afraid of drafts, and frequently suffered from colds. Usually he spent his time reading about Eastern religion and philosophy while dressed only in his underwear. From his reading he evolved a peculiar cult which the family shared, but which allegedly was understood by only a few select people. This Eastern philosophy somehow included certain Christian traditions so that Christmas and winter-solstice celebrations were combined. A ceremony of the lighting of candles was preceded by a long speech by Mr. Dolfuss on the holiness of light during which the entire household were required to stand listening.

Mr. Dolfuss' intelligence and ingenuity were put to a test when the family business failed. He invented a device which he manufactured and sold with great success, so that no change in the family's income or living standard occurred. Mr. Dolfuss claimed other inventions, however, and the family believes that he was cheated out of several patents.

Mrs. Dolfuss considered her primary duty to be at the service of her husband: she felt he was a great man and came to share his beliefs to which she still adheres. After his death she continued to believe that her husband was still alive, dead but in another reincarnation. The family members refused to elaborate their religious beliefs to us because the religion was not to be discussed with people not devoted to it. Even the daughter maintained this reticence out of reverence for her father, although she supposedly disavowed the creed.

The patient and his sister as children were cared for by the Fräulein since the parents were frequently absent on long trips. The Fräulein favored Emil over his sister, she treated him like a little prince, and habitually slept with him. This nursemaid also worshiped the father and claims even now that she understood him better than did Mrs. Dolfuss. Thus, to the patient, his mother who devoted most of her time and energy to her husband represented remoteness, whereas the Fräulein mixed motherliness and seductiveness with rigid reinforcement of the father's cold formality and religious preoccupations. She had used harsh methods of toilet training.

When the patient was seven or eight, the nursemaid was dismissed by Mrs. Dolfuss, partly because of their competitive feelings, but also because Emil's teachers complained that he had not been taught the rudiments of self-care and that he was being severely "spoiled" by his nurse. Supposedly, Emil did not react to this separation. He showed little emotional disturbance until shortly after his father's sudden death. For a few days following this crucial event, Emil behaved appropriately, acting as the head of the household during his mother's transient incapacitation in the period of her acute bereavement. The patient has been quoted as saying, "I have to be the man in the family now." Soon thereafter he became delusional, believing that a light beam from a tall building was following him. He told one of his psychiatrists, "The loss of my father set me back, and I don't know how to describe the incomparable harm it did to my development of all descriptions."

Other characteristics of the family interaction and attitudes must be mentioned. In line with his beliefs, the father disapproved of and never expressed any hostility. Everybody was "happy" in this family. The mother, however, despite her subservience, belittled and criticized the father's disinclination for fresh air, sports, and physical activity. She was a food faddist and considered physical culture extremely important for herself and her children. She was always very parsimonious, leading the patient to say, "I always gave my family large presents, but they never gave me anything."

COMMENT

It is easy to note the many parallels between the parents' behavior and the patient's symptoms. Their haughty demeanor, their withdrawal into a religious world accessible only to a selected few, their preoccupation with health and food, their demands for ritualized service, and much of their detailed thinking seem of one piece. However, because of overdetermination the patient's symptoms also contain minor but important modifications and indicate some of his distorted primitive object relations (Szasz, 1957). For instance, during one of the accidental periods of darkness in his room, Emil became frightened, grabbed a flashlight, and held it erect over his penis, thus revealing castration fear. Between hospitalizations he made sexual overtures to his sister. His oral dependent needs also asserted themselves. As his father might have done for business trips, Emil studied airline time tables to find interconnecting flights that could provide him with a continuous food supply from all over the world. Moreover, the symptomatology was based not only on identification with his father, but also contained important elements of the mother's overt and covert attitudes and of the entire family interaction. Emil's hostile insistence upon fresh air parodied the father and ceded a point to the mother. Hoarding was a mockery of her stinginess, and he collected and ate foods which she avoided.

We should like to point out that in a number of patients we have observed a brief period of relatively effective but pathological identification with the dominant and usually sicker parent figure shortly before the outbreak of more overt psychotic manifestations. But whereas the parents may entertain abnormal beliefs or grandiose schemes in a contained fashion, the patient carries them out. Adele, Emil's sister, also shared with their mother and with the patient the bizarre, grandiose religious beliefs; but both women had maintained sufficient reality adaptation and social presence to exercise great reticence in discussing those ideas with others. In neither the mother nor the sister did these delusional beliefs interfere with productivity or social competence, in contrast to the devastating effect of these same beliefs upon the patient's life. One may surmise that Adele's sex and more distant relationship with the Fräulein facilitated greater and more effective utilization of the mother as a model. The patient, in a sense, could believe that to gain his mother's affection and approval, he should identify with his father and fill the gap in his mother's life by becoming a deity like his father. Under the stress of the father's death, his preoccupation and behavior became increasingly limited to the examples of which he saw the most, and which were reinforced and gratified by the entire family: his father as a demigod at home. In the face of his mother's expectation that he be the man of the house, incestuous proclivities also became rekindled, abetted by his nurse's earlier seductive manipulations.

Another important facet in this picture of *folie en famille* is the family use of clichés and the mislabeling of feelings and attitudes—for instance, the recurrent emphasis that this was an entirely happy family, superior to others. Nobody was permitted to show hostility, and if it appeared, it would have to be denied or rationalized. After hitting somebody, Emil always made up with handshakes and embraces. Transformation of such a pattern into behavioral skills tolerable to and effective with other persons would obviously involve a formidable task in relearning. Adele, who managed this belatedly with the help of analytic treatment, once remarked in discouragement when she began to understand the similarity between the patient's behavior in the hospital and her father's ideas and behavior, "Oh, the poor boy, how can he get over it, he is so right." Emil was right, in terms of the family's teachings.

But withdrawal, social isolation, and household-wide dereistic thinking are what we observe in this family, and when we consider Emil's learning opportunities in his family, it becomes clearer how the development and structuring of his personality must have suffered. What the patient knew and could learn of his father was not of the successful businessman and inventor, but the sour, cold, withdrawn, and formal authoritarian who was being babied and deified at the same time. What he saw mostly in his mother was stinginess, disinterest in the children, duplicity, and subservience to the megalomanic father. This must have been confusing to Emil, because her ambivalence together with the Fräulein's inconsistent alternation between harshness and seductiveness must have left him with incompatible part objects for identification. Moreover, the range and character of adaptive techniques that could be acquired in this skewed family structure were unsuited for living in the larger community.

Thus, we discern in the patient and related behavior and attitudes in the parents and in the family interaction all the characteristic primary and secondary schizophrenic manifestations as outlined by Bleuler (1911). The family as a whole was withdrawn from the community, thought deviantly from it, and there was ambivalence, lack of warmth and shared delusional thinking. The patient "learned" most of his symptoms from the parents' behavior; he caricatured and combined them, his basic personality organization lacked cohesiveness, and his behavior reflected the *folie en famille*.

If patients' difficulties and symptoms on which we base our diagnosis of schizophrenia can thus be identified as the product of faulty learning within the family, learning related to identification with deviant parental figures and their skewed or schismatic interaction, broader questions suggest themselves: does the trouble lie with the teaching process; with deficiencies in the "teachers"; with communication; with a learning disability in the child; or are all of these implicated? Here we have provided only a descriptive framework for the study and understanding of psychotic behavior as learned phenomena.

Postscript

We have not sought to imply that all schizophrenic symptomatology can be understood as learned phenomenon. Much is regressive, and, as we have presented elsewhere, many aspects of the thought disorder can be understood as egocentric cognitive regression to "preopera-

tional" and "concrete" stages of cognitive development and many symptoms as regressions to "preoedipal" phases of development. However, as we have noted in previous chapters, paranoid distrust is often learned from parental example and in some instances, clearly taught by a parent. The complex symptomatology of Bill Forel who had become a schizophrenic vagrant can be understood in terms of his severe rejection by his mother and aunt and his denial that anything that had happened in his life could be connected to his unhappiness for he could not live if he thought his mother's behavior and his aunt's meanness had anything to do with his misery.

IX

Comparison of Parent-Child Relationships of Male and Female Schizophrenic Patients

(1962)

This chapter draws together and sharpens concepts that have been broached in previous chapters about the different configurations of families that produce male and female schizophrenics, and considers why the different patterns have basic similarities if the differences in the developmental tasks of boys and girls are taken into account.

Having drawn attention to the serious disturbances that permeate virtually every area of interaction in these families, we wish to focus upon the differences between families containing schizophrenic sons and those with schizophrenic daughters. Scrutiny of these differences serves to clarify many of the apparent inconsistencies in the literature concerning characteristics of the parental personalities and their ways of relating to their schizophrenic offspring. Mothers of such patients have been designated variously—as rejecting, aloof, unempathic, cold (Abrahams and Varon, 1953; L. Hill, 1955; Tietze, 1949), overprotective, intrusive, or symbiotic in their relationships with the patient (Alanen, 1958; Mark, 1953; Prout and White, 1950). Fathers have been observed and studied less frequently but have been described as distant, aloof, passive, neglecting (Frazee, 1953; Gerard and Siegel, 1950; Hajdu-Gimes, 1940), seductively close, hostile, or brutal (Alanen, 1958; Reichard and Tillman, 1950).

Stephen Fleck, Theodore Lidz, and Alice R. Cornelison: Comparison of Parent-Child Relationships of Male and Female Schizophrenic Patients. *Archives of General Psychiatry*, Vol. 8, 1963, pp. 1-7. Copyright © 1963, American Medical Association.

When we examined the seventeen core families in our study according to the sex of the schizophrenic child, certain parental characteristics and abnormalities of family interaction fell into definite clusters for male and female patients respectively. Alanen (1958) in his study of the mothers of schizophrenic patients had noted some differences between the parents of male and female patients. The mother with a schizophrenic son tended to be closer to the patient than to her other children, and was "possessively protective" of him, whereas mothers of schizophrenic daughters were apt to be aloof and "inimically protective" of the patients. Although Alanen did not study the fathers, he gained an impression that fathers of schizophrenic sons provide poor models of masculinity because of their passivity and their submissiveness to their wives. Having gained similar impressions, we were led to focus upon the problem because we noted that the siblings who are of the same sex as the patient are, as a group, clearly more disturbed than the siblings of the opposite sex (Chapter XII). It is clear that different tasks in achieving maturity and identity formation confront boys and girls, and there are strong indications that some family environments are more conducive to the development of schizophrenia in male offspring, and others to the development of schizophrenia in female children; or in less definitive terms, that some families are more deleterious to integrating ego development of sons than of daughters, and vice versa.

Amidst the complexities of the interaction patterns three issues appear critical and help to unify the findings. These are (1) the faulty model for identification provided by the parent of the same sex as the patient; (2) the impediments to proper resolution of the patient's oedipal attachments created by the disturbed parental interaction; and (3) the failure of the parents to maintain proper generation boundaries between themselves and the patient, either by being seductive with a child or by being more like a rivalrous sibling than a parent, with both patterns sometimes occurring in the same family.

The configurations that we shall outline are abstractions that fit some families very precisely and others less distinctly. One or two families have patterns more commonly seen when the patient is of the other sex, and a few families seem equally detrimental to offspring of both sexes, but the trend is clear and serves to clarify the dynamics of the parent-child relationships in all but a very few of our cases.

FEMALE PATIENTS

A greater consistency could be noted in the configuration of the families containing female schizophrenic offspring than in the families with male patients. Strikingly similar dynamics could be abstracted from the families of six of the eight female patients—and only one differed markedly, bearing a greater resemblance to the pattern discerned in families with male patients.

The mothers of the schizophrenic daughters formed very poor models of a woman both because of their own characteristics and because of their husbands' contemptuous and derogatory attitudes toward them. These were highly schismatic marriages with but one or two exceptions. The parents were in open conflict, each undercutting the worth of the other to the children, and commonly both sought to win the daughter to side with them in the conflict. The mother's insecurity and deficient self-esteem as a woman further declined in a marriage in which the husband constantly derogated her worth as a wife and mother. Usually she struggles against her husband but cannot maintain her ground against a dominating man who may be grandiose, if not overtly paranoid, a man who is embittered because the wife does not bolster his narcissism by constant admiration. The mother becomes the defeated and devalued parent, particularly in the eyes of the patient. Anxious about raising a daughter, unable fully to accept her or be at ease with her, possibly because of homosexual concerns, the mother remains aloof, and fails to invest the relationship emotionally and erotically as required for the proper nurturance of the infant and small child. However, we cannot designate these mothers by the catch-all term "rejecting." Most of them were very attentive to their daughters and aspired to be maternal. Their efforts were impeded by their insecurities, their marital unhappiness, and at times, by their jealousy of their husbands' greater interest in their daughters. The mother's aloofness prevents the daughter from establishing a proper preoedipal attachment and impedes identification with the mother, and directs the female child to the father for affectionate nurturant responsivity. While some of these mothers were seriously disturbed, only one was definitely psychotic, the remainder tending toward resentful depression, perplexing vagueness, and imperviousness to the daughter's feelings and needs.

In contrast, three fathers of schizophrenic daughters had clear-cut paranoid tendencies, and a fourth had a depressive psychosis with paranoid trends. With perhaps one exception, they were highly narcissistic men who needed constant admiration because of their concerns about masculinity. As one father stated, "When I married I was only half a man and could only marry half a woman." Failing to gain the obedience, loyalty, and admiration they required from their wives, they turned to a daughter in a seductive manner that in some instances verged upon physical incestuousness, and used the girl to fill the place unsatisfied by the wife. These daughters in seeking their fathers' love must attempt to differentiate themselves from their mothers who are so unsatisfactory to the fathers instead of endeavoring to emulate a woman whom father loves. With the mother-daughter relationship poor from the start, early identification with the mother is impaired; later, instead of following her mother into womanhood, the girl has a negative directive in trying to become different from the devalued mother. The absence of an acceptable role model in the mother greatly complicates the developmental process, especially if the daughter's desire to gain her father's love is fostered by his seductiveness and his clear indications that she is more important to him than his wife. The oedipal attachment is not resolved or adequately repressed even at puberty, and the girl moves into adolescence disturbed by an incestuous entanglement that eventually terrifies her, if not the father. The girl's ego development is further impaired because insofar as she finds herself resembling her mother, she despises herself and lacks self-esteem as a woman; a situation that can be aggravated because most of the fathers have little respect for any woman.

Because of the parental schism, the girl is usually caught in a bind of the type in which satisfying either parent means rejection by the other (Weakland, 1960). The situation is further complicated when the daughter, in search for warmth, trust, and affection, turns from her aloof mother to become involved with a father whose needs cannot be satisfied by a woman, and is subjected to the father's confusing combination of seductiveness and his disparagement of women.

There are, of course, variants of this generalized and abstract description of the daughter's position in the family. However, only one mother who was also overtly schizophrenic demonstrated maternal closeness to her daughter, and all of the fathers of female patients with the exception of the one who had been seriously depressed had been seductive. There are one or two families in the series in which the mother avoids open conflict by giving in to the dominant father, leading to a marriage that is more skewed than schismatic. In some such instances—more apparent outside of our series—the mother remains emotionally withdrawn from her husband and virtually hands the daughter over to the father as a substitute for herself, thus fostering a sexualized relationship between the father and the daughter.

MALE PATIENTS

Maternal aloofness was also prominent during the infancy of male patients, but the most striking findings concern the very poor masculine model provided the son by his father, and the mother's dependency upon this son for her own emotional satisfaction and completion, often with failure to set boundaries between herself and the boy.

Deficiencies of the father in furnishing an adequate role model of a man, husband, and father with which the son can identify and gain guidance into adulthood derive both from the characteristics and behavior of the father, and also from the mother's condescending or hostile attitudes toward her husband. Five or six of the nine fathers behaved more like sons to their wives than husbands, and several of these were unusually passive adjuncts to their dominant but seriously disturbed wives, nonentities in the home who never countered their wives' eccentric ideas of family life and child rearing. Other fathers, feeling excluded from the mother-son coalition, filled rivalrous rather than paternal roles toward their sons. Two were extremely distant men who were away from the home for long periods. Three of the nine fathers were virtually psychotic, and one was an alcoholic who created grave difficulties for the family whenever he was at home, while three others disrupted the home life by their emotional instability and frequent outbursts. For a son to become a man like his father meant either to be psychotic, or a passive castrated figure belittled by a woman, or a highly inconsistent figure who created confusion and suffering for the family. With but three exceptions, these men were less aggressive than the fathers of schizophrenic daughters, providing little if any instrumental leadership within the family even when adequately effective in their occupations. The children of two of these three fathers considered these men to be homosexual, while the son of the third was seriously perturbed by his father's homosexual seductiveness. Somewhat paradoxically of all the fathers of schizophrenic sons these three were among the four who were most competent in their occupations. The other fathers were all passive men who were insecure in their masculinity.

The mothers made it clear to their sons that they were dissatisfied with their husbands, and even the one mother who admired her husband as a deity and shared his grandiose delusions was condescending toward him as a man. The mothers clearly conveyed to their sons that they must grow up to be different from their fathers. Some mothers sought to have the son who became schizophrenic live out the life she would have liked had she been a man. For the son to grow up in his father's image would not gain him a love object like his mother.

All of the mothers of schizophrenic sons were also very insecure in their marital and maternal roles. Although they had difficulty in being close and maternal to a son as an infant, they soon became oversolicitous and overprotective and unable to differentiate their own anxieties from those of the child—which in a few cases reached the extreme of almost total failure of the mother to differentiate herself from the child. Some mothers, because of their insecurities in child rearing and their awe of a male child, were unable to set limits for their sons. In contrast to the aloof mothers of daughters, the mothers of sons tended to be engulfing and, at times, highly seductive. Even the one mother who openly rejected her son could be extremely sexually seductive with him when she was intoxicated. One other mother was distant from her son, but the governess who raised him filled the role of the intrusive, adulating, and seductive mother, sleeping with him and perhaps stimulating him sexually throughout his childhood.

One might venture to say that in contrast to the early relationship between mothers and schizophrenic daughters, the original mother-son symbiosis with its erotic components and the initial identification of the boy with his mother were never properly surmounted. Then, as the son found himself more important than the father to his mother, the oedipal attachments were never properly repressed. Retaining a stronger identification with the mother and, in a sense, remaining a part of the mother rather than seeking to identify with the father, the boy was left with a predominantly feminine superego and without proper ego boundaries between himself and his mother. In such situations, particularly when the father was highly rivalrous, the son had realistic grounds to fear both the father and the engulfing mother who was turning him into an adjunctive castrated figure like his father.

COMMENT

These male and female patterns are basically similar in many respects, almost mirror images rotating about the sex reversals in the oedipal configuration. The child who becomes schizophrenic has a poor relationship with the parent of the same sex who is aloof and often rivalrous, and who provides a very poor model for the child's identification. Such a child then seeks to be different from this parent to gain the love and approval of the parent of the opposite sex who tends to be engulfing or seductive, using the child to gain completion or gratification. In both constellations the patient's image of the parent of the same sex as a model to follow into maturity is damaged in two ways: (1) by that parent's conflicts and deficiencies concerning sexual identity and parental functions; (2) by the interaction with the other parent who accentuates the poor image either by acquiescing in the aberrant modes of child nurturing, or by actively devaluating and undermining the spouse.

However, this characterization of the similarities in the configurations in the families of male and female patients is an oversimplification because the developmental tasks in respect to the oedipal situation are not mirror images. In a hypothetical normal developmental pattern, the girl can retain much of her primary identification with her mother, and optimally can seek to gain a love object like her father by growing into a woman like the mother. In contrast, the boy must be able to rescind his early identification with the mother and gain security as a male, optimally by becoming a man like his father who can gain a love object like his mother, and be able to provide for a woman rather than remain dependent upon her.[1]

In the skewed family configurations of our male schizophrenics the patient retains his primary tie with the mother and is not guided into a masculine role by having an effective father or a father admired by his mother. Furthermore, without a clear division in these families into two generations, the son cannot find a secure and separate position as a child, since his father may be rivalrous instead of parental and his mother may rear him to extend and complete her life.

The female patient, however, because of the mother's lack of empathy, attains neither the essential primary mutuality with her mother nor a solid identification with her. Seeking affection and nurturant care from the father, she develops an ego ideal based upon what she believes father needs and wishes from a woman instead of taking on attributes of the devalued mother.

While it must remain a matter for conjecture, it seems to us that a boy's ego development will be injured more seriously than a girl's by having a mother who cannot establish ego boundaries between herself and a child, because a daughter need not break away from the initial mother-child symbiosis as completely as the boy, who must gain a masculine identity. In addition, a father who fails to fill an instrumental role in the family will be more detrimental to a son who needs to learn a masculine role than to a daughter.

Conversely, a girl will be harmed more seriously than a boy by a father who dominates and derogates the mother and who tends to be antagonistic and belittling of all women. While a boy will certainly be affected deleteriously by an aloof and cold mother, the attainment of an "affectional-expressive role" (Parsons and Bales, 1955) through the empathic absorption of maternal feelings is more critical to the girl's development than it is to the boy's.

---

[1]These models differ from classic analytic theory which has emphasized the difficulties confronting a girl because of her need to shift her love object from the mother to the father, as well as the differences resulting from castration anxiety and penis envy. These theoretical differences are important, but their thorough consideration is not germane to the immediate topic.

These gender-linked differences in the issues confronting children in the families of schizophrenic patients appear to be borne out by our study of the patients' siblings, where we noted that the siblings of the same sex as the patient were more seriously disturbed than the siblings of the opposite sex (Chapter XIV). Our findings also suggest that the seemingly contradictory descriptions of the parents of schizophrenics may be reconcilable if the patient's sex is taken into account instead of correlating parental personality profiles with a patient's diagnosis regardless of sex. While it is beyond the confines of this report, we wish to record that the differential examination of the patients' psychosexual development according to sex also helps to clarify and establish more definite patterns of family dynamics pertaining to sociopathic patients and in other emotional disorders.

We wish to re-emphasize, however, that one must look beyond individual parental characteristics and study the nature of parental interaction and the entire family behavior in order to trace pathologiccal developments in an offspring. Furthermore, we do not consider that such family patterns are in themselves specific to the production of schizophrenia in an offspring, but that other factors enter into the etiology of schizophrenia, in particular the disturbed thought processes and paralogic ways of one or both parents that provide faulty training in reality testing and distrust in the validity and utility of verbal communications (Chapter XIX).

POSTSCRIPT

There were three families that did not fit the patterns presented, at least not clearly. We were kept from formulating the family configuration for female patients we have presented because the Lerner family did not seem to fit. However, the masking of the actual situation by Mrs. Lerner was so pervasive that we never knew very much about Mr. Lerner's relationship to his wife or daughter, but it became apparent that Mrs. Lerner was unempathic toward the patient. The Dolfuss family was atypical because it was the Fraulein rather than the mother who was unable to establish boundaries and was highly seductive, and though the mother adulated the father, the patient's assumption of the father's role in the family almost required him to be psychotic. The Forel family shifted from a schismatic to a skewed family when the patient was young. Insofar as the father could not provide a masculine model for his son and was scorned by his wife, the situation was more exaggerated than most. Mrs. Forel was not close to her son but overtly rejecting. However, after the patient reached adolescence, she became threateningly close in being overtly sexually seductive when intoxicated, an almost daily occurrence.

We had not sufficiently considered the homosexual tendencies of some mothers of female patients or the homosexual tendencies of some fathers of male patients (Chapters X and XI). How the parents' personalities, including their sexual orientations, and the manner in which the parents relate impair the patient's development of a firm sexual identity requires further study. One such study concerning the problems of a boy overcoming his early identification with his mother as well as his libidinal attachment to her can be found in the articles "Male Menstruation: A Ritual Alternative to the Oedipal Transition" (Lidz and Lidz, 1977) and "Oedipus in the Stone Age" (Lidz and Lidz, 1984).

X

Incestuous and Homosexual Problems

(1958)

We find, in retrospect, the following chapter on incestuous and homosexual problems to be inadequate for several reasons. At the time we were primarily interested in demonstrating that the incestuous and homosexual tendencies that frequently lead to the panic that often initiates the onset of overt schizophrenic disorders are not simply the resultants of preoedipal and oedipal fixations, as was commonly believed, but rather reflect continuing flaws in the ongoing family dynamics and structure, and could clearly be related to the psychopathology of the parents and the family transactions. We had also not yet appreciated how common such tendencies were in our series. Thus, the sister of Emil Dolfuss, a woman who made a reasonable adjustment with the help of many years of psychotherapy, told that she had been seduced at an early age by the butler, and she was fairly certain that the governess had repeatedly sexually stimulated her brother while sleeping with him. The psychotherapist of the schizophrenic sister of our Robb patient informed us after the book had been written that Mr. Robb, the educator who had displaced his wife with a young teacher, slept with his adolescent daughters when they were upset. We had also not included some material provided in previous papers. Mr. Lamb, a promiscuous and alcoholic man, had confided to his wife that he had become a professional athlete in part because of the erotic stimulation provided by seeing his fellow athletes

Stephen Fleck, Theodore Lidz, Alice R. Cornelison, Sarah Schafer, and Dorothy Terry: The Intrafamilial Environment of the Schizophrenic Patient: Incestuous and Homosexual Problems. In *Individual and Familial Dynamics*, edited by Jules H. Masserman. Copyright © 1959, Grune & Stratton, New York. This paper was presented in part at the annual meeting of the Academy of Psychoanalysis, May 1958.

naked, and that he had a strong attachment to one of them. The patient, his son, had been quite certain that his very "macho" father was homosexual. Similarly, the several sons of Mr. Schwartz, a man with whom we had little contact, considered their father to have been homosexual, but for reasons we could not establish. Then, for reasons we shall present in the postscript to this paper, we did not seem to appreciate fully how incestuous and homosexual behavior or tendencies of parents influenced the family transactions and created difficulties for the patients in virtually all of these families. Finally, newer concepts concerning the nature of the oedipal transition have clarified our understanding of the interrelationship between homosexuality and incest.

The critical import of incestuous problems in the onset, symptoms, and therapeutic management of youthful schizophrenic patients has became increasingly apparent. We have come to anticipate the patient's fear that incestuous impulses will overwhelm the ego leading to panic, further withdrawal or intensification of rigid defenses. Often the patient, particularly the male patient, will fluctuate between incestuous and homosexual concerns and fantasies. Several striking examples indicate that the patient's incestuous preoccupations were based upon tangible difficulties in their relationships with their parents. We therefore turned to the sixteen patients in our study to clarify the issue. In at least half of these patients, judging conservatively, incest problems were critical. When the patient's difficulties are viewed against the family setting rather than simply intrapsychically, these problems like many schizophrenic symptoms gain new meaning and a more tangible etiology.

We are not concerned here with actual incest which various authors have noted as an occasional traumatic factor in the lives of some schizophrenic patients. However, the incidence of incest in schizophrenic patients, like that of other pathological events, rises when attention is focused upon it. In another series of seventeen consecutively admitted schizophrenic patients, pertinent inquiry on admission disclosed that four of these patients had had incestuous relations (Endicott, 1958). As far as we know, actual parent-child incest did not occur in any of our cases, but a social class variable may be involved here as almost all of our patients belong to the upper economic classes. On the other hand, we are not referring simply to personality distortions traceable to faulty resolution of oedipal problems. We are considering here how the family configurations and parental problems led to the continuation of incestuous wishes or strivings into late adolescence and adult life, and/or to homosexual longings or proclivities in the parents.

CASE ILLUSTRATIONS

The area of interest may perhaps best be clarified by an illustration. Bill Forel, a twenty-year-old schizophrenic youth with vagrant tendencies and grandiose delusions, had at the age of eleven lost his father who had been a maternal, affectionate figure to him. Bill tried to convey his dilemma about being near his mother to his therapist approximately as follows. When his mother drinks too heavily she becomes softhearted, affectionate, and unrestrained in contrast to her usual cold and preoccupied attitude. At these times Bill feels that she wants to engulf him, perhaps to eat him up, or she kisses him in a revolting sort of way. He becomes tight inside, experiences an unbearable tension, and must get away. He goes out for a walk, seeking relief. A feeling goes all through his body. He does not ejaculate, but it is a sexual feeling which like an orgasm reaches a pitch and becomes so unpleasant that it is unbearable. Still, it would be a pleasant feeling if directed toward a young and pretty girl. At such times he must exert extreme control because he feels that if he let himself go it would end in his having intercourse with his mother. When sober, his mother acts like a stranger. He prefers this for he can then feel comfortable in her presence, but when he gets those sexual feelings he cannot stay near her. He notes his comfort with his therapist because he feels that his therapist, in contrast to his mother, has control of himself and will not let anything happen if the patient should lose control.

The occurrence of such incestuous preoccupations in schizophrenic patients has long been recognized and understood in such terms as a concomitant of the regression to an intense preoedipal attachment to one parent or the other, or as evidence of the constitutional ego weakness with inability to cathect boundaries between the self and others (Szasz, 1957). We learned, however, from Bill's older brother who is not psychotic that he too became very uneasy around his mother because of her seductive fondling and unmotherly kissing, and that when he would seek to get away, or became angry with her because of her neglect of his invalided father, she would seek to woo him back and pacify him by becoming even more amorous. The brother had been disturbed to find shortly after he married that he would awaken from dreams uncertain whether he was in bed with his wife or his mother. And when, for example, during her first interview, the mother of another young man tells the social worker, "He is not just part of my life, he is all of my life. Why, when he became upset, I slept with him just like man and wife," there is reason to consider that the schizophrenic patients' concerns with incest are based on more than their own regressive propensities or restitutive efforts.

Incestuous problems are not being presented as etiological of schizophrenia but as a focal issue in the development of the patient's faulty ego structure and sexual identity that are related to the seriously disturbed family settings in which schizophrenic patients have grown up. Although incestuous problems are common among schizophrenic patients, we do not know whether they occur in all such patients, and, of course, conscious incestuous concerns can occur in other types of patients. However, Glueck (1957) studying sex delinquents in general found that those who had been involved in incest all belonged to the most disturbed group he labeled "schizo-adaptive," and Weinberg (1955) who surveyed 203 court cases involving incest concluded that the problem cannot exist without serious family disorganization, and family disorganization also appears to be a prerequisite for the appearance of schizophrenia in an offspring.

These and still other issues are interrelated with the topic isolated for purposes of presentation here. Homosexuality in particular, implicated in the etiology of schizophrenia ever since Freud's (1911) study of the Schreber case, seems to be intimately related to the problem of incest; at times they seem almost like two sides of the same coin. A thorough discussion of the interrelationship would involve consideration of some fundamental psychoanalytic concepts and we shall here simply indicate the nature of the relationship by noting that both are narcissistic problems in which love of the self, love of someone like the self, and love of someone undifferentiated from the self are apt to be quite confused. This state is to be anticipated in a schizophrenic patient with poor boundaries between the self and a parent, often a parent who also has poor self boundaries and an uncertain sexual identity (Lidz and Lidz, 1952).[1] While active seductive or incestuous interplay may be limited to one parent and one child, the other family members and especially the other parent almost always participate, at least by their passivity or denial (Chapter XIII; Parsons, 1954; Weinberg, 1955).

Flugel (1921), Parsons (1954), and Parsons and Bales (1955) have studied the family from a psychoanalytic orientation and both stress that a precarious balance exists between the erotic bonds essential to the cohesiveness of the nuclear family and the normal development of the children, as against incestuous impulses that are disorganizing for the family and its members. Thus, the de-erotization or at least the desexualization of the child-parent attachment is one of the cardinal family functions. The fate of the oedipal situa-

---

[1] The reevaluation of the Schreber case by Macalpine and Hunter (1953) with its emphasis upon hyponchondriacal delusions related to ideas of physical transformation into the opposite sex does not contradict the homosexual hypothesis but rather places emphasis on another aspect of the patient's uncertainties concerning sexual identity.

tion holds its central position in psychiatry because it is here, in particular, that the developing child traverses a knife edge with potential disaster on both sides. On the one side, his development will be stunted and distorted unless he receives affectionate love—one might say, erotically motivated parental love—during the preoedipal periods. On the other side, the erotic quality of his attachment must gradually be frustrated and the child-parent love freed of sexuality in preparation for the latency period. We believe that this process depends not on biological subsidence of erotic drives, but on the child's finding a reasonably conflict-free place in the family, with his position in relation to both parents established and his identity as a childhood member of his sex accepted.

When a parent, particularly the mother, needs to gain affectional and erotic satisfaction predominantly from the parent-child relationship rather than from the marital relationship and promotes uncontrolled erotization of the bond to the child, the essential frustration of the child required for satisfactory resolution of the oedipal relationships cannot occur. Other serious deficiencies in the essential family structure and in the filling of the paternal and maternal roles also open the way for incestuous tendencies. In particular, marked violations of the boundaries between the generations will disrupt the imperative structure that holds incestuous trends in check, as when one parent is more of a child than a spouse to the other parent, or a rival with a child, or when a child is used as an emotional substitute for a spouse as noted above. Other failures of parents to fill their essential roles can also court trouble, for instance, when the mother is cold and unyielding, thus pushing a daughter toward the father, or when the father is passive and ineffectual and so fails to strengthen the repression of the son's oedipal wishes. Schismatic differences between parents when each seeks to undercut the other and win the child away from the spouse can permit the child to feel that he is more important to one parent or the other than is the spouse. When one or both parents are psychotic or borderline schizophrenic, the parent may have difficulty in establishing clear boundaries between himself and the child, and the child's progression from narcissistic love to object love is impeded because of the difficulty in differentiating the parent's needs from his own. As all of these circumstances are prominent findings in families of schizophrenic patients, one might anticipate that failures of essentials for the resolution or the repression of oedipal strivings would lead to incestuous trends in schizophrenic patients. When incestuous impulses remain or become more or less conscious, they further upset the balance of the family; other distortions of the family life and of the personality structure of its members will follow upon the need to avoid infringement of the strong taboo.

How such family situations can foster incestuous ties and fears as well as homosexual proclivities is illustrated in Chapter XIII concerned with the Nebb twins, both of whom were seriously troubled by fantasies of incest with their mother and by impulses toward homosexual incest with each other. Mrs. Nebb had clearly been unable to establish boundaries between herself and her twin sons, was flagrantly seductive with them, and taught them that they were all-important, whereas their father was a dull man who meant little to her. This mother often slept with her sons well into their adolescence, bathed them, and gave them enemas in a highly sexualized manner in which she was the intrusive aggressor. Mr. Nebb's inability to fill the roles of husband or father further opened the way for incestuous fantasies and strivings and for confusions of sexual identity in the twins.

Another clear example is provided by the family relationships of Dora Nussbaum. Dora had been hospitalized after lengthy analytically oriented therapy and an even longer period of increasing disorganization which included episodes of impulsive sexual acting out. She had shouted in public that her father wanted to rape her. Dora had conscious incestuous fantasies, and suffered periods of panicky concern that incest might occur. When, for example, her father had sat on her bed in the hospital when she had the flu, Dora had jumped up, fled from the room, and immediately had become more disorganized.

The Nussbaum's marriage had been marred from its inception by their discrepant personalities and by their intense conflicting loyalties to their respective parental families. Mr. Nussbaum was highly narcissistic, needing demonstrative affection and given to gregariousness and effeminate flashiness. His wife was aloof, penurious, and a rather misanthropic woman with a vituperative tongue and given to marked depressive mood swings. Her primary emotional attachments remained with her own family, especially one sister. She was proud of her oldest child, a boy, and very attentive to him. Before the birth of the patient, four years later, the Nussbaums became emotionally estranged because of a conflict between their families in which Mr. Nussbaum's brother was accused of business dealings that led to the suicide of Mrs. Nussbaum's father. The spouses became deeply resentful toward each other, and though they continued to live together, the marriage became a hostile encounter in which constant open conflict was avoided by mutual withdrawal and silence. Mrs. Nussbaum suffered an injury to her neck when Dora was born, and the infant's care was left to a maid. Later, Mrs. Nussbaum attempted to be a good mother but became impatient with the child, and, as her own unhappiness increased, she became increasingly critical and hostile. When Dora's behavior became very trying after the age of twelve, the mother expressed her frank hatred. When Dora left for college, her mother reputedly said, "I hope you come home in a coffin." In contrast, Mr. Nussbaum turned to his daughter and lavished affection upon her with much physical demonstrativeness, to his wife's great disgust. He would hug and kiss Dora excessively and often lie on her bed until she went to sleep. When Dora awakened at night frightened, she would get into her father's bed until she learned the facts of life and feared that she would become pregnant. As she became ill in adolescence, the father would frequently comfort her by holding her in his arms until she went to sleep.

Mr. Nussbaum was highly critical of his wife, letting his daughter know that he had little regard for her mother. He insisted for some years that there was nothing really wrong with Dora but only with his wife. Indeed, Mrs. Nussbaum must have been profoundly disturbed at times, expressing extreme hopelessness about Dora's behavior, telling the girl she wished she were dead and suggesting dual suicide. The family situation was further aggravated because Mr. Nussbaum avoided his family problems by spending most evenings in his office, encouraging his wife and daughter to think he was having an affair. However, as he was impotent, or said he was, the fictional mistress served not only to aggravate his wife but also to bolster his narcissism. Despite his intense feelings that his wife was rejecting and destructive to Dora, he assumed little real responsibility himself.

These are fairly typical illustrations of the intrafamilial environments of schizophrenic patients with incestuous problems in the research series of upper- and upper-middle-class families: the Nebb family on the bizarre side, and the Nussbaum family less dramatic than most; but both were among the more intact families and neither included overtly schizophrenic mothers or paranoid fathers as is the case in some of our other families. These families which raise an offspring who develops the most serious psychiatric illness fail to provide directives for repressing incestuous interests. Thus, they fail in one of the fundamental tasks of families. The taboo against parent-child incest is among the most intense and universal taboos. The potential for incest exists in every family in the erotically toned parent-child attachment, but its progression into an incestuous bond would not only disrupt the structure of societies based on kinship systems, it also would threaten the existence of the nuclear family in all societies, prevent the child from channeling energies into socializing activities, interfere with peer relationships, and block his emergence as an adult. The prevention of incest does not, however, ordinarily rest on conscious evocation of the taboo. The family structure and distribution of essential roles contain the requisites which normally keep incestuous trends from invading consciousness. When conscious avoidance of incest becomes necessary because of defective family structure and role confusion, the personalities of the family members become further distorted because spontaneity becomes impossible and role conflict inevitable. We do not believe that we have fallen into a circular argument. When we examine Talcott Parsons' (1954) analysis of factors essential in family structure for the preservation of the incest taboo, we find them to be notably lacking in these families. We shall concentrate, therefore, on these deficiencies of family structure and interaction rather than on the intrapersonal pathology of its members.

Discussion

The family is a special type of small group; it is an organic unity with certain structural requisites and imperative functions which, if distorted, will seriously affect the functioning of its members and the personalities of the emergent generation. The family is also a unit in that the action of any member affects all members. Unless all find reciprocally interrelating roles within the unit, role conflict ensues. Its structure and functions are dictated in part by biological imperatives and in part by social mores and needs. Two biological givens establish the family's framework. It is divided into two generations and into two sexes. The parents, having grown up in two different families, seek to merge themselves and their backgrounds into a new unit which satisfies both their needs and completes their personalities. They serve as leaders, educators, and models for their offspring who gain the essentials of group living by learning how to fit into this family. Yet, in contrast to the parental generation, the children must learn to live within the family and yet become capable of emerging from it. The parents subserve different family functions according to sex and transmit these sexually linked roles to their offspring through their behavior. In a general way, the father's functions are more instrumental (i.e., concerned with the family's well-being in society) and the mother's more expressive (i.e., concerned with intrafamilial interaction and the affectional relationships of its members). However, the parents must act in coalition, united by their marital attachments and needs for complementarity in providing for themselves and their offspring. Deficiencies or aberrations in the sex-linked roles of parents, or in the parents' sexual identities, can sometimes be absorbed by role shifts as far as the parents are concerned, but gross distortions jeopardize the sexual identity of the offspring.

We have mentioned only a few of the requisites of family functions and organization. We shall now focus on the severe deficiencies in the maintenance of essential boundaries between generations, in the parental coalition, in the fulfillment of maternal and paternal roles, in the parents' basic sexual identities, and in effecting sociocultural integration of the family unit. All these deficiencies have been important findings in the families we have studied. They are often so interrelated that they cannot be kept isolated even for purposes of discussion.

The Generation Boundaries

The obvious and chronic sexual seductiveness of a parent that was apparent in the illustrative cases was just as flagrant in several other instances. Here a parent's need for affectional and erotic gratification was being served rather than the child's need for a close and erotic bond to the parents during the preoedipal period. The child's erotic attachment was fostered and continued into adolescence rather than being frustrated to permit the child to enter the latency phase. Even in the two cases involving female patients where frank sexual seductiveness was not overt, the basic family configuration was the same as in the Nussbaum case. Their mothers had been aloof from the patients and husbands. They were highly neurotic or borderline psychotic women and were also very restricting and controlling. The fathers were clearly narcissistic, requiring constant bolstering of their masculinity in the form of admiration and implicit obedience from their wives. The marriages were highly schismatic almost from inception with each spouse derogating the other to the children. The father wooed the daughter to his side of the conflict, and sought in her the admiring woman he needed but could not find in his wife. The patient learned early that she was more important to the father than his wife, and sensed his need for erotic gratification from her. She was aware that she could widen the breach between her parents and gain the father for herself. One of these patients suggested that the solution to her problems and those of the family was to split up. She would live with her father and her sister with her mother. When the father of the other patient suggested an identical solution, the patient emerged briefly from her catatonic muteness to state, "I'll do anything my father wants, but he can't have me that way." Such use of a child to replace a spouse by a parent whose own affectional and erotic needs are poorly controlled constitutes a most flagrant violation of the boundaries between generations and courts disaster.

The parents are supposed to be guides and educators who both foster growth and set limits. They must serve as objects for identification and as models of love objects who can be relinquished as the child grows from the family into society. Further, when there is confusion between the generations, it inevitably fosters conflict in the role relationships between the family because no two persons can simultaneously occupy the same position. As can be noted in the illustrative cases, there were other breaches in the boundaries between the two generations as well: Rivalry of a parent with a child, one parent behaving as a child of the spouse rather than as a parent, abdication of decision-making for the family to a child, etc.; all contributed to the difficulties in one family or the other. However, the use of the child to complete the life of a parent, particularly the erotic needs of the parent, disrupts the entire familial pattern of a generation that leads and one that follows, one that educates and one that is educated, one that gives from maturity to enable the child to grow and the other that assimilates in order to mature.

The Parental Coalition

There were various reasons why parents sought gratification and fulfillment through a child, including the serious psychopathology of a parent such as Mrs. Nebb, who could not establish boundaries between herself and her twins. Mrs. Narab, the schizophrenic mother of a schizophrenic youth with severe incestuous fears, resumed her artistic pursuits at our suggestion. She became upset when she recognized her painting of a mother caring for her sick son turning into a picture of a mother having intercourse with her son. However, in every case the parental coalition and the parents' mutuality in relation to the child who became ill were not simply deficient, but had degenerated into disregard, contempt, or overt hatred, with one parent undermining the worth and authority of the other. Each parent was left without emotional support in carrying out role functions, and without a source of erotic gratification from the marital relationship. Thus deprived, such parents are prone to turn to the relationship with a child for fulfillment. Then, too, the child who should be confronted with the fact that each parent's primary emotional and erotic attachment is to the other parent can instead seek to widen the gulf between the parents rather than learn frustration of erotic attachments and cede one parent to the other. Cessation of the child's sexualized attachment need not occur under these circumstances. When it does, the motivation is conscious fear of revenge or the child's projected hostility rather than through experiencing the necessary frustration ameliorated by affection which can lead to early identification with the parent of the same sex and strengthen the child's superego and sexual identity. But when the child is used to gratify a parent's needs, a symbiotic relationship can develop in which the child continues in an object relationship that is essentially narcissistic for both. The child feels undifferentiated from the parent and the sexual strivings are incestuous, not moving toward another discrete person but remaining, in infantile fashion, bound to the parent who is part of him.

The Parental Roles

The family equilibrium was also disturbed in every instance because the fathers of the schizophrenic sons and the mothers of schizophrenic daughters failed in their paternal or maternal roles either because of severe psychiatric illness, or because they were the devalued partner in the marriage, or sometimes both. When the father fails to fill the instrumental leadership role and is instead another child to the mother or acts the part of a defeated castrated husband, as did Mr. Nebb, the son can disregard him as a rival for the mother. Here, the fear of retaliative castration from the father does not operate to repress the oedipal strivings. Rather, observation of the father's plight can lead to fear of castration or engulfment by the mother which increases trends toward homosexuality. When, as with the Nussbaum family, the mother is cold and unyielding and a rival to the daughter, a girl has little reason to appease the mother to retain her as a love object. She is pushed by the mother to the more femininely oriented father. Another type of parental role failure occurred in some families in that the center of gravity lay outside the nuclear family because the parents' primary attachments and the center of their interests lay in their own parental families. The parents' dependence on their siblings, particularly the homoerotically tinged attachment of a mother to her sister, as occurred in the Nebb family, the Nussbaum, and Forel families, deprived the spouse and in some instances the child as well of these parents' primary attention and affection.

The Sexual Identity of the Parents

Related to role failure but more difficult to establish and discuss briefly is the matter of a parent's insecurity in his or her sexual identity. A satisfactory identification as a member of one's own sex in a parent seems essential in order to serve as an adequate model of a primary love object or an identification model to a child. We have a distinct impression that in all the families in which clear-cut incestuous problems existed, either the father had strong feminine or homosexual tendencies, or the mother sought phallic completion from a son and had little interest in a daughter. The parents' respective homoerotic tendencies may well have contributed to the choice of a marital partner. The child is caught in a serious dilemma when needed to redress the imbalance created in the family organization by the defective sexual identity of a parent. Such parents are apt to gain satisfaction by identifying with a child of the opposite sex, as seemed to be the case with Mrs. Nebb and with Mr. Nussbaum. The parent may then also gain vicarious pleasure from the sexual behavior of the child.

Such considerations are also pertinent to the problem of homosexuality. Mr. Benjamin, for example, the father of a boy with intense fears of incest, seemed to identify with his son homosexually. Relatively impotent and unable to gratify his wife, Mr. Benjamin often spoke as if the boy should sleep with his mother. He would suggest, for example, that the boy would be helped by sleeping with a movie star and then specifically named an actress whom he had repeatedly said resembled his wife. He had also shown homosexual seductiveness toward the son by taking showers with him, comparing genitalia, massaging him in his bath, etc. When one of his friends who he knew was a homosexual visited over weekends, Mr. Benjamin permitted him to share a room with his adolescent son, and he took no stand when this man made advances to the boy. In this case, the father's faulty sexual identity had many other repercussions including the failure to maintain the separation between the generations, a confusion in the assumption of a parental role, the father's primary attachment to an older sister who dominated this family, constant quarrels between the couple with mutual

disparagement, as well as many other problems not immediately germane to this paper such as the construction of
highly irrational defenses by the father to protect his pseudo
masculinity.[2]

Sociocultural Isolation of the Family

Because the children must emerge from the family into
the larger society, the family milieu must in many ways reflect
the cultural setting. Stated another way, the family must be
sufficiently in harmony with its social environment to enable
the child to emancipate himself. Our families often fall short
of this prerequisite, although the parents may as individuals
function adequately and even successfully in jobs and in the
community. However, as a family group, they remain relatively isolated from other groups, and this is particularly true
of the eight families with the most severe incest problems.

It is possible that we are faced with a circular situation:
sociocultural isolation may promote incestuous trends in a
quasi-closed system whose inner shaky equilibrium would be
disturbed intolerably if the family group were to interact with
other groups. On the other hand, the existence of incestuous
problems together with the family's other prestige-endan-
gering vicissitudes could lead to their encapsulation. So far
our material seems to point to the marital problems between
two disturbed partners (how ever well they may function
outside the family as individuals) as the primary link in a
chain of events which gets further complicated by the arrival
of children who become enmeshed in the pathological parental interaction. Incest is only one facet in the development
of this drama.

This condensed presentation of an extremely complex
topic can offer only an impression of our approach and thinking about the subject. It is hoped that at least three points

[2]Such problems are not uncommon in these families. The Nebb twins, Narab
sons, and Daryl Lamb all considered their fathers to have homosexual tendencies,
and our attention has been drawn to the homosexual interests of some mothers of
schizophrenic daughters.

have been conveyed: (1) that problems of incest are extremely important to the understanding and treatment of many, if not most, schizophrenic patients; (2) that incestuous impulses cannot be understood simply as a symptom of schizophrenia—as a symptom of regression, restitution, or of blurring of ego boundaries due to constitutional ego weakness. The material indicates the continuing interactional nature of the incestuous tie to a parent; (3) the incestuous problems indicate serious family deviations as well as individual psychopathology. These families which produce schizophrenic offspring suffer flaws in family structure conducive to the provocation of incestuous trends which are so alien to the functioning of the nuclear family and to the socialization of children that they are banned by the most widespread and intense taboo of mankind.

In closing we wish to indicate the importance of incestuous problems in the development or onset of schizophrenic reactions.

1. The patient does not become a distinctive individual with needs and impulses clearly differentiated from those of the parent. He instead subserves the needs of a parent, and the establishment of clear ego boundaries is hindered.

2. The patient's emergence from the primary object relationships is blocked, with energies tied to the parent rather than freed for extrafamilial socialization and for learning processes.

3. The schizophrenic patient's tendency to sexualize all object relationships may well rest on the absence of experiences where he is being forced to desexualize his primary object relationship to a parent, be it the parent of the same or of the opposite sex.

4. The incestuous concerns can lead to panic because of fear of being overwhelmed by the forbidden incestuous urge with ensuing punishment by the self and others for infraction of this basic taboo.

5. The patient cannot regain security by regression to a dependent position on the parents because it is proximity to

the parents that is feared. The regression must either be profound to the earliest preoedipal periods or be accompanied by withdrawal maneuvers.

POSTSCRIPT

A child starts life in a symbiotic or, perhaps more correctly, a dependent unity with the mother. As the symbiosis breaks up, the mother becomes both a primary love object and an object for identification. The potential consequences differ for boys and girls. The girl can retain her primary feminine identification with her mother, and as the ties to the mother as a primary love object wane (because of the mother's de-erotization of the attachment, the recognition of the father's place in the mother's life, the generation difference, and perhaps, because of the antipathy to the mother for not making her a boy or because she devalues the mother for not having a penis, etc.), she finds a new love object within the family in the father (or older brother). The attachment to the father does not threaten the girl's individuation as would a continued attachment to the mother, for it has not been symbiotic. The girl often only rescinds her oedipal attachment to her father at the time of pubescence when both father and daughter are likely to take distance because of the increased sexualization of the relationship. The girl is subject to several miscarriages of the process. The oversolicitous, and particularly the homoerotic, mother may foster a homosexual tendency in her daughter, or a tendency to regress to seeking homosexual protection when disillusioned with men, etc. The attachment to the father may not be frustrated at puberty because the mother pushes the daughter to the father as a substitute for herself, or because of the father's seductiveness; and the oedipal attachment turns into a latent or actual incestuous attachment. Homosexual trends in the mother, as we shall present in the next chapter, can lead the mother either to distance herself from a daughter or be seductively close to her.

The boy's situation is somewhat more complicated. In order to gain a firm identity as a male but also to individuate, he must overcome his primary feminine identification with his mother, and then repress or overcome the erotic aspect of his love for her. The process is fostered by the mother withdrawing the sensuous component of her care; the intervention of the father who has prerogatives with the mother; the fear of the father's rivalry, real or projected; the identification with the father whom the mother loves, admires, or simply depends upon, etc. The dangers of an incestuously toned attachment to the mother can derive from the mother's continual erotic investment of her son, her substitution of the son for her husband in her affections, the failures of the father to provide a block to the boy's continued preemption of the mother or his failure to provide a model for identification. Homosexual tendencies can arise from a continuing feminine identification with the mother, from flight from incestuous concerns; from the search for a father figure who will instill (including through insemination) needed masculinity (Lidz and Lidz, 1984); from attachment to a father who has been the nurturing person when the mother is cold, unyielding, or withdrawn; and commonly from a combination of several such factors.

We cannot here enter upon the complexities of the developmental processes that can lead to incest or homosexuality. We have simply sought to indicate that the two developments that commonly threaten schizophrenic patients have rather similar roots and that the family configurations in which schizophrenic patients grow up that we are describing in this book are configurations that can readily lead to homosexual and incestuous tendencies and fears in the offspring.

XI

Homosexual Tendencies in Mothers of Schizophrenic Women

(1969)

The following paper, which does not concern the seventeen families studied intensively, and, indeed, is based primarily on material gained from the authors' patients rather than from the studies of families, is included because of its relationship to the preceding chapter. We had therein considered the impact of homosexual tendencies of both mothers and fathers on their sons. Here, we are concerned with how the incestuous homosexual tendencies of some mothers affect their daughters.

The mothers of schizophrenic patients have been the subject of intensive study during the past several decades, and some of the divergencies in the descriptions of such mothers and in the hypotheses concerning their pathogenic influences upon their offspring were resolved through the differentiation of the mothers of schizophrenic sons from the mothers of schizophrenic daughters. Alanen (1958) noted that whereas the mothers of male patients were closer to their sons who became schizophrenic than to their other children and were "possessively protective" of them, the mothers of female patients were likely to be aloof and their overprotection has an inimical quality. These findings were amplified in Chapter IX where we noted that mothers of female patients had little

Ruth W. Lidz and Theodore Lidz: Homosexual Tendencies in Mothers of Schizophrenic Women. *Journal of Nervous and Mental Disease*, Vol. 149, pp. 229-235. Copyright © 1969, Williams & Wilkins, Baltimore, MD.

empathy for their daughters, lacked maternal warmth, were often vague and colorless, and failed to provide a suitable model of a woman with whom the daughter could identify—a situation that was often aggravated because the father derogated the mother and conveyed to the daughter that, to gain his affection and esteem, she must be very different from her mother. These women have a nebulous quality that makes then difficult to describe (Chapter III). Their communications characteristically have an illusive, scattered content that conveys distance in interpersonal relationships. They had poor relationships with their own mothers and felt unwanted as girls and, retaining a poor opinion of women and femininity, they not only have difficulty in cathecting a daughter but also convey a sense of defeat and helplessness as part of woman's lot. Although they have difficulty in establishing boundaries between the self and the child, in contrast to mothers of schizophrenic sons, they do not seek to use the child to complete their lives or to compensate for the frustration of being women and gain little, if any, gratification from their daughters.

We wish to direct attention to the manner in which the homosexual tendencies of some mothers of schizophrenic women influence their relationships with their daughters and create serious developmental problems for them. Our interest was drawn to the problem by a woman who had a sister who was schizophrenic.

A young woman, Mrs. A., entered analysis because of severe sexual inhibitions and anxiety that was becoming incapacitating. Her sister's hospitalization with the diagnosis of schizophrenia increased her concerns about herself. During the early months of her analysis, she depicted her mother as a kindly person who had always been strangely aloof from both of her daughters. However, on some occasions, Mrs. A.'s mother had related to her more as a sister than a mother, confiding how she had at her husband's insistence sought to abort both of her children and told intimate details of her sexual life and her difficulties with her paranoidally suspicious husband. While Mrs. A. was trying to unravel the perplexities of the strange relationship in her parental home, her mother died. The patient found a posthumous letter for her in which her mother told that she knew that she had been an ineffectual wife and mother. Now that Mrs. A. was old enough to understand, the mother wished her to know that her only real love had been a woman with whom she had lived for several years before eloping from this woman with the patient's father. She had hoped to live a normal married life and become a good mother, but she had never been able to really love her husband or forget the earlier relationship that had been more meaningful and gratifying. It was very clear from the contents of the letter that the mother was posthumously seeking absolution from her favorite daughter for her homosexuality which she believed had been the major cause of her unhappy marriage and her daughters' emotional problems. After Mrs. A. absorbed the painful communication, she began to attain new insights concerning her parents' strange marriage, her mother's masochistic acceptance of her father's unfounded accusations of infidelity, her inordinate aloofness from her older daughter who had become schizophrenic, and the reason why her father's relationships with his daughters had verged on the incestuous.

The definite homosexuality of this woman who had a schizophrenic daughter reminded the authors that several schizophrenic women whom one or the other of them had treated in psychoanalytic psychotherapy had been adversely affected by their mothers' homosexually toned relationships with them. We shall summarize the material that is pertinent to the topic from the treatment of three patients.

Miss B. had become acutely delusional and seriously disorganized while in college. After several years of treatment in a hospital, she managed to live in the community and resume her education with the help of intensive therapy. She remained socially inept but constantly sought to establish intense relationships in which she could be dependent. She carried on numerous heterosexual and homosexual flirtations as well as some relationships with homosexual men. Miss B. attracted both men and women by her frankness and wit, but she sought to hold others by making them anxious about her which, together with her inappropriate behavior and her ability to direct barbs at others' sensitivities, drove her friends from her. She would then attribute the desertions to her physique and to the acne pits on her face. Actually, she would have been reasonably attractive if her makeup and dress were not sloppy despite the inordinate amount of time and attention that she devoted to her appearance.

Her mother had died when Miss B. was adolescent. She had been an intellectual who had competed with her brilliant husband, a man who, although almost as inept socially as the patient, was sought after because of his unusual intellect and breadth of knowledge. Miss B.'s mother had been unable to provide much nurturant care or warmth for her children, and Mr. B. had been obliged, despite his awkwardness and scholarly preoccupations, to try to mother the children. The patient could recall her father bottle feeding her younger brother or pacing the floor to quiet the baby while reading a book. When Miss B. became pubescent, her mother would frequently have her undress after she came home from school and would then scrutinize the naked girl, commenting unfavorably upon her breast development, the shape of her buttocks, and her acne. She expressed her concern that her daughter would never attract a man unless her physique and her skin improved. She would then have the nude girl perform a series of exercises intended to correct the way she held her breasts and to change the contours of her rear. When the mother became bedridden with a chronic illness, she continued to have her daughter appear for these inspections and exercises, and she would also require the girl to massage her, an action which the patient experienced as a sexual intimacy.

Mrs. C. managed to remain at home and care for her two young children during a schizophrenic episode when she was delusional and sometimes hallucinated. Keeping a tight hold on her behavior, she sought treatment knowing that she was seriously disturbed. She was a highly competent professional woman despite her inordinate shyness. She was concerned over her inadequacies as a wife, fearing that she was homosexual and was worried by her fantasies of practicing fellatio with her father. Fears that she was becoming as shrewish as her mother led to suicidal thoughts. An unmarried sister with whom Mrs. C. had been extremely close caused her intense concern, for the sister was notably promiscuous with married men and also engaged in flirtations with women, if not in homosexual relationships with them.

Throughout her analytic psychotherapy, Mrs. C. expressed her antipathy for her mother, conveying disgust when speaking of her. She believed that her father had been made miserable by her mother's carping criticisms of him and by her constant reminiscences of the joys of her life prior to marriage. Mrs. C. related her oral fantasies about her father to the mothering care he had provided her in lieu of her mother. She recalled her excitement as a child when her father bathed her and stimulated her genitalia in the process. Still, the reasons for her feelings of disgust with her mother remained obscure until she returned from a week's visit with her parents. She reported that the visit had gone better than previous ones—she had refused to sleep with her mother. She hesitantly explained that she had told her mother that her children would be uneasy in a strange house unless she remained in the same room with them. Her mother always expected to sleep with her when she visited, even as she had often insisted that they sleep together when she was still at home. Her mother would lie behind her, body to body, and fondle her breasts. Even when telling of these experiences as a woman of thirty, Mrs. C. seemed uncertain if it were proper to refuse her mother, saying that she had decided to take a stand because these experiences left her feeling disgusted.

Mrs. D. had become psychotic in college following the resignation of a woman instructor for whom she had developed an intense "crush." She was able to resume her education after a year in a hospital but she made several suicidal attempts, cutting her wrists after drinking heavily. With continuing psychotherapy, her adjustment gradually improved and she became an instructor in a women's college. Her condition remained precarious and she suffered occasional paranoid episodes. She continued to form attachments to older women from whom she demanded attention. She shifted to a woman analyst and, after a couple of stormy years, improved markedly. She managed to complete her doctoral dissertation and then was married for a year or two to a passive and somewhat paranoid man. An intense homosexual relationship following her divorce ended in a very brief psychotic episode. Eventually, Mrs. D. settled into a successful academic career.

Mrs. D.'s mother was a vague, poorly organized woman with few friends. Although her life centered in her home, she was a poor housekeeper. The mother was markedly oversolicitous toward her daughter, differentiating poorly from her, and transferring her own insecurities and anxieties to the child who, she believed, was unable to care for herself. The mother's anal preoccupations were marked, and she involved her daughter in them. The mother persisted in wiping and cleaning the girl after bowel movements even after she started school and had difficulty in letting her go to the first grade because she worried that she could not wipe the girl if she had a bowel movement while at school. She frequently gave herself enemas, taking them while in the bathtub lest she soil anything, and often had her daughter keep her company during the procedure. The overprotectiveness and anal preoccupations extended into the night and the sleeping arrangements. Until Mrs. D. left for college, she often slept between her parents, nestled against her mother in "spoon" fashion. As a child and adolescent, Mrs. D. believed that mother and she signaled one another during the night by passing wind. Although the mother permitted herself such behavior, she would scold the patient for it and send her to the bathroom. Mrs. D. grew up feeling her mother's great need for her to need her mother, and believed that she had to remain a needy infant to hold her mother together. She became extremely sensitive to her mother's needs and unspoken signals and, after she left home, she had intense longings for an older woman who would be completely preoccupied with and take care of her.

In all three cases, the mother's relationship to the daughter who became schizophrenic contained an erotic quality, including sensuous physical intimacies. None of the mothers had been able to provide good nurturant care to the patient as a child but, at the same time, did not establish clear boundaries between herself and the child. The vacillations between disinterested aloofness and inappropriate physical intimacies that continued into adolescence or even adult life perplexed these patients. The mothers confused their daughters' needs with their own, transferred their anxieties to their daughters, and seemed to need the daughters' dependence upon them. Still, they gained little pleasure or gratification from a daughter but related by being concerned—and conveyed concerns that undermined the daughter's self-esteem and autonomy.

Studies have indicated that the homosexual concerns and tendencies of schizophrenic patients, as well as their incestuous strivings and fears, reflect the incestuous or homosexual proclivities of a parent and, concomitantly, the failure of parents to maintain their own gender-linked roles and the essential boundaries between the two generations in the nuclear family (Chapter X). The child's development becomes confused when identification with the parent of the same sex does not promote formation of a proper gender identity that is fundamental to the achievement of a stable and coherent ego identity. The de-erotization of the child-parent relationship is one of the cardinal functions of the family. Whereas the infant's proper development requires erotically motivated attention and love, the attachment must gradually be frustrated in order for children to overcome their egocentric orientations toward their mothers in which they consider themselves the center of the mother's existence, to permit them to find their places as members of the family, and then to be free to invest their energies in peer relationships and schooling.

Both the mother's continuing erotization of her tie to a son whom she needs to complete her life and the father's seductive behavior toward a daughter have been described (Chapter X). In a general way, the incestuous closeness of a mother to her son is more deleterious than father-daughter incestuous attachments because the son remains caught up in the initial symbiotic relationship with his mother, which blocks the development of his autonomy as a separate individual, and because his continuing identification with his mother impedes the development of a firm male identity. The girl's attachment to her father does not involve the primary symbiotic bond or interfere with her feminine identification, although it tends to block her emergence from the family and fosters the undue sexualization of object relationships, as occurs in hysterical personalities.

The impact of the homosexuality of fathers upon their sons has also been noted. The development of a son's proper gender identity is impaired by the faulty object for masculine identification and, when the father is also sexually seductive with his son, serious developmental confusions result. Raybin (1969) has described father-son incest extending over three generations with the member of the third generation becoming schizophrenic.

Although the homosexual tendencies of some mothers of schizophrenic patients have been surmised (Chapter III), neither the studies of Alanen (1958) nor those of Lidz et al. (Chapter III) provided clear evidence of a mother's homoerotic behavior with a daughter or material to study the impact of such relationships upon the daughter's development. These mother-daughter relationships, like those that so often exist between mothers and sons who become schizophrenic, had the malignant quality of continuing the erogenous aspects of the preoedipal mother-child closeness because of the mother's inability to establish boundaries between herself and her child and between her needs and those of her child. The patient was left with feelings of being an adjunct to her mother and to her emotional and physical needs and was burdened by the need to support the mother from whom she had insufficiently differentiated. The mother's failure to frustrate the child's preoedipal attachment impeded the child's attainment of adequate initiative and autonomy. It did not force the child to overcome the egocentric orientation of believing that she is the primary focus of the mother's life and to find and accept her proper place as a child member of the family. The symbiotic ties remained, rather than being supplanted by more clear-cut identifications and object relationships.

In some respects, however, the situation was here even more deleterious than it was with sons who become schizophrenic. The mother gained little, if any, real gratification or sense of completion from the daughter. It seemed as if the mother was overprotective because she was sorry for the child rather than because she loved her. Feeling incomplete and inadequate herself, the mother could not feel that a daughter could learn to care for herself. The erotic closeness was intermittent and did not compensate for the sparse maternal nurturance. For all three of the schizophrenic women, the continuing erotism with the mother was of a primitive sort, involving such matters as skin contact, anal preoccupations, and physical intimacy while asleep. The mother's fluctuations between overconcern and aloofness increased the child's insecurities, fixated upon erogenous aspects of the attachment to the mother, and reinforced ways of gaining maternal attention through provoking anxiety, inability to care for the self, needing protective closeness at night, etc. In some such cases, at least, the problem becomes accentuated when the daughter reaches puberty and her mother avoids homosexual temptations by placing greater distance between herself and her daughter. The shift not only creates further inconsistencies concerning aloofness and intimacy but is also apt to increase the dependency needs of the girl whose development of autonomy has been impeded. Such needs create longings for the tangible sheltering person, the need to touch and feel, and reawaken sexualized longings for the old intimacies and the childhood means of capturing the self-absorbed attention of the mother.

These patients could not pursue their education and career or foster peer relationships with any consistency, for the dominant striving for a mothering person intruded repetitively. For Mrs. D., crushes on teachers and the desire to be close to them were more significant than schooling, and the intensity of her attachments led many teachers to move away from her. When a high school teacher rebuked her and called her a bad person, Mrs. D. felt crushed, believing, perhaps correctly, that her homosexual longings had been perceived and rebuffed. Soon after she started her analytic psychotherapy with a woman, she was caught peering into her therapist's home at night and was found to have been sleeping on the ground near the therapist's bedroom.

As might be anticipated, the difficulties in achieving a comfortable distance in interpersonal relationships became a central problem in therapy. The therapist, rather than therapy, became the patient's prime objective. Miss B., for example, when entering and leaving her woman therapist's office, found ways of touching her and of brushing against her breasts if possible. She sought to seduce her therapist into an intimacy with her, and the only feelings that she experienced toward her therapist were "needy" ones. But if the therapist appeared interested in her somatic complaints, she felt rejected and even panic-stricken because of the homosexual implications. Mrs. C. was extremely sensitive to the precise position of her chair in relation to her therapist's: a few inches closer than usual, and she was anxious that her incorporative needs would get out of hand or she felt stifled by the therapist's intrusiveness, whereas, if a few inches more distant, she felt that he was aloof and disinterested. The intensity of her oral cravings and fellatio fantasies transferred from those she had for her father would intrude and frighten when regressive longings for dependency mounted. In all of these women, the longings for closeness based upon prolonged physical intimacies with their mothers opened the way for polymorphous perverse fantasies and behavior and for tendencies to confuse sexual behavior with men with desires for feminine love objects.

Because the patients' relationships with their mothers remained erotized into adolescence or even into adult life, and also because of their identifications with mothers with homosexual tendencies, a paranoid trend upset their relationships; they were apt to feel that any woman who showed an interest in them had homosexual motives. Such attributions of homosexuality to others were, in part, projections, but also were transferences from the mother. Mrs. D. disrupted several important friendships in college by accusing her friends of homosexuality. Miss B. avoided an important teacher in graduate school because she interpreted this woman's concerns about her unstable behavior as evidence that the teacher sought to seduce her, even as she became acutely anxious that she might be seducing her therapist when she forced an interest in her physical appearance or health.

The mother's confused or nebulous gender identity had widespread repercussions on the daughter's gender identity. A mother who gains erotic gratification from another female, even if it is from a child, promotes confusion concerning appropriate object choice in a daughter who identifies with her. Furthermore, these patients were aware of the poverty of their parents' emotional relationships and of the mother's meager cathexis of the father who, in turn, conveyed his dissatisfaction with the mother as a spouse and sexual object. Mrs. A. escaped from the dilemma adequately (as did another woman with a similar parental configuration analyzed by one of the authors) by identifying in childhood with her father's mistress who remained for her an ideal of a sexually desirable woman. Insofar as these patients identified with their mothers, it was with persons who had little self-esteem as women, which was reinforced by their husbands' disinterest, contempt, or hostility.

The mother's homosexual orientation can also profoundly influence the daughter's relationship with her father. In all of these cases, and very notably in two of them, the father assumed many maternal functions very early in the child's life, tending to fixate the daughter's attachment to the father at a preoedipal, nurturant level. Mrs. C., as we have noted, related her fellatio fantasies to her longings for mothering from her father. Mothers may also seek to avoid heterosexual responsibilities to their husbands by offering the pubertal daughter to the father as a substitute, a circumstance that probably occurred in Mrs. A.'s family—and a collusion that has been noted in many cases of father-daughter incest.

We have sought to examine some of the adverse influences of a mother's homosexual tendencies upon a daughter, particularly the effect when such tendencies include erotic, incestuously toned relationships with the daughter. The nature of such influences cannot be stated precisely for they are, in actuality, blurred, inconsistent, and confusing. They were, in the cases studied, such an inherent part of the way in which the patients grew up that, even in the analytic process, they emerged with difficulty. We have suggested that such mother-daughter relationships are as injurious as incestuously toned mother-son relationships and, in some ways, even more detrimental to the development of the child. The material serves to clarify some aspects of the peculiar relationships that exist between mothers and daughters who become schizophrenic. However, not all schizophrenic women have mothers with the types of difficulties described. Although much remains to be clarified, we have designated and discussed a subject that requires careful scrutiny in order to elucidate further factors that enter into the etiology of schizophrenia and also into the genesis of some types of female homosexuality.

POSTSCRIPT

We had in Chapter III emphasized the antipathy of the mothers of schizophrenic patients to their own mothers, and particularly the frankly expressed hostility of all but one of the mothers of schizophrenic daughters toward their mothers. The homosexual tendencies of the mothers described in this chapter may well relate to their craving for a caring and physically close maternal figure. Various complications of mothers' erotic interest in, or needs for, their daughters have been presented, including how they can lead to homosexual needs and projections in the daughter, but also the daughter's incestuous involvement with the father.

XII

Schizophrenic ·Patients and Their Siblings

(1961)

One of the most frequent questions we have been asked is, "If the intrafamilial transactions are so critical to the appearance of schizophrenia in an offspring, how is it that their siblings are normal?" It will be recalled that we planned the study to include only families with at least one child other than the schizophrenic patient in order to examine the question. The data assembled in this chapter clearly indicate that the problem is not as puzzling as it first appeared. Few of the siblings could be considered "normal" or well integrated; three of the twenty-four were clearly schizophrenic and seven of the remainder were deemed "borderline." The differences between the personality integration or adaptations of the siblings cannot be explained by any single factor, but we believe that it will be apparent from this chapter, as well as from other chapters in the book, that the schizophrenic offspring was subjected to different influences than their siblings, sometimes to extremely different intrafamilial influences.

We recognize that the assessments of the psychopathology of the siblings are retrospective and thus open to rater bias. However, we had not anticipated that siblings would have so much severe psychopathology but rather had originally hoped that comparison between the patients and their reasonably well-adjusted siblings would enable us to isolate more clearly why a particular child in the family became schizophrenic. Still, the differences in the influences affecting the children seem clear enough and some generalizations emerged from

Theodore Lidz, Stephen Fleck, Yrjö O. Alanen, and Alice R. Cornelison: Schizophrenic Patients and Their Siblings. *Psychiatry*, Vol. 26, 1963, pp. 1-18. Copyright © 1963, The William Alanson White Psychiatric Foundation, Inc.

the study, particularly concerning the different impact of a family on sons and daughters.

The question has been raised repeatedly: If the family milieu is critical for the production of schizophrenia in a particular offspring, if it exerts a serious pathogenic influence upon this child, what about the siblings? Why are they not affected?

We designed our entire intensive study of the families of patients around this question, selecting only families in which the schizophrenic child had at least one sibling who could be studied. This permitted a comparison of the patients with persons who were not schizophrenic but who had been raised by the same parents and exposed to many similar intrafamilial influences. The siblings rather than some other arbitrarily selected persons form a comparative group—and we are pointedly avoiding the term *controls*, since we do not believe that a true control series can be established in this type of study.

Of course, we do not aspire to a definitive answer, for if the question of why one child in a family rather than another becomes schizophrenic could be answered, the cause of schizophrenia would be virtually found. Genetic investigations, despite the impressive findings of twin studies, have thus far failed to produce evidence for either a dominant or a recessive trait. Their failure may be due to primary reliance upon hospital records and the incidence of overt and flagrant schizophrenia. The contribution of the various genetic studies has recently been reviewed by Jackson (1960b), and currently Rosenthal (1959, 1960) is carefully examining their methodologies and findings. The evidence indicates that extragenetic influences play a very significant role. The scrutiny of our data can help clarify the problem, particularly along two lines: (1) by noting the incidence of serious psychopathological conditions among the siblings; (2) by examining the differences in the intrafamilial influences impinging upon the siblings within a family with particular reference to (a) the changes in family circumstances and intrafamilial role relationships that alter the conditions under which siblings are raised; (b) the mother's capacities to provide affectionate nurturant care to the various siblings during infancy; (c) the different role allocations and role assumptions of the children in the family dynamics; (d) how the parental personalities and the configuration of their relationship lead children of one sex to be confronted by greater developmental problems than children of the opposite sex; (e) idiosyncratic problems; and (f) the influence of the siblings upon one another.

Comparing the intrafamilial factors influencing the schizophrenic patient with those affecting his siblings obviously presents difficulties. The investigators are aware of the bias that can arise from the knowledge that one sibling is schizophrenic and another is not. As the difficulty is inherent in the study, nothing could be done except to take it into account. Another problem is that an intensive study including all family members could not encompass a large sample, and unless the study was intensive, it could not expect to gain meaningful answers. In the sixteen families the various combinations and sequences of brothers and sisters were limited, and some factors of potential pertinence require study of various permutations of gender and sequential placement within the family. Another limitation arises in presenting the material. It is difficult to compare the developmental situations of the siblings briefly, for the material is inordinately complex and properly would require a thorough exposition of each family.

The "Normal" Sibling

Any intent to compare the development of the schizophrenic patient with that of "normal" siblings had to be modified greatly for the simple but incontrovertible reason that only a small minority of the siblings could be considered reasonably well adjusted. While normality cannot be readily defined, everyone who has examined the material has been struck by the serious personality problems of the siblings as a group. The sixteen patients have a total of twenty-four siblings. Only five or six of the siblings are making reasonably adequate adjustments, and of these only three are considered well adjusted, even if the assessments are slanted favorably.[1] Examining the siblings for the presence of serious psychopathology, we find that three are clinically schizophrenic and another six or seven, including one who is a severe psychopathic personality, are making borderline and very tenuous adjustments. The remaining eight or nine siblings suffer from a variety of clinical neuroses, acting-out tendencies, and psychosomatic ailments, alone or in combination, for which four had required psychiatric treatment prior to the time of study (see Figure 1).

FIGURE 1

RANGE OF ADJUSTMENT OF 24 SIBLINGS OF SCHIZOPHRENIC PATIENTS

| Well
Adjusted
3 | Adequately
Adjusted
3 | Emotionally
Disturbed
8 | Borderline

7 | Schizophrenic

3 |

The listing of psychiatric diagnoses for the siblings would serve little. The range and severity of their problems can be illustrated by citing the problems of the children in the two families with the largest number of siblings. By chance, one contained four sons and the other four daughters. In the Schwartz family, the youngest son was the patient, a paranoid schizophrenic with delusions that people were against him, accusing him of homosexuality. His oldest brother was a severe sociopath, an embezzler, forger, and gambler. The second son had been disturbed in adolescence and may have been transiently delusional in early adult life, but had become a successful mathematician and had moved far away from the family and its problems. The third son was seriously

[1]Margaret Thaler Singer, in an unpublished investigation, estimated the stability of fourteen siblings of eleven schizophrenic patients through a study of their projective tests. She considered four to be constricted normals, five as moderately or severely neurotic, and five as clearly schizoid or latently schizophrenic.

phobic, suffered from anxiety, and was unable to practice his profession, although he managed to hold a routine job and to marry, living with his wife in the parental home.

The second daughter in the Thomas family had been schizophrenic for many years, the most chronic and withdrawn patient in the series. Her older sister had been in analysis for several years because of serious and diffuse emotional and marital difficulties. The third daughter, who also was in psychiatric treatment, had severe marital problems, had a violent temper, and felt chronically frustrated, tending to be highly suspicious of the motives of others. The youngest sister had withdrawn from the family and had married. She refused to use her inherited wealth, tying herself down to her housework and children in a bizarre, obsessive manner, maintaining a very precarious balance. She is a borderline or ambulatory schizophrenic.

While the nonschizophrenic personality disorders of the siblings may be of little interest to those who consider schizophrenia to be a clearly circumscribed disease entity, or to those seeking a predominantly genetic etiology, these disorders have pertinence to psychiatrists who entertain the hypothesis that schizophrenia is related to deviant personality development. If the intrafamilial transactions play a major role in shaping the personality of the offspring raised within the family, each child in these seriously disturbed families may well be affected in different ways and to differing degrees, and not all need reach the extreme of a schizophrenic reaction.

The personality problems of the siblings will receive further scrutiny during the discussion of the influences affecting their development within their families. However, two defensive maneuvers, marked constriction and flight from the family, require special comment because they were strikingly characteristic, particularly of the siblings who had made reasonably good adaptations.

Of the four best adjusted siblings, only one, a girl who had two psychotic brothers, seemed reasonably free and imaginative. The other three, as well as many of the more disturbed siblings, suffered from marked constriction of their personalities with notable limitations in their range of emotional maturity, their perceptiveness, and the use of their intellectual resources.[2] A sibling may, for example, successfully pursue a scientific career that requires minimal interpersonal awareness and remain relatively impoverished in other areas. The constricted personality usually utilizes the defense of isolation to prevent recognition of the extent of the intrafamilial difficulties, for facing the total situation would be shattering. In some, whole periods of the past have been completely repressed and particularly traumatic experiences have produced amnesias. In the investigation, where intensive therapy could not be offered the siblings, such defenses had to be respected as essential to the sibling's ego integrity.

A sister of a young schizophrenic woman had managed to avoid involvement in the parental conflict in which her sister had been enmeshed, carefully placating both parents.[3] She was a relatively poor informant about the family, insisting that she could remember very little about her childhood, or even about many recent occurrences. She went on to explain that life in her family had been so painful that she had taught herself very early in childhood to think as little as possible about the family's quarrels, never letting herself review a day's happenings. She tried to concentrate upon avoiding trouble, pleasing her parents, and doing well at school until she could leave for college and lead her own life. She did not consciously know how she felt about her strange and difficult parents. While we have counted this young woman among the more stable siblings—indeed the most stable sibling of the same sex as the patient—Margaret Thaler Singer, who interpreted the projective tests of the members of this family without any knowledge about them, wrote the following excerpt:

---

[2]Margaret Thaler Singer has also emphasized personality constriction as a major defense of siblings of schizophrenic patients from her unpublished study of the projective tests of a series investigated at the National Institute of Mental Health by Lyman Wynne and his coworkers.

[3]More detailed data concerning this young woman can be found in Chapter VI.

To coin a phrase, this girl is "her parents' child." One can see the impact of their communication styles upon her. She uses fragmented remarks, tells a story [on the TAT], then takes it back saying that she didn't find a meaning! Nothing gets validated and confirmed. She often describes interactions as rather pointless, fragmented affairs which she then denies. . . . people are not responsible for their own wrongdoings . . . children might need their attention brought back to concrete realities—they are seen as inattentive and drifting—people in general are not good, and interactions hardly ever lead to anything pleasant. She is more than willing to leave crazily incompatible acts hanging together as if they made sense or were sequitors. . . . Men are seen in very poor light. . . . Mother is not seen in a positive way at all. On one card she told no story at all where a mother is usually seen. In another two stories the wife poisons the husband. . . .

Thus the projective tests bore out the clinical impression that this woman had managed to deal with potentially serious disturbance by constriction, isolation, and denial.

One of the most successful siblings, the brother of a schizophrenic girl, had knowingly or unknowingly gratified his parents' ambitions for him by choosing a wealthy spouse and becoming a capable physician. He was pleasant and affable, but communicated little of pertinence. Singer, again without knowledge of the subject, stated, on the basis of the projective tests:

He is obsessive. He has learned from his father to take an intellectual position and try to seem detached. On the Sentence Completion Test he talks of viruses, chemistry, Beethoven, pharmaceutics, and politics. He senses he is nonrevealing and unimaginative. . . . He is repudiating imagination and fantasy . . . particularly on the TAT where he says things are a . . . matter of course . . . innocuous . . . status quo . . . nothing drastic . . . just a passing thing . . . no outcome . . . just simply another thing, etc. He has learned the Pollyanna-like style both his parents have. . . .

Although personality constriction was prominent in the siblings in this study, we know that some siblings of schizophrenic patients are reasonably stable and also highly sensitive and productive. A number of outstanding authors have had schizophrenic siblings, and some have apparently abreacted their traumatic lives in their artistic productions. Some psychiatrists with schizophrenic siblings have sensitively used the insights gained within their own families to understand and treat schizophrenic patients.

Some siblings realize that they must flee from the disturbing family environment as soon as possible in order not to be overwhelmed. Several of them recounted how they had maintained an emotional aloofness for several years until they could get away; in others, the predicament of the schizophrenic sibling became so intolerable and frightening that they impulsively left home, as did a character in Tennessee Williams's *The Glass Menagerie*. In leaving the home, they are apt to try to block out the past and disengage themselves from their families. Of course, these siblings are often more able to leave the parents and survive on their own than are the patients, in whom such attempts at disengagement may precipitate an acute psychotic break. The sister whose constriction has just been noted had no intention of returning home after finishing college and married promptly upon being graduated. In another instance, a college girl became bedridden soon after her brother was hospitalized, and then with the support of her psychiatrist moved away from the home and severed contact with her mother; even many years later she continued to avoid her parents, and she visited her brother, who was hospitalized very close to her home, only two or three times in four years. The brother of a male patient kept away from his mother—who was schizophrenic, divorced, and pathetically lonely—because, in his frenzy at her engulfing ways, he found himself planning ways of murdering her. The most stable of the four Schwartz brothers was the only one who had left the family; he lived at a great distance and kept himself absorbed in his mathematics. One sister in the Thomas family, but not the best adjusted, had made a complete break with her family, not only avoiding contact with them but also consciously seeking to lead a totally different type of life.

DIVERGENT INFLUENCES UPON THE
OFFSPRING WITHIN A FAMILY

The Effects of Changing Family Circumstances

The family is not static but is an organization with a dynamic configuration in which role relationships change constantly. Time is a factor in these changes, as children enter new developmental phases and parents grow older. Sometimes marked shifts in the family occur, leading to a loss of equilibrium or to deleterious defensive measures to maintain a semblance of role reciprocity between members. In some instances the family situation and the parental attitudes altered so markedly that the patient was raised altogether differently from his siblings, and a similar outcome of the developmental process could not be expected. The Forel family offers a clear example.

The Forel marriage had never been compatible. The father, a weak man, had struggled ineffectually against the domination of the family by his wife, who was abetted by her two older sisters. All three sisters were contemptuous of men, and the oldest was a virago who despised and sought to control men. Mrs. Forel was cold, highly narcissistic, and a teasing flirt. She refused to move away from the neighborhood where her mother and sisters lived, and each summer abandoned her husband to vacation with them for two months. The marriage became increasingly schismatic, with Mr. Forel feeling himself an outcast in his own home, his opinions devalued, and his wishes ignored. His frequent tantrums increased his wife's contempt for him.

There were three children; the patient, a boy, was the youngest child, with a sister thirteen years older and a brother eleven years older. All of the children suffered from the family atmosphere. The older brother considered his childhood to have been abysmal, but far better than the patient's. For the two older children the parental influences had been modified by close contact with the extended families of both parents. The older son had been a favorite of his grandparents and aunts, gaining their admiration and praise by ingratiating himself in an obsequious fashion that enraged his father. He became highly neurotic, terrified of male authorities. He believed that he had escaped very serious disorganization by, first, his attachment to a male teacher, identifying himself with him and trying to follow in his footsteps, and then by developing a psychogenic dermatitis that led him into intensive psychotherapy. The sister became a seriously constricted and anxious woman.

Shortly before the conception of the patient, the parents had verged upon the separation they had often considered. Mr. Forel had been offered an opportunity to establish a business in another state, but his wife refused to move away from her sisters. When Mr. Forel issued an ultimatum and threatened divorce, his wife capitulated and agreed to move, and also agreed to resume the sexual relationship she had terminated eleven years before. The patient was a product of the brief reconciliation. Finding herself pregnant, Mrs. Forel became enraged at her husband and sought unsuccessfully to terminate the pregnancy. After the child was born, she paid little attention to him, and feeling lost without her sisters, upon whom she had always been dependent, she began to drink heavily and to entertain male friends. During the patient's childhood, both parents were frequently intoxicated, and the older children reported that the father often carried his wife home dead drunk. The older siblings and the father tried to fill a mothering role toward the patient. Then, when the patient was six, Mrs. Forel was seriously disfigured in an auto accident which occurred when her husband fell asleep while driving. She became depressed and refused to leave her room until her appearance could be restored surgically, more than a year later. Feeling guilty, the father sought to make amends by becoming subservient to her, and was treated more contemptuously than ever. Then in rapid succession, the brother left for college, the sister married, and the father failed in his business. The family moved again, and shortly thereafter the father developed a malignancy. As he went downhill, his wife totally neglected him, fearing that she might catch cancer from him. The father died when the patient was eleven, and from then on the boy never had a real home. They lived with his married sister for a time; and then his mother moved in with her oldest sister. This aunt hated the patient, who was defiant toward her, and refused to permit him to live in her house. He boarded in the neighborhood, visiting his mother when his aunt was not at home.

In at least half of the families, the sequential position of the offspring formed a significant differentiating influence because of changing family circumstances, although the changes were less dramatic in the other cases than in the one described above. The children's position in a family can, however, make considerable difference in the parents' attitudes toward them even when they are of the same sex and closely proximate in age because of the places they fill in the dynamic equilibrium of the family. We have considered two of the most difficult problems of differentiation in our series in other papers: the differing role and identity assignments of a set of identical twins (Chapter XIII); and the very different situations confronting two sisters born less than two years apart, the older of whom is schizophrenic and the younger reasonably well adjusted (Chapter VI). The mother of the twins had selected the older twin to live out her masculine fantasies of the life denied her because she was a woman and was herself a less favored younger twin, while she identified the younger of the twins with her feminine, passive, and masochistic self. In the other case, the older of the sisters had become the focal point and scapegoat in a conflict between her parents that had antedated her birth and had been brought to a crisis by her conception, whereas the younger sister had remained relatively peripheral to the continuing parental quarrel.

The Mother's Capacity to Provide Nurturant
Care During the Patient's Infancy

In half of the cases studied, a clear disturbance was found to have existed in the relationship of the mother with the patient as an infant—a disturbance that was not present, or at least not to the same degree, in her relationship with her other children. This is in keeping with theories of the importance of infantile deprivation and maternal rejection in the genesis of schizophrenia. Three mothers had been physically incapacitated for many months following the patient's birth, disabilities that had been aggravated by their emotional problems at the time. One mother had been fearful of handling her oldest child, particularly of bathing him, a task which the father had to carry out. The mother of the two schizophrenic Robb sisters had been too insecure to take care of her oldest daughter and had turned her care, as an infant and small child, over to a nurse; when her son was born, three years later, she had cared for him herself; but when the younger daughter was born, she paid little attention to her, for she was preoccupied with hostility toward her unfaithful husband, and was considering divorce. Mrs. Ubanque, another mother of two daughters, had suffered "gloomy thoughts" following the birth of the younger girl, who became the patient, whereas the birth of the older child had been a joyous occasion—and a clear preference for the older child continued during the ensuing years. Mrs. Forel, already referred to, had sought to abort her youngest child, who became the patient, and had been emotionally withdrawn from him during his infancy as well as during his later years. At least one other mother's efforts at mothering were seriously impeded by her husband's extreme jealousy of any attention she sought to give her son, a situation that did not recur after the birth of a daughter. In several other instances, the mother had difficulty in providing proper nurturant care for her children as infants, but notable differences in the care provided the patient and the siblings were not apparent.

It is difficult properly to assess such influences in the first year of the patient's life. The problem is partly one of retrospective assessment, but even more one of sorting out what is pertinent and decisive in families where serious difficulties had existed prior to the patient's birth and then continued throughout his developmental years. Two things are apparent: that these difficulties in nurturing the infant did not occur in all cases, and that this problem was but one among many parent-child difficulties. However, such deprivation may be important in predisposing the child to schizophrenia. It may also indicate the start of a chronically faulty mother-child relationship, and such unsatisfactory parent-infant interaction may set a pattern aggravated by constant feedback from child to mother, mother to child, and one parent to the other, involving the sibling relationships as well.

The Child's Role in the Family Dynamics

The Child and Parental Conflicts.—In those families that we have designated as "schismatic," the parents were in open conflict, trying to coerce each other, each encountering from the other either defiance or, at best, a temporary hostile and resentful submission. Each undercut the worth and self-esteem of the other and divided the family, the mother wooing the children to side with her, and the father wooing them to side with him in the conflict, each parent fostering distrust and devaluation of the other. In many cases a constant threat of family dissolution hung over the children. The parents were preoccupied with their marital problems, and, in the absence of affection and support from each other, turned to a child to fill their emotional needs. In our experience, the child who becomes schizophrenic is caught in the schism to a greater degree than are the others in a variety of ways. First, he may fill the role of the "scapegoat" whose difficulties preoccupy the parents and mask their basic unhappiness with one another. Second, he may insert himself into the split, seeking to widen the gap between them to gain one parent for himself. Third, he may devote his energies and attention to bridging the gap between the parents. He straddles issues, divides his loyalties, and seeks to become a different person for each parent in order to fill the emotional needs of both, consuming his energies in preserving the parents' marriage and in salvaging their lives, rather than in the interests of his own independent ego development. Fourth, he may be caught in a bind in which loyalty to one parent means rejection by the other; because of their opposing standards and needs, he cannot satisfy and feel accepted by one without arousing dissatisfaction or hostility in the other. The widely discrepant attitudes and directives of the parents cannot be integrated within the single child—the irreconcilable parents become irreconcilable introjects.

The reasons why one offspring rather than another becomes most intensively involved are diverse: the sequential position, the child's sex, changes in the family situation, childhood illnesses, and others not so readily categorized. However, the patient's involvement commonly relieves the other children of much of the burden.

The case of Dora Nussbaum illustrates how one child became more caught up in a family schism than her sibling. Her parents, preoccupied with their own problems and their feud could invest little in their baby daughter, resenting her birth that blocked consideration of divorce. The baby became irritable and difficult, filling the role of a scapegoat and diverting attention from more basic sources of dissension in the home; eventually she widened the gulf between her parents by displacing her mother to the extent of near-incestuous involvement with her father.

In contrast, Mrs. Nussbaum had been delighted by the birth of Dora's older brother who was born before the chronic dissension with her husband had started. She continued to take pride in her son, whereas she was never able to act warmly toward her daughter. Although Mr. Nussbaum gained gratification from having an admiring daughter, he also used her in his conflict with his wife, spiting the latter by the alliance with Dora. Because of the alignments within the family of mother and son as against father and daughter, the situations in which the two children grew up were very different. Mrs. Nussbaum because of her behavior toward Dora and because of her husband's devaluation of her and hostility toward her could not form a model for Dora to follow into womanhood; and her hostility toward Dora posed a realistic danger. The son, in contrast, received affection from both parents, for his father was very much interested in him. Although he, too, was affected by the parental conflict, he was never the center of it, or made to feel that he was the cause of it—and he was two years old before it started. Further, his father provided an excellent career model for him to follow even in his mother's eyes.

The older of the two daughters in the Grau family was caught in a particularly difficult bind because of the parents' dissensions that antedated her birth and their irreconcilable ideas about religion, which focused upon how the child should be raised.[4] Her Protestant father refused to permit her to be baptized into Catholicism despite his written promise, he constantly condemned Catholicism and all Catholics, and he later refused to permit her to go with Catholic boys. Her Catholic mother fought back, sought to woo the girl to Catholicism, and secretly circumvented her husband. She was constantly anxious about her unbaptized child, and eventually had her baptized without her husband's knowledge. The parents' religious quarrels were but symptomatic of many areas of discord.

The patient struggled with these irreconcilable introjects until she finally defiantly sided with her paranoid father and sought to win him away from her mother. The younger daughter, while also subjected to the conflict, never became the focus of it. To some extent, the father relinquished her to his wife; since the older sister preempted the father's attention and affection, the younger could form an alliance with her mother. As we have noted previously, the sister learned at an early age to sidestep the difficulties in which the patient became involved.

In the Benjamin family the son who became schizophrenic sought to satisfy the disparate ambitions his parents held for him, to fill their unmet needs, and to keep them from separating. When they were at odds, he would become fright-

---

[4]See Chapter VI.

ened by their seductiveness toward him; yet he would become jealous and more disturbed whenever they became more compatible. Both parents used the son's indications of affection and his criticisms of the other parent as a vindication of themselves, wooing him as an ally. At the same time, the father could not permit his son to gain a better education than he himself had obtained, and he unconsciously sabotaged his wife's hopes and the boy's ambitions. The confusions in the sexual sphere were even greater, with both parents behaving seductively toward their son. The patient's older sister could simply side with her father and did not seek to hold the parents together. She was not threatened by seduction from the mother, and her father was less physically seductive toward her than toward his son. Less involved in the parents' difficulties and hence less burdened by guilt, she could also exploit the parents' disagreements to gain goals of her own, which her brother could not do.

The Child's Role in "Skewed" Families.—Not all of the parents were in overt conflict. In the families that we have termed "skewed"—predominantly families with male schizophrenic offspring—the serious personality problems and deviant ways of the dominant parent were not countered by the spouse. The patient, in contrast to his siblings, is the object of a particular intrusiveness by the dominant parent, usually the mother, which blurs the boundaries between parent and child and ties the patient to satisfying the parent's needs and to continuing a primary relatedness with her. The boy's differentiation from the initial symbiotic bond to his mother and the development of identification with his passive father are impeded. The symbiotic attachment leads to confusion of sexual identity, incestuous concerns, and a greater assimilation of the disturbed parent's deviant and paralogical ways. The siblings may resent the patient's special relationship with the mother, but they are freer to develop into independent persons. The oldest child may be selected as the object of this intrusive relationship, but in some instances the mother holds on to the youngest child as the older children grow away from her.

In the family with the identical twins (see Chapter XIII), the mother never established ego boundaries between herself and her twins. From the time of their birth, her entire life was wrapped up in these phallic extensions of herself. The older brother of the twins, together with the father, became outcasts. The mother banished the father from her room and bed, and she considered the older son to be uncouth and unimportant. The older brother hated the twins, envied them, and suffered; and he became accident-prone, seriously unstable, and tended to act out. Yet he could identify with his father, who, despite his wife's contempt and ridicule, was a far more stable person than she. The older brother did not need to struggle to differentiate himself from his mother or to escape her bizarre demands; and eventually he felt very free to leave home and seek fulfillment elsewhere.

The Siblings' Gender

While most of the siblings were emotionally unstable, our data indicate that the most generalized and consistent factor related to the severity of the disturbance was the sex of the sibling. This factor is complex; since it is a function of the parental personalities and their interrelationships, its origins can antedate the birth of any of the children. The significant finding is that siblings of the same sex as the schizophrenic patients were, as a group, clearly more disturbed than siblings of the opposite sex. The developmental tasks confronting children of opposite sexes in a particular family were very different. While the sample in this series is small and unsuited for statistical analysis, the finding is in accord with the studies of concordance rates for schizophrenia in dizygotic twins, with studies of *folie à deux*,[5] and with the findings of Penrose (1945) and others concerning concordance rates for schizophrenia in siblings of schizophrenic patients. Such findings

[5]For concordance rates in siblings, see Greenberg (1956) and Kallmann (1953).

have led to the consideration of a sex-linked genetic factor, but Rosenthal's (1960) analysis of the collective data from the various studies shows that the gender-linkage within the more extended family does not appear to follow genetic lines.

As shown in Figure 2, the nine male patients in our series had fourteen siblings—eight brothers and six sisters. Three had only brothers, two had a brother and a sister, and four only a sister.

Figure 3 shows the female patients and their siblings. The seven female patients had a total of ten siblings—seven sisters and three brothers. The paucity of brothers is unfortunate and limits the usefulness of the data. Four of the female patients had only sisters; one had a brother and a sister; and two had only a brother.

The Sisters of Male Schizophrenics.—The only sibling of a male schizophrenic who could be considered emotionally healthy and well adjusted is a sister. One other sister, now a young adolescent, may attain reasonable stability despite some acting-out tendencies. Two other sisters of male schizo-

FIGURE 2

ESTIMATED ADJUSTMENT OF MALE PATIENTS AND THEIR SIBLINGS

Each vertical column represents a child in the order of his birth in the family. The patient is identified by "Pt" above the column. Symbols for males and females are shown above.

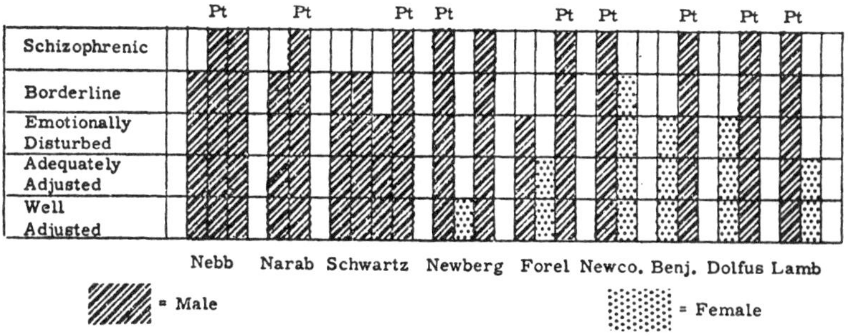

FIGURE 3

ESTIMATED ADJUSTMENTS OF FEMALE PATIENTS AND THEIR SIBLINGS

Each vertical column represents a child in the order of his birth in the family. The patient is identified by "Pt" above the column. Symbols for males and females are shown above.

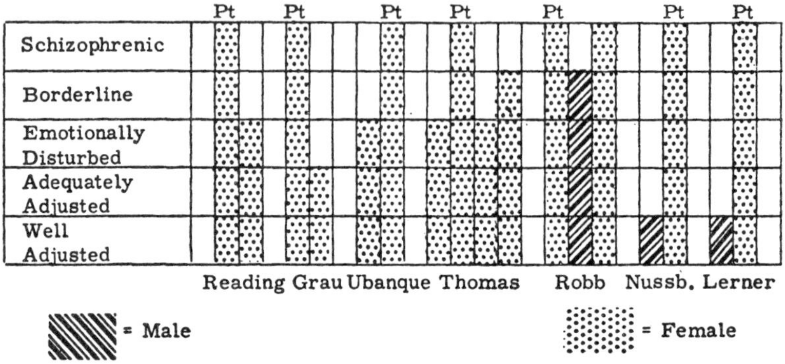

= Male   = Female

phrenics are living reasonably satisfying lives despite fairly serious personality problems; one is seriously constricted and insecure in her marital relationship, and the other has psychopathic traits that have thus far not led to serious difficulties. The remaining two women, the sisters of the most chronic male patients, were both seriously disturbed at one time, and both sought psychotherapeutic help; one is now pursuing a profession effectively, and the other has married and is raising a family, but is seriously constricted and insecure and is making a tenuous adjustment.[6]

The Brothers of Male Schizophrenics.—In contrast to the sisters, none of the eight brothers can be considered to have remained reasonably stable. Two have been psychotic; one became paranoid in childhood, and the other, an identical twin of a patient, has been a transvestite with bizarre fantasies and thought processes. Another brother is a criminal sociopath; a fourth is making a tenuous borderline adjustment and shows many schizophrenic features on his projective

[6]*Since the original publication of this paper, she has had a fairly serious schizoaffective episode.*

tests. The fifth, the older brother of the identical twins, is accident-prone and severely obsessive, and has many other disrupting personality problems. The sixth is phobic and limited, and has serious career and marital problems. The two remaining male siblings are now doing fairly well, but both went through many years of serious turmoil. One may have been transiently delusional in adolescence, and the other suffered from a severe neurodermatitis, had serious concerns over his masculinity, and at times was incapacitated by anxiety, but he worked out his major problems in psychotherapy.

The Brothers of Female Schizophrenics.—Two of the three brothers have successfully pursued professions and have remained emotionally stable, although they are both limited by constriction of their personalities. The third brother, a man with two chronically schizophrenic sisters, has had considerable difficulty in both work and marriage and is rather schizoid.

The Sisters of Female Schizophrenics.—Only one of the seven sisters of the female patients has made a reasonably stable adjustment, and her limitations have already been mentioned. Her skillful avoidance of crippling involvement in a very bad family situation has been discussed in detail in Chapter VI. One sister is chronically schizophrenic, and another, who completely withdrew from her family, is making a borderline schizophrenic adjustment. The remaining four sisters are rather seriously unstable, but the extent of the disabilities of two could not be clearly determined because of their fear of involvement and avoidance of frequent contact with the investigators. One of them had left home precipitately soon after her sister was hospitalized.[7]

Two Illustrations of the Factor of Gender.—The indications that certain family constellations and interaction patterns cre-

[7]Data concerning the seventeenth patient and her family are not included in this paper. The patient had only one sibling, a sister who is emotionally disturbed and suffers from ulcerative colitis. The parental relationship is schismatic, and the mother is incapable of closeness or of acting warmly toward her daughters.

ate greater vulnerability to the development of schizophrenia
for offspring of one sex than for the opposite sex (Chapter
XI) are highlighted by the two families with alternate gender
sequence of their three children. In one, two sons were separated by a daughter, and, in the other, two daughters were
separated by a son. In both families the oldest and youngest
children were schizophrenic, while the middle child of the
opposite sex was not. While this finding probably is partly
a matter of chance, the family situations will be presented
briefly to illustrate how the family configurations created
very different developmental tasks for the boys and girls
within these families.

In the Newberg family the oldest son became acutely
schizophrenic at the age of fifteen. The daughter, who was
thirteen at the time, has remained well and is probably the
most stable and adaptable of any of the siblings in our series.
The third child, a boy who was then nine years old, suffered
from night terrors and paralyzing separation problems, and
soon after his brother's hospitalization developed delusional
beliefs about his teachers and schoolmates.

The Newberg marriage had been filled with mutual recrimination and frequent threats of separation almost from
its inception, with most of the quarrels focusing on the intense
attachment of both spouses to their natal families. Mr. Newberg was the most poorly organized father of any of the male
patients. Raised in a disorganized family abandoned by the
father, he had at an early age assumed responsibility for the
support of his mother. He remained intensely attached to
her, was jealous of his brothers, and spent much of his spare
time in his mother's home. He was equally rivalrous with his
sons, behaving in many ways like another child in the family.
He talked incessantly, in a driven way that the interviewers
found difficult to endure for even an hour at a time. He was
scattered, pursuing one fixed idea after another. Although
a steady provider, he was caught between his ambitions and
his needs for security, and he constantly threatened to leave
his job to pursue some hairbrained scheme. In his free time

he worked upon a sequence of inventions that never materialized or a succession of hobbies each of which he was going to turn into a business. He talked constantly of his great abilities but accomplished little, and he created great confusion when at home.

Mrs. Newberg, in contrast, was one of the most stable mothers in our series. She depended greatly upon her older son, and sought compensation for her unhappy marriage in her children. Although she was oversolicitous, she maintained a reserve that probably impeded her relationships with them. She was firmly attached to her three sisters and refused to move away from the street on which they all lived, which caused her husband great inconvenience. While she justified this, in part correctly, by her husband's unreliability and her need for companionship and help in raising the children, her husband resented her lack of confidence in him. Mrs. Newberg's sisters intruded themselves into the affairs of the Newberg household, and one in particular was openly hostile and contemptuous of Mr. Newberg, constantly belittling him even in the presence of his children.

In this family, the sons had a very faulty paternal model in a man who boasted much and achieved little, who was highly inconsistent and given to suspiciousness, and who was more of a rival to them than a father. The mother and her sisters constantly denigrated him and placed little trust in him, conveying to the boys that they must not resemble him. They lived in an atmosphere where women dominated the extended family and were highly critical of men. For a son to become like the father meant becoming virtually psychotic, subject to constant hostile criticism and contempt, and almost intolerable to the mother whose love they sought.

The daughter's situation was very different. Surrounded by women who were mutually supportive, she had a number of positive feminine models. Although her father was frequently angry with her mother, he also expressed considerable admiration for her. The daughter was clearly her father's favorite, and her mother was not jealous or rivalrous.

Further, the daughter did not need to fill the place in her mother's life, that her father had left unsatisfied; she did not have to achieve as a man in a world in which her grandiose father could accomplish little; nor did she have to face the issue, which confronted her brothers, of how a man could satisfy and be lovable to a woman when the father was so unsatisfactory to their mother and aunts.

The Robb family, in which two chronically schizophrenic daughters were separated by a son who, despite serious difficulties and several bad starts, has managed to achieve a career and marry, presents an analogous situation. Mr. Robb, a professor of education, married a troubled heiress who was seriously lacking in self-esteem. The couple had very different ideas of family life, child rearing, and the types of people with whom they wished to associate. Mrs. Robb accepted her dominating husband's decisions and choice of friends and quietly suffered in associating with people whom she despised. When, however, her husband started a series of sexual liaisons, she followed suit to vent her anger and gain quiet vengeance. Then Mr. Robb invited female exchange students from abroad to live with the family, ignoring his wife's protests. Soon he was spending evenings talking with them and ignoring his wife, and he turned to one of these, who was a teacher doing advanced study, for guidance in raising the children. For many years Mrs. Robb had had little authority in her own home, but now her inadequate self-esteem and confidence fell markedly as her opinions were pointedly ignored and belittled. Deeply resentful and preoccupied with her unhappiness, she could invest little in her children.

The oldest daughter was cared for by a nursemaid during her infancy, but when the son was born the nurse was discharged, and the mother gained considerable satisfaction from caring for him. However, it was soon after the second daughter was born that the mother discovered that her husband was having affairs. From then on she gave little thought or attention to her children. Even though the situation has been presented only in barest outline, one can note that the daughters were uncherished by their mother and that they gained a strange view of the worth and role of a woman, since she was unempathic as a mother, and consistently devalued and held in contempt as a wife. The girls could readily feel that they could not satisfy or gain the affection of their oversolicitous and seductive father by growing up to resemble their mother. The son, who also developed rather serious problems, had at least received maternal affection and attention during his infancy and early childhood; and he had a successful and renowned father who provided a model—and whose example he eventually followed by marrying a wealthy woman from an unstable family.

When the families with schizophrenic sons and those with schizophrenic daughters were examined as separate series, notable differences in their configurations became apparent. Because of the parental personalities and the nature of their interactions, the families with schizophrenic sons presented more serious impediments to the integrated ego development of boys than of girls, and the opposite was true for the families with schizophrenic daughters, although a few families were probably equally noxious to children of both sexes.

The parent of the same sex as the patient—the fathers of sons and the mothers of daughters—formed a very poor model for the patient to internalize in order to gain identity as a man or woman because of the parent's serious psychopathology, because of the parent's attitudes toward the child, or because of the spouse's derogatory and undermining behavior toward this parent, and commonly for all three reasons. To maintain the approval and affection of the parent of the opposite sex, the child sought to differentiate himself from, rather than identify himself with, the parent of the same sex, and thus lacked a positive sex-linked model to follow in order to gain maturity as a man or a woman. The situation was aggravated because the parent of the opposite sex from the child seductively used the child as a replacement for the unsatisfactory spouse in filling his own emotional needs and thus interfered with the child's development into an independent person. Although the case illustrations have emphasized the child's difficulty in achieving identity as a member of his own sex, the problems created for his development go far beyond this. The resolution of the oedipal ties is impeded, and incestuous wishes remain conscious into adolescence; fears of vindictiveness by the parent of the same sex are heightened by the realistic rivalries existing in the family; and narcissistic and homosexual proclivities are fostered by the confused and confusing sexual identities of the parents.

The case material reveals that with but rare exception the mother of the male patient is engulfing of the son, seeking to maintain a symbiotic closeness with him, while the father is distant and rivalrous toward the son or is himself but a weak, emasculated appendage of his wife. In contrast, the mother of the female patient is aloof and distant from her, either because she is unable to accept in a daughter the femininity she rejects in herself or because she seeks to ward off homosexual impulsions, while the father tends to be derogatory of women in general but seductive with the daughter, whose admiration he needs to bolster his insecure masculinity and narcissism. A more detailed examination of these differences suggests that satisfactory ego development and integration in boys and girls depend upon different requisites in the family structure and interaction (Chapter IX). A boy's ego development will be injured more seriously than a girl's by a mother who cannot establish clear ego boundaries between herself and the child, since to achieve a firm masculine identity he must break away from the initial mother-child symbiosis more completely than a daughter needs to. In addition, a father who fails to fill a masculine instrumental role in the family will be more detrimental to a boy, who needs to learn this role, than to a girl. Conversely, a girl will be harmed more seriously by a cold and aloof mother, for the attainment of maternal affectional characteristics through empathic absorption of maternal feelings is more critical to

a girl's development than to a boy's; and a father who dominates and derogates the mother and tends to be antagonistic
and belittling toward all women will affect a girl's development more deleteriously than a boy's. The exposition of the
different developmental tasks confronting boys and girls and
how they are furthered or impeded by the family configuration goes beyond the purposes of this paper; here we are
seeking only to indicate why a child of one sex may be more
vulnerable to personality disorganization within a given family than a child of the opposite sex.

Idiosyncratic Problems in the Parents'
Relationship to the Schizophrenic Offspring

The comparison of some of the patients with their siblings
must take into account certain special problems related to
unique circumstances. Expectations before birth as well as
many circumstances at and following confinement can set the
stage for certain interaction patterns in the family or certain
attitudes toward a particular infant. For example, differences
in temperament present at birth may influence the ensuing
child-parent relationship and interaction, although this, like
many other such influences, is difficult to assess retrospectively.

The Nebb twins, one of whom was overtly schizophrenic
and the other a transvestite who might also be considered
schizophrenic, were, in contrast to their older brother, placed
at birth in a special and unusual situation because their
mother had been competing with her own twin sister to see
which of them could produce twins. The birth of the twin
sons was a major triumph for Mrs. Nebb, who had been the
deformed and neglected member of her family, and they
were to be her means of achieving prestige and dominance.

In another family, the daughter who became the patient
had manifested artistic talent to an unusual degree by the
age of three. Two relatives in the maternal line who had been
similarly gifted from earliest childhood had become psychotic. The patient's mother had been directed away from

developing a similar talent lest it lead to insanity, but the patient's unusual ability could not be suppressed. The mother was naturally ambivalent about the patient's dominant activity and vacillated between encouraging it and seeking to guide the girl into more conventional channels. The bright but untalented older brother had not been subjected to such ambivalent guidance or to an *a priori* expectation of great vulnerability to psychosis.

It must be noted, however, that there were other problems in both families that were just as serious as in the other families in the series.

The Interaction Between the Siblings

In our scrutiny of the divergent influences upon the siblings within a family, we must also note the effects of the interaction between the siblings themselves, although this topic extends beyond the limits and purposes of this paper. In the Narab family, the overtly schizophrenic mother considered both of her sons to be geniuses—even, at times, Messiahs—and her extreme intrusiveness into the lives of both was not countered by the father. The younger son became schizophrenic while the older traversed a narrow path, skirting overt psychosis. He was filled with venom toward his mother and feared that he might act out his homicidal fantasies about her if he remained near her; and, at times, he was almost equally hostile toward his younger brother. While *ex post facto* analysis is particularly hazardous in this instance, several factors seem important. Mrs. Narab had been smotheringly dominant of her firstborn, but with the birth of the second son she turned her major energies toward him; and as the older son began to move away from her, she clung all the more tenaciously to the younger. The firstborn could express his jealousy and anger toward his brother, dominating him and forcing him into a passive and masochistic position—one might say into developing a more Messiah-like personality and possibly emulating his father, whom both sons considered homosexual. The absorption of the mother's needs by the younger son appears to have provided greater freedom for the older.

Illness in one offspring—whether the schizophrenic patient or the nonschizophrenic sibling—affects the siblings differentially. At least three of our patients experienced comparative neglect when the prolonged illness of older siblings—rheumatic fever in one instance—required a great deal of the mother's attention. In the Schwartz family, the severe psychopathy of the oldest brother pre-empted the economic and emotional resources, as has already been noted. It was the youngest son who became psychotic. Not only had his father become ineffectual as a husband and father shortly after his birth, but his mother's attention had become absorbed by the oldest son's markedly antisocial and delinquent behavior. The family lived in a "tough" neighborhood, and the next older brother had protected the patient, as the baby of the family, and fought his battles for him—abetting his development as a passive, dependent child who was very insecure in his masculinity.

In the Grau family, the patient's difficulties throughout her childhood had had a very different impact on the younger sister. She explained that her older sister had borne the brunt of her mother's insecurity in raising children; the mother had relied on books with her first child but raised the second daughter according to less rigid directions. Moreover, the second daughter had avoided involvement in the parental conflicts by noting how her sister became embroiled with one or the other parent at each phase of development, and her major guide in life had been sidestepping situations that had caused difficulties for her sister. It also became clear that her antagonism to her older sister who created so much difficulty had led her to side with her mother rather than to seek the affection of her paranoid father.

The influences of the siblings upon one another may be diverse, but the child who becomes schizophrenic often lessens the impact of the parental pathology upon the siblings by serving as a target of the parents' intrusiveness, as a scapegoat, or as an example for the siblings of what not to do.

COMMENT

This comparison of sixteen schizophrenic patients with their twenty-four siblings, in an effort to clarify why the patient rather than his siblings became schizophrenic, has presented only a general survey of the problems, for any careful scrutiny from a genetic-dynamic orientation would require a separate article, if not a monograph, for each family. Several general findings that warrant attention have emerged from the study. One of these is that the question of why one child within a family becomes schizophrenic while the others remain "well" or "normal" requires restatement. As many siblings were psychotic as reasonably well integrated, and all except five or six of the twenty-four siblings suffered from serious personality disorders.

A definite gender-linkage was found in the occurrence and severity of the psychiatric disturbances in the siblings. The brothers of the male schizophrenic patients were clearly more disturbed than the sisters; and the sisters of schizophrenic females were sicker than the brothers, although the value of this finding is limited by the paucity of brothers of female patients in our series. Only one sibling of the same sex as the patient was considered to be reasonably stable; and no sibling of the opposite sex from the patient was overtly psychotic.

The influence of the parents and of their interaction with each other upon sons and daughters differed. In general, different configurations and parental personalities existed in the families with male and female schizophrenic offspring (Chapter IX).

Other differentiating influences upon the development of the children occurred with varying frequencies and in various combinations. In half of the cases, the mother had been either physically incapacitated, too intensely preoccupied with her marital problems, or too anxious and insecure to provide nurturant mothering care during the patient's infancy, while such conditions did not apply during the infancy of the siblings. In half of the families the patient was raised under conditions that were different from those under which the siblings were brought up; in a few families the difference was very marked.

When the siblings were close in age—and even when they were identical twins—they were also subjected to very different intrafamilial influences. The child who becomes schizophrenic may become a pawn or scapegoat in the parental conflict; he may be caught in a bind between the conflicting needs and wishes of the parents, who become irreconcilable introjects; he may invest his energies in seeking to salvage the parents' marriage and to satisfy the needs of both; he may insert himself into the split between the parents, and become a needed complement to one parent. The patients' energies during their developmental years were deflected from developing an integrated independent ego, and failure of closure of their oedipal attachments left them prone to incestuous conflicts during adolescence. The influence of the siblings upon one another may create more or less precarious circumstances and greater or lesser vulnerability.

We have not, of course, included all of the factors that may have been conducive to the production of schizophrenia. Little attention has been given to family characteristics that were reasonably similar for all of the siblings, particularly the paralogic modes of thinking and communicating of one or both parents that were present in all the families.

Although any reconstruction of the intrafamilial circumstances that influenced the development of these patients and their siblings cannot be fully satisfactory, the material offers clear and reasonable grounds for the understanding of why one child rather than another in a family becomes schizophrenic. The data support rather than refute the hypothesis that the intrafamilial environment plays a critical role in the etiology of schizophrenia.

POSTSCRIPT

A number of factors make one child more vulnerable to becoming schizophrenic than the other children in the family. The child who remains relatively well is sometimes able, because of the problems encountered by the disturbed sibling, to utilize the defense of constriction and to escape from the family milieu. The configuration of the family and its dynamics change with time and is clearly more deleterious for one child than the others. For various reasons, the mother may be unable to be nurturant to the child who becomes schizophrenic. Specific idiosyncratic families may have pertinence, etc. However, the sex of the child appears to have been a major factor, though far from the only influence in determining the degree of psychopathology in the offspring in a given family. Whereas none of the families provided an adequate environment for its children's development, some were more noxious for children of one sex than the other for reasons we have presented. In the three families with two schizophrenic offspring, the schizophrenic children were of the same sex, though the Newcomb sister whom we had rated as "borderline" later suffered from a schizoaffective psychosis. However, our description of the Newcomb family conveys that Mrs. Newcomb, among the most "schizophrenogenic" mothers, was amazingly impervious to her daughter. In all instances, except one, offspring who were considered to be adequately well adjusted or integrated were of the opposite sex from the schizophrenic offspring.

The finding that the sisters of male schizophrenics did considerably better than the brothers of male schizophrenics and two of the three brothers of female schizophrenics did considerably better than the sisters of female schizophrenics fits into our developing hypothesis that, in general, the families that gave rise to male schizophrenics differed from those that produced female schizophrenics, a concept that was approached in Chapters V and IX, and which we develop into a more comprehensive theory about schizophrenic disorders than formulated in the original edition of this book.

The material concerning the families provided in the chapter has been somewhat limited and depends on the knowledge of the families the reader has gained from the remainder of the book. In order to obtain a more detailed and definitive understanding of how the family transactions affect sons and daughters differently, we recommend the book A Mingled Yarn by our first coworker, Beulah Parker (1962), which provides a detailed study of a family with a schizophrenic son and two seriously troubled but nonpsychotic daughters.

XIII

Ego Differentiation and Schizophrenic Symptom
Formation in Identical Twins

(1958)

A primary intent of the following article was to highlight some of
the unique developmental problems of identical twins and how the
similar family environment in which they grew up affected them
differently. However, the chapter provides another striking example
of the bizarre family setting in which many schizophrenic patients
grow up and irrationalities foisted upon them, as well as a sketch
of a "schizophrenogenic" mother. The chapter, as also the next, pre-
sents a somewhat different perspective of homosexuality and incest,
indeed of homosexual incest, in the developmental pathology of schiz-
ophrenic patients, and of the potential relationship between failure
to achieve a firm gender identity, schizophrenia, and polymorphous
perverse sexual compulsions.

Among the patients in the study was an identical twin
whose co-twin became extremely disturbed immediately after
the patient was hospitalized. The patient was treated in the
Yale Psychiatric Institute and continued in analytically oriented psychotherapy after discharge, while his twin managed
to remain at home receiving analytically oriented treatment
from a therapist who kept detailed process notes of each
session.[1] The study of these twins, together with all of the

Theodore Lidz, Sarah Schafer, Stephen Fleck, Alice R. Cornelison, and Dorothy
Terry: Ego differentiation and schizophrenic symptom formation in identical twins.
Journal of the American Psychoanalytic Association, Vol. 10, 1962, pp. 74-90. Copyright
© 1962, American Psychoanalytic Association. This paper was presented at the
Midwinter meeting of the American Psychoanalytic Association, December 1959.
[1]We are greatly indebted to this psychiatrist who must remain anonymous to help
conceal the identity of the family.

other members of the family, and the intrafamilial environment they created permitted a unique opportunity to examine the special problems of ego development confronting twins and the impact of the family dynamics in shaping the personalities and the pathology of these twins in particular. We believe that if we wish to use twin studies in exploring the genesis of schizophrenia (Kallmann, 1946; Kallmann and Bondy, 1952; Schlegel, 1955, 1957), we must understand and take into account the dynamic problems of twinship because the ego development and ego structure of twins is apt to differ markedly from those of nontwins. The specific problems of identical twins, however, contribute to the understanding of ego formation and integration in general. In this chapter, we shall seek to focus on these matters while for the time being we neglect the intrafamilial conditions which seem to us to have particular pertinence to the development of schizophrenia.

The literature concerned with the personality development of twins, though sparse, calls attention to a group of problems highly relevant to our case. It reminds one of Aristophanes' poetic fable concerning the nature of love in Plato's *Symposium*. Originally, he tells us, humans were double with two heads and eight extremities and of three sexes, male, female, and androgynous. Because of their challenge to the power of the Olympians, Zeus split them in half. Since then, the halves wander the earth, unable to rest in their incomplete states, seeking their other halves. Identical twins were originally thus united. Kent (1949) in her study of a series of disturbed twins during their childhood remarked upon the frequent symbiotic relationship which she believed was fostered by the presence of a rigid, unloving mother. Most pairs divided into a dominant and a submissive twin, the twin with acting-out tendencies being the dominant one. Many mothers related to the twins as if they were one child, but at the same time treated them differently emotionally. In this setting, twins were intensely rivalrous for the mother's affection, and some reacted with extreme dependency upon the mother while others became aggressively rebellious. Such twins had great difficulty in establishing relationships with other children. Freud (1922) in considering normal and pathological jealousy commented upon the pattern in which early intense rivalry with and hostility toward a sibling turn into love and identification with the envied sibling, and can lead to one pattern of homosexuality. This developmental pattern may be particularly common among twins. Solomon and Bliss (1956), Weatherly and Deabler (1954), Hartmann (1934-1935), and others have reported homosexuality in schizophrenic identical twins, while Orr (1941) and Karpman (1953) both found homosexuality a major problem in the fraternal twins they reported. Karpman (1953) studied the passive member of the twinship who reported that he had been hostilely competitive for the mother but felt doomed to disappointment because his twin was more attractive and so transferred his love to the twin he had originally hated. When separated from his twin upon entering college, he had an upsurge of compulsive sexual urges as a defense against homosexuality. He struggled with his need for his brother and further felt he needed his brother as a protection against his incestuous impulses toward his mother. These problems can be seen clearly in the twins we are presenting. Orr's (1941) patient was also driven by a constant wish "to find a twin" after separation, and having feared to excel or be excelled, sought to be a mirror of his twin, sacrificing his individuality, and considering himself feminine and castrated. This man complained that his chronic dilemma was whether he was a half person or a whole person. Demarest and Winestine (1955) found the necessary focus of treatment in the five-year-old twins they reported to be the children's inability to differentiate themselves from each other and from the mother. Cronin (1933) describes adult identical twins in whom the lack of differentiation was outstanding. They experienced greater love for each other than for any other person. One was assertive and masculine, and the other passive and feminine. They had not only shared their mother, but had sexually shared the maid who had helped raise them, and then lived in a polyandrous relationship with a woman legally married to one of them. Joseph (1959) analyzed an identical twin who had a passive, feminine orientation but who took the initiative in performing fellatio on his brother. When he separated from his twin, he sought to assuage his loneliness by lying in bed and gazing in a mirror, imagining the image to be his twin.

CASE PRESENTATION

We can present only a small fragment of our data, and will seek to utilize illustrative examples symbolic of the family situation in lieu of completeness.

Peter Nebb was admitted to the hospital from college at the age of twenty. He had been unable to study, feeling incomplete and lost without his twin, being preoccupied with a ritualistic means of controlling himself, and expressing paranoid beliefs about a former homosexual partner. He was confused, and suffered from ill-defined states of "dissociation" when he would "become another person," dress as a bum and wander the streets. His younger identical twin, Philip, became intensely upset when Peter was hospitalized. Having been dependent upon Peter who was his ideal, he felt that he verged on becoming acutely psychotic. His talk was driven and disorganized, and his projective tests appeared schizophrenic in many respects. Transvestite homosexual activity had increased markedly following his brother's hospitalization. However, with the help of intensive psychotherapy Philip managed to avoid a clear-cut psychotic break, and was able to remain at home.

We must turn back to the preceding generation in our effort to understand these twins. The mother was also a twin, a fraternal twin who from birth had never matched her vigorous, attractive, and dominant sister, probably because a dysplastic habitus gave her a peculiar appearance. Although she had envied and hated her twin, she was nonetheless strongly attached to her and either saw her or spoke with her on the telephone almost every day throughout her life. Her sister had been openly favored by the parents. When their mother had become a chronic invalid, they had withdrawn Mrs. Nebb from school to take over the household chores and raise an infant brother named Philip, whereas they encouraged her sister to finish high school and gave her many advantages. Mrs. Nebb turned her energies toward grooming her brother to become a great man. She prided herself on his every achievement, enforcing strict and rigid discipline while prodding him onward—only to become bitterly disappointed when, after making a brilliant record in college, he became an alcoholic ne'er-do-well. The brother's failure was a serious blow to Mrs. Nebb which affected her conscious attitudes in rearing her twins.

Mrs. Nebb identified with her father who had kept a general store in a rather remote mountain community and dispensed patent medicines to the local inhabitants who came to him for medical advice. She became a practical nurse, and eventually a registered nurse. Her access to the homes of some wealthy families fanned a consuming determination to acquire higher social status for herself. She worked successfully as a nurse until she was almost forty years old, when her twin sister became engaged to a wealthy man. Mrs. Nebb, who had previously never considered marriage, now set about finding a husband for herself, and, according to her own statement, deliberately corralled her husband, five years younger than herself, in order to have a double wedding with her twin sister. Although Mr. Nebb was a competent and friendly man, he was extremely shy and passive. He had never gone out with women before and, in general, behaved like a stepchild who must remain in the background and placate women. Indeed, his mother had died when he was born and he was raised by a foster mother whom his father later married. He became a reasonably successful real-estate broker, but never aspired to the renown of his father, a professor of literature, or to the eminence of his older brother in the business world.

Following the draw in finding husbands, competition now turned to efforts to produce twins. The sister "led two children to one" when Mrs. Nebb triumphed by giving birth to twins. From that moment on, the twins were her glory and the focus of her life and, because of her domination of the home, the focus of the family life. The story of the birth of the twins became a family legend: Peter had kicked Philip out of the way and into a breach position, which required a prolonged delivery for Philip. The story contained the implication that Peter, as a fetus, had deliberately displaced his twin to gain priority. Whatever the reasons that made Peter more aggressive, the birth set a pattern. Peter was preferred by his mother and from the start was more aggressive, more daring, and more charming—like Mrs. Nebb's sister. Philip, on the other hand, was more docile and passive like Mrs. Nebb herself. Whether Peter was selected because he was more aggressive, or became more aggressive because he was selected, cannot be determined.

The twins belonged exclusively to the mother, and the family was consequently divided into two groups: the father and oldest son, comprising the outgroup, were supposed to adjust to the primary purpose of raising the extraordinary twins to live out their full capacities. Mrs. Nebb let the twins know that because of her pain at their birth and her sacrifices for them, they must never leave her. They were her indirect means of surpassing her twin.

Mrs. Nebb insisted that the twins were geniuses whose activity must not be inhibited by any restrictions. She believed she had failed with her brother because she had been punitively controlling, and she would succeed with the twins by using obverse methods. She categorically eschewed any discipline, but she was nonetheless extremely controlling and intrusive in other areas, particularly in all matters that threatened her serious phobia concerning contamination. This applied to bowel habits, bathing, food fads, and abhorrence of animals, where any breach in the practices she dictated produced severe rebuff. She had banished her husband from her bedroom and bathroom when he had a mild transient fungus infection of the groin, and thereafter he could only use the basement lavatory. The older brother and father were labeled "dirty," and the brother "dirty-minded" for refusing to let mother bathe him and examine his stools after he was fourteen.

The twins were raised as a unit. They were dressed identically until nine or ten, and they were practically indistinguishable in appearance. Often they were not differentiated by the parents, and both were punished or praised for the deeds of one. Further, Mrs. Nebb had trouble differentiating their needs from her own: the twins were part of her, and her relationship to them was shaped by her own problems which predisposed her to treat the twins as phallic extensions of herself. Often, when she was ill and received medicine, she also gave it to the twins. At one time, the boys could not keep awake in school, and learned that Mrs. Nebb had been placing the sedative she had received for herself in their breakfast food. They were both bowel trained starting at three months. Suppositories and enemas were liberally used, and enormous amounts of parental affect and energy were concentrated on bowel functions. Later, indeed until late adolescence, mother would give both twins enemas together, often because one was angry with her, which meant to her they were constipated. The enemas were administered according to a ritual in which both boys lay naked on the floor, and mother lubricated their anuses with her finger and inserted the nozzles with water as hot as they could stand. The twin more dilatory in getting into position would have to dash to another floor to the toilet. She continued to bathe them and to wash their genitals until they were fifteen. The mother constantly praised the twins to her friends and strangers and asked them to perform for guests. Friends were often amazed to learn that Mrs. Nebb had another son.

Already in their preschool years, they gained the reputation of pint-sized terrors. They had to be withdrawn from kindergarten because Peter, in particular, was an exasperating behavior problem. They found that they could feign asthma (a disease from which they suffered intermittently after the age of three) to gain their way or be left alone; and before long they learned that mother would believe any story they made up to please or circumvent her. The twins were virtually always together, sharing thoughts, and had secret ways of jabbering that conveyed "I love you most," which they did not say outright. Mother discouraged other playmates, and later she frowned on girl friends. The twins shared interests, hobbies, and pranks. Together they dared much, for there were two of them. Still, there was a profound difference between them, for Peter was the leader and initiator of trouble, while Philip loyally followed his ideal. At six or seven, Philip stabbed a boy who had attacked Peter, thus proving his loyalty. Philip often felt intensely anxious and fearful of the dangers that Peter's behavior brought. He took to religion, praying that Peter would be good. During treatment he recalled that he had been frightened by thoughts of killing Peter and had changed "kill" to "kiss" in childhood obsessive rituals.

Each twin, then, related to his mother and co-twin in an interconnected manner. Peter was the phallic, acting-out aggressor identified with his mother's twin, and Philip was more identified with the mother's passive, feminine, and devalued castrated aspects, and they assumed similar roles with each other. They complemented each other, with Philip ceding the masculine role to Peter. They were rivalrous for mother, but sought to gratify different aspects of her needs. In accord with this role division, Peter concentrated on the task of carrying out action with a relative impoverishment of his inner life, while Philip specialized in internal elaboration of experience, both affective and ideational, and was inclined to be the passive spectator.

Mrs. Nebb not only systematically abjured setting controls and limits herself, but, in addition, undermined her husband's sporadic efforts at discipline. By her scorn of his actions and by her contempt for him, she let the twins know that they could disregard their father. Still, when they were young, he would occasionally fly into a fury and beat the boys who were then terrified. Even when the boys were in college she encouraged them to disregard their father and even her own authority. She would try to get her way in the home by having hysterical "fits" and spells of uncontrolled crying. When Philip was in college he took it upon himself to stop her outbursts by taking her over his knee and spanking her. Once, when Mr. Nebb tried to interfere with a spanking, Mrs. Nebb abruptly stopped shrieking, told him to mind his own business, and ordered Philip to continue to spank her and then started to scream again.

When the twins were nine, they precipitated a major family crisis. Peter, fascinated by fire since the age of four, started a fire in some hay and blocked Philip's attempts to extinguish it. The fire spread, burning down a nearby barn. Soon they were involved in more serious troubles. Peter broke into a boarding house vacated for the winter, and formed a gang which systematically ransacked and vandalized the place. Peter was incriminated by the police as ringleader, and although Mrs. Nebb continued to deny that her twins were involved despite their confessions, the boys were ostracized. The episode with the involvement with the police remained a serious trauma to the boys despite Mrs. Nebb's negation of it. These events at least contributed to the family's move from the mountain resort to a metropolis, though Mrs. Nebb still insists that they moved only to afford the twins the superior education they required. Mr. Nebb, for valid business and social reasons, refused to move, and arguments extended to threats of separation. However, it was Mr. Nebb's last stand, and after he finally capitulated, he ceased trying to assert himself concerning family decisions and the control of the twins.

In the city, the twins seemed to settle down. Their interests focused on scientific experiments. They were good students but had little to do with others, even refusing to eat lunch in school as was customary. During this period, Philip had his first sexual contact when he masturbated with another boy, which shocked Peter when Philip told him of it.

When, as small boys, they had first asked their mother about female genitalia, she answered as directly and openly as she could—by pulling up her skirt to illustrate her explanation. Still, Philip recalled, he continued to think that she had a penis hidden somewhere. The mother's overt seductiveness continued after the twins reached adolescence. She not only examined each bowel movement, continued the enema routine, bathed them, and often displayed herself naked before them, but she would get into bed with them until they were fifteen. When Peter made a visit home from the hospital and was trying to converse seriously with his father, which was a new interest and experience for him, Mrs. Nebb, unable to intrude and gain his attention despite various ruses, finally came into the living room naked in her effort to regain her son's favor.

The break in the twins' symbiotic existence came at fourteen when, sent to a boarding school, they were placed in widely separated dormitories. Peter's aggression toward Philip came to the surface in a shattering rejection of Philip as he sought to rid himself of his alter ego. Peter, using his charm and unbridled imagination, soon became the center of an admiring group from which he actively excluded his twin. When Philip also sought to gain prestige by fabricating stories, Peter exposed his lies and Philip was ridiculed. Philip who had always been loyal, felt betrayed and abandoned. Presently, he found a homosexual boy and became the passive partner of a pair who embraced and played with each other even in the presence of other boys. Philip was generally regarded as a "queer" and became an outcast. He was dropped from school at the end of two years ostensibly because of poor grades, but his overt homosexual behavior was, at least, equally important. Transferred to another school, Philip immediately formed a firm homosexual relationship with his new roommate and started to practice various perversions aside from mutual masturbation.

During their last summer vacation in boarding school, the twins went on a camping trip together with Philip's homosexual partner. Within a short time, Peter, who had not been overtly homosexual until then, sought to insert himself between his twin and his friend. His triumph became clear when he and the other boy went to bed together naked in Philip's presence. Philip cried inconsolably and the trip ended precipitously.

Peter's hostile acts did not disrupt their close relationship. Philip behaved like a rejected but adoring suitor, well aware that his homosexual attachments were substitutes for the relationship with Peter. The development of the homosexual defense against disorganization following the loss of his cardinal object relationship occurred relatively early in adolescence and was, in a sense, not ego-alien to Philip. Very early in childhood he had accepted the role of a passive partner who was incomplete without his twin, and, much as a wife might, lived to augment and complete Peter's life.

Philip did not gain admission to as select a college as Peter did and he attended college in his home city. Without Peter around, the family found Philip to be pleasant, considerate, and quiet. He assumed a more parental role in the family, making decisions for his indecisive parents, and taking a firm hand with his mother. However, he began to dress himself as a girl and admire himself in the mirror, wishing and wondering whether he were developing breasts. He had thoughts that perhaps he might have female internal genitalia. He began to roam the streets dressed as a girl, or as a bum, to be picked up by men and willing "to do anything," to be kissed by them. When his twin became psychotic, such behavior not only became a dominating compulsion, but he insisted on telling his father (and as soon as possible, Peter) every sordid detail of his homosexual experiences. Several interesting motivations for these needs emerged in therapy.

While the twins' rivalry for their mother had been intense in early childhood, Philip had ceded her to Peter, needing and fearing Peter and identifying with him. As his father was a devalued and castrated figure whom the mother did not want as much as she did Peter, Philip's oedipal conflict revolved about his twin and mother as much or more than the parental relationship. With Peter away at college, the major figure that prevented recrudescence of his incestuous attachment was out of the way. He warded off his incestuous impulses and his castration fears by becoming a transvestite—a phallic woman and thereby denied the absence of a penis in the woman. Peter's collapse threatened his entire integration. When his mother now turned to Philip for completion, his fears heightened to verge upon panic. He not only feared Peter's wrath, but with Peter no longer mother's favorite, Peter no longer stood between him and fears of castration by the displaced father. He now had a great need to demonstrate to both his father and to Peter that he was a girl and had no designs upon his mother. The understanding of the transvestite, homosexual behavior also requires recognition of his wish to be a girl—in a continuing identification with his mother and as a complementary mate for Peter to retain their unity. During treatment he had a dream, which he interpreted as a wish to tell his twin: "You do not have to castrate me. I can hide my penis and be a wife to you." The failure to achieve a masculine identity was abetted because his father was a devalued figure, unwanted by the mother. The wish to be a girl led to fantasies of having female sexual organs that verged on the delusional.

Although Peter's difficulties and symptoms were similar to Philip's in many respects, they contained critical differences. Peter finished prep school with high academic and athletic honors and was fulfilling his mother's ambitions. He selected a college distant from home because of its prestige, but also to place distance between himself and his mother whose sexual seductiveness troubled him. He took with him to college a ventriloquist's dummy which he had learned to manipulate with unusual skill. He was a competent ventriloquist and amused his classmates by putting on "acts." The dummy was not consciously a substitute for Philip, but when it made him popular, as he had wished, he became jealous, destroyed it, and then grew lonely without it. He concentrated on gaining popularity, and his grades were poor. More serious difficulties started in his second year. With increasing frequency he suffered from "tension periods" which he sought to master by a system of ritualistic thinking combined with breathing and muscle control. He sought the correct mathematical formula for his system rather than questioning its validity. Masturbation became compulsive to gain relief from tension. He felt incomplete without Philip. At times he would sit in the library next to some boy who resembled Philip. While Philip had started his transvestite wandering, Peter, too, would wander about dressed as a bum—but he could never clarify this behavior and did not know why he pursued it. Some time during the year, he started a homosexual relationship with another boy named Peter.

During a school vacation Peter and his partner, Peter, took a long trip together with a third boy. In a striking repetition of the earlier vacation when Peter had stolen Philip's partner, the third boy took the homosexual partner away from him and now Peter was in Philip's position. He probably had been attempting to identify with Philip by selecting a partner named Peter, and loving the boy as he needed Philip's love, even as some homosexuals seek to love boys as they wish their mothers to love them. Following the rejection he now became paranoid toward his former boy friend, believing the boy was trying to destroy him. The classic pattern—I love him . . . I do not love him . . . I hate him because he persecuted me—was resounding against his own destructive behavior toward Philip, and his ambivalence toward his twin whom he was trying not to need and love (Freud, 1922).

We can discuss only certain critical problems confronting Peter. He emphasized his search for a substitute for his mother, his flight from her seductive wiles, and his terror of all women as overpowering and engulfing. Drawings made during his psychosis showed women with biting mouths and dentate vaginas, and intercourse as an anal-sadistic act. He felt lost with his twin at home pre-empting his mother's attention for the first time while he felt excluded and rejected by her admonitions that Philip was less selfish and self-centered. He was bitter toward his mother for basing her existence upon him, and he was contemptuous of his father. Heterosexuality was filled with terror for him, and homosexuality was not sufficiently ego syntonic with his previous dominant exhibitionistic and phallic trends. In contrast to Philip, Peter was not burdened by severe castration threats from his twin or his father. The greater danger remained preoedipal—of incorporation by the mother and loss of identity by remaining her phallus. The castration threat, one might say, came primarily from women—a fear that had strong roots in the reality of his relationship with his strange mother.

The twins' intrapsychic configuration differed at the time they became ill. Philip had attained a defensive equilibrium—albeit a highly tenuous, pathological, and dangerous one—through his feminine identification and transvestite role that neutralized the dangers from both parents and his twin, though it required compulsive acting out. Peter, however, struggled with a dilemma common in adolescents who become schizophrenic. He found himself a part of his mother, and the burden of achieving success to complete her life and her phallic strivings weighed heavily upon him. He was supposed to be a man and yet remain part of a woman. He was struggling for an identity discrete from her, and in this case from his twin as well. His mother's seductive behavior made him fearful of losing control of himself, and he feared being near her—and for similar reasons of being close to Philip. Now his mother's reversal in turning from him to Philip undermined the worth of his more masculine identity. He felt betrayed, and murderous impulses mingled with the incestuous, creating panic over loss of ego control. Needing constant admiration to support his failing narcissism, he regressively felt the need for his twin's adulation—and attempted to find a homosexual solution. The restitutive maneuver failed when he was rejected, even as he had rejected his twin. The rejection of his love was destroying him.

There were quite obviously many other important aspects in the family dynamics. Anality played an unusually prominent role in his family—but in this paper we cannot discuss the influence of the mother's sadistic and intrusive anal assaults on her twins upon their development of passive, homosexual, and masochistic fantasies.

While the basic problems of these twins are very much alike, we wish to emphasize the critical differences between them and how they seem to be clarified by the twins' positions in the family configuration. Raised as a unit and as rivals for their mother, they could not occupy the same space or role in the family, and established a complementarity by sharing the space. The nature of the pattern which evolved was greatly affected by the way in which mother identified them and reacted emotionally to them. Peter, because of birth priority, his greater constitutional vigor, or his phallic name, came to be preferred by the mother and identified with her aggressive, envied twin sister. Through him she would live out the dominant, aggressive role to which she had always aspired. Mother deliberately led both twins to be rebellious against authority, to consider themselves beyond rules, and to ignore their father. Without counteracting sources of a positive paternal identification, Peter was phallic, grandiose, antisocial, constantly needing admiration, and when excluded by his twin and his mother, became homosexual in the pattern of seeking a boy to love as he wished to be loved. Philip, in contrast, identified by mother with herself, represented the passive and feminine aspects she despised in herself. In this role he could complement Peter, repress his own hostility, and lean upon him for leadership. He relinquished his mother to Peter and thus protected himself from her engulfment and Peter's hostility, and he could retain Peter as a love object. In his fantasies he was a girl, and his transvestite homosexuality was ego syntonic and protective. Philip's safety depended, however, upon having Peter about as mother's favored object, and with Peter psychotic, Philip was in danger. Both twins, then, were still part of their mother, but each was identified with a different aspect of her, which, in turn, permitted a symbiotic ego structure between the twins.

We have, in this presentation, neglected the older brother of the twins. His situation was difficult and unenviable —rejected by his mother who wished to use him as she did the father as a pawn in preparing the way for her twin kings. He did not escape unscathed and had serious emotional problems, but his rejection by his mother made it easier for him to accept his hostility toward his obnoxious brothers and to differentiate from them and his bizarre mother. He was identified with the father who, despite the mother's opinion, had some positive values and at least a relatively stable integration.

Discussion

Certain problems in ego development confronting identical twins, particularly those raised as a unit, noted in the review of the literature are clarified by this study. Perhaps, they stand in sharp relief because of the pathology of this family, including the mother's efforts to compensate for her own ego deficiencies arising from her own development as a twin.

1. Identical twins seem disposed to develop symbiotically without adequate ego boundaries between them. Initially, at least, each has difficulty in differentiating his own behavior, thoughts, and wishes from those of his twin. The developing ego also responds to needs and drives in the twins as well as within the self. Whereas every child must differentiate the self from the mother, such twins have the additional problem of differentiating from the co-twin.

2. A primary object relationship is established with a person who is not different from a mirror image and with whom most experiences are shared. Problems of narcissism become accentuated, and love of the object remains self-love. As the object reacts much the same as the self, it becomes more

difficult to differentiate the internal motive from the external, and, in a sense, reality from fantasy. Relating to other persons less empathic than the twin is hindered or blocked. The narcissistic object choice imposed upon the child would seem to heighten homoerotic trends.

3. No matter what efforts are made to treat twins as one person, and this case forms a rather extreme example, they cannot be one, and differentiation and separation are inevitable, however painful or unwelcome they may be. In the effort to occupy a single place within the family and particularly with the mother, a complementarity develops. The twins divide roles. One is apt to become more dominant and the other more passive. In our example, we have indicated that the role relations established by the mother and with her also patterned the complementary roles of the twins with each other, and they each identified with different aspects of the same mother. Here, as in many other twins, the initial rivalry for the mother led to hostility between the twins, which was resolved by the passive twin ceding to the aggressive twin, thus gaining security by denying masculinity, but furthering the passive homosexual attachment and aborting resolution of the oedipal conflict. The hostility is repressed but reappears in jealous rivalries when either twin forms a new relationship, because the bond to the co-twin remains narcissistic and symbiotic. It does not become a true object relationship like the affectional bond between father and son that occurs in an ideal resolution of the oedipal situation.

4. Because of identical or complementary expectations from parents, the sharing of the resolution of the oedipal situation, and the division of roles between them, the superego structure of each twin tends to remain incomplete. Behavioral standards and expectations for the self depend upon response of the twin rather than being properly incorporated as a self-controlling structure. Ego ideals may be followed that fit the partial identity of the twin, and a pattern that requires complementing by another.

We believe that the use of twins to study the etiology and

psychopathology of emotional disorders—which has focused largely upon genetic factors in the past—requires consideration of such special problems of ego development in twins and their ensuing vulnerabilities.

In closing, we wish to note that the problems of homosexuality and homosexual panic, linked with paranoid schizophrenia since Freud's study (1911) of the Schreber case, cannot be considered separately from problems of incest and incest panic, which often ushers in the schizophrenic break, or separately from the hypochondriacal delusions involving change in sex that Macalpine and Hunter (1953) stressed in their review of the Schreber case. Incest and homosexuality are often two sides of the same coin—narcissistic problems in which love of the self, love of someone undifferentiated from the self, and love of someone like the self are not clearly differentiated—but this interrelationship and its roots in the family interaction are the topic of another study (see Chapter X).

POSTSCRIPT

Conventional statistical comparisons of concordance rates of schizophrenia in monozygotic and dizygotic twins usually consider the environmental background to be similar for the twins whether mono- or dizygotic. The article serves to illustrate that monozygotic twins can have very special identity problems, and suggests that investigators such as Kendler (1983) who believe that familial and other environmental influences are the same for mono- and dizygotic twins are making an untenable assumption. However, the following chapter shows that dizygotic twins can sometimes behave very much as identical twins. Such differences can affect concordance figures. The article further demonstrates that even for identical twins who were raised together and whose environment was unusually similar, the intrafamilial influences affecting them were quite different, starting with their mother's identification of one with herself and the other with her dominant sister. Further, the division of roles between them led to notable differences in their personalities. Moreover, are these twins to be considered concordant or discordant for schizophrenia?

Similar questions arise concerning a schizophrenic monozygotic female twin treated by one of us. The patient was schizophrenic for several years, but her twin was flagrantly bisexually promiscuous, and in many ways less stable than the patient who before and after the several psychotic years was a highly competent professional, wife, and devoted mother.

Several studies have noted that the second-born twin with a lighter birth weight is the twin who is likely to become the passive member of the pair and, to a statistically significant degree, is more likely to become schizophrenic. Single case studies cannot counter such findings but in both of these pairs, it was the firstborn and more dominant twin who became schizophrenic.

XIV

Interrelated Schizophrenic Psychoses in Fraternal Twins

(1963)

The article on fraternal twins was not part of our study of the families of schizophrenic patients. Indeed, with both parents dead, our only informants were the psychotic twins. The article is included for comparison with the preceding chapter. Fraternal twins who did not resemble one another any more than siblings might were raised as if they were monozygotic twins and, indeed, continued to share a life together well into adult life, not even being separated in the military. Their school performance and aptitudes remained almost identical, and as has often been noted in monozygotic twins who became schizophrenic, the psychosis of the second followed closely on the psychosis of the first, and were clearly interrelated.

Although not emphasized in the article, these twins came from a seriously disturbed family. The father became an alcoholic vagrant who did not fill anything of a paternal role for his sons; the mother sought fulfillment through the achievements of her twin sons, and her early death fostered a marked interdependency between the sons that developed into a relationship akin to that of husband and wife, and neither could attain a sense of completion and stability without the other.

The onset of psychoses in both identical twins, often with a striking similarity in symptomatology, time of onset, and

D. Clint Smith and Theodore Lidz: Interrelated Schizophrenic Psychoses in Fraternal Twins. *Archives of General Psychiatry*, Vol. 10, 1964, pp. 423-430. Copyright © 1964, American Medical Association.

severity of illness is an impressive phenomenon that has often been recorded as common (Kallmann, 1946; Rosanoff et al., 1934; Slater, 1953), and occasionally described (Astrachan and Simon, 1963; Jacobs and Mesnikoff, 1961; Solomon and Bliss, 1956; Swanson, 1961; Weatherly and Deabler, 1954; Chapter XIII). We wish to report a similar occurrence in a set of fraternal twins who, despite differences in appearance, had been raised in a manner usual only among identical twins and who had continued to live syncytially until a few weeks before one became overtly psychotic at the age of 26.

Interest in schizophrenia in twins has until recently focused primarily upon the high concordance among identical twins in contrast to the lower concordance among fraternal twins and siblings. Luxenburger (1934), Rosanoff et al. (1934-1935), Essen-Moller (1941), Kallmann (1946), Slater (1953), and others have documented such findings. Kallmann reported the most distinctive difference, a concordance of 86 percent in identical twins in comparison with only 14 percent in fraternal twins and in siblings. Although the concordance rates for identical twins found by other investigators are considerably lower than those reported by Kallmann, they have been accepted as impressive evidence for a very strong hereditary factor in the causation of schizophrenia. However, careful scrutiny of the data has revealed some inconsistencies that require explanation. Alanen (1958) raised the pertinent question of why female dizygotic twins have a concordance rate for schizophrenia that is far higher than that for opposite-sexed twins, and which approaches rates for identical twins. Jackson (1960a) has noted various reasons why the findings cannot be accepted uncritically as evidence of a genetic determination of schizophrenia. Rosenthal (1959, 1960, 1961a, 1961b) in his systematic study of the twin literature pertaining to schizophrenia has progressively become less impressed by the evidence that had once been considered as virtually incontrovertible.

Concomitantly, a renewed interest among psychoanalysts in the psychology of twins has influenced the evaluation of twin studies of schizophrenia. Identical twins, because of their common genetic endowment, because they share the same parents at the same time, and because they often have more experiences in common than any other persons, provide a particularly favorable opportunity to compare the personality developments of two individuals. Various investigators have noted differences in the ego development and ego structure of a twin, particularly of an identical twin, from those of nontwins. Among the special problems confronting twins are the difficulties in achieving a sense of identity and an adequate self-image (Arlow, 1960; Burlingham, 1952; Joseph, 1961; Kolb, 1960; Leonard, 1961; Orr, 1941; Chapter XIII). Identical twins have the problem of differentiating from each other as well as from the mother. They tend to develop with inadequate ego boundaries between them. A primary object relationship is established with a mirror image with whom most early experiences are shared, and problems of narcissism become accentuated because love of a primary object is almost akin to self-love. The narcissistic object-choice heightens homoerotic tendencies. Intense rivalries are fostered by the need to share the mother but are usually repressed and balanced because of the need for the twin and the lack of clear differentiation of the twin from the self. In an effort to occupy a single space within the family and diminish conflict, a complementarity develops with the twins tending to divide roles. One is apt to be more dominant and the other more passive, and their identifications with different parents may accentuate this complementarity. The repressed hostility may reappear in jealous rivalries when either twin forms a new object relationship. Kolb (1960) considers that twins usually find one of two solutions for the twin relationship: the more common is an "inverted identification" which involves a mutual identification with the same person with repression of rivalrous hostility, and which leads to deficiencies of personal identity; less common is the "everted identification" in which each twin identifies with a different parent; but even with "everted" identifications strong libidinal ties continue to exist between the twins. Along with the sharing of roles, and because of the shared resolution of the oedipal situation, superego formation in each twin tends to remain incomplete, with behavioral standards and expectations for the self depending upon the response from the twin rather than upon a properly internalized means of self-control and self-direction (Chapter XIII). The use of twin studies in exploring the etiology of schizophrenia must take into account such problems of twinship as well as the common genetic endowment of identical twins.

These studies have emphasized that identical twins have much in common aside from their genetic endowment, and, further, that even the differentiation between the twins through different identifications, role assignments, and role assumptions often increases their interdependency because of the complementarity of the ego developments. Thus, if one twin becomes schizophrenic, the co-twin is apt to be highly vulnerable because a cornerstone of his integration has been shattered; a situation that is aggravated because intense anxiety is virtually unavoidable when the twin becomes ill with a condition considered to be hereditary.

The substantial evidence that the disturbed family environment in which schizophrenic patients grow up is highly important to the genesis of schizophrenia (Bowen, 1960; Fleck, 1960; Lidz and Fleck, 1960; Wynne et al., 1958) is not controverted by twin studies. The pathogenic influences of the disturbed family are apt to be very much alike for both twins. This is particularly so for identical twins, and more so for fraternal twins of the same sex than for fraternal twins of the opposite sexes (Alanen, 1958; Chapter IX).

Leonard (1961) has observed that whereas the mirror image similarity of identical twins creates difficulties in self-differentiation and the establishment of ego boundaries, the difficulties are usually overcome in the course of development unless heightened by one or more of several factors: the cultural attitude toward twins of dressing them alike, considering them as a unit, and promoting their unity; the parental attitude, including the narcissistic pride in having produced twins and the desire to emphasize the twinship; socioeconomic factors—"parents under economic stress are hard put to find time and energy to give twins individual attention," and leave the twins "to entertain each other" a great deal. She has also noted that relatively uneducated parents may accept the cultural attitude toward twins more readily and further emphasize the twin relationship.

In the case which we are reporting only the genetic identity and close physical similarity were lacking. The patients were born in a single birth, dressed and raised as a unit by a mother who accentuated their twinship. They were subjected to the same intrafamilial difficulties—parental conflict, the inadequacies of the father, the mother's rejection of the father, and her intense need for the twins to achieve. The loss of the father, the economic deprivation that left them to care for one another much of the time, and the premature loss of the mother led to accentuation of their dependence upon one another. Even though fraternal twins, they behaved more like identical twins than most identical twins, and their psychoses were more clearly interrelated than the psychoses of most identical twins.

The patients, Alan and Ben, are black male fraternal twins, the only children of poor parents. Alan was born a few hours before Ben in an otherwise uneventful birth. Alan was somewhat larger and remained so throughout childhood. They were always easily distinguishable; Alan reputedly looked much like his mother whereas Ben resembled the father.

The family life was marred by serious discord with frequent arguments between the parents over the father's excessive drinking and his inability to hold a job. When the twins were five years old, the mother left the father and the metropolis in which they had been living to return to her small home town in the South. The twins had no further direct contact with their father who continued to drink and eventually died on "skid row." The mother was an extremely ambitious and self-sufficient woman. She worked in a factory and her dominant interest in life was to promote the ultimate success of her twins. From their early years, she emphasized her expectation that they would achieve educational and social success. Even as children, the twins never doubted that they would complete college and enter a profession. The mother died when the twins were in early adolescence and they went to live with a maternal aunt. The twins withdrew somewhat from their peers and spent long periods together silently mourning for their mother.

The twins were dressed identically from birth and were always kept together. However, neither felt that they were treated identically by the mother, each reporting that she had favored the other. Alan believed that the mother had preferred Ben because he was smaller and weaker and protected him at Alan's expense. Ben considered that the mother favored Alan because he resembled her in appearance and personality. From first grade through college they attended the same classes, sitting in adjacent seats, and making essentially the same grades. In grade school they would often sign the other's name to homework and test papers. When they had to find part-time work in adolescence, they maintained their unity by finding a single job in which they could share the work and responsibility.

An active-passive role division became apparent following their mother's death. Alan assumed the more feminine role, identifying with his mother, and the role differentiation continued in adult life. Alan assumed all of the domestic duties and functioned as a mother and a wife, preparing meals, attending to the laundry, handling the day-to-day budget. However, in accord with the matriarchy in which they were raised, Alan, in his more feminine role, had more control and power in making decisions. The manner in which they balanced roles is of interest: Alan the older and stronger, identified with the strong mother whom he resembled, and took care of the more masculine younger brother, much as a wife might care for a husband. Although both were outstanding students, Alan always remained in second place scholastically—Ben finished first and Alan second in the class in high school; and in college Ben's average surpassed Alan's by less than one per cent.

Alan had his first homosexual experience in early adolescence, and continued to have sporadic homosexual relationships in response to feelings of intense loneliness. Ben insisted that his homosexual experience was limited to one encounter in college. Alan, however, reported that some of his homosexual partners told of previous homosexual experiences with Ben. In accord with Kallmann's (1952) findings (but in contrast to the twins studied by Joseph and Tabor [1961] and one of the cases reported by Arlow [1960]), there was no direct homosexual involvement between the twins.

Throughout two years of military service following their graduation from college, the twins maintained their closeness: they were assigned to the same unit and lived in the same quarters. They then entered the same graduate school and continued to live together and take the same courses. However, they now, for the first time, began to dress differently. Although Alan was the more actively homosexual, he also had more heterosexual experiences. During their first year in graduate school, Alan became engaged to marry. The academic performance of both twins then declined so seriously that they were dropped from school. Their failure surprised the faculty as well as the twins for they were intellectually capable and their academic achievement had previously been high. During the next few years they again tried and failed in a graduate school and worked at various jobs while continuing to live together.

Then, immediately preceding the onset of Ben's psychosis, they decided to separate, giving as their reason their concern that they were too close to each other. Later they indicated that Ben had become concerned over the homosexual attraction between them. At Ben's suggestion they separated to the extent of living on different floors in the same rooming house.

Within two weeks of the separation Ben became acutely

schizophrenic. It is, of course, possible that the separation followed the development of delusions. Alan arranged for Ben's admission to a psychiatric hospital. Ben had been hearing voices and expressed a variety of paranoid ideas. Two delusions were prominent: that various people were accusing him of having an affair with a woman who lived in their rooming house; and that he could communicate with anyone by thought waves. Ben's agitation gradually subsided but he remained very delusional. Attempts at psychotherapy helped little, and he was given a course of insulin coma therapy which brought some improvement. He remained in the hospital for approximately two years, and then with the help of tranquilizing drugs and supportive psychotherapy found and maintained employment.

Alan visited his brother every day during the first year of Ben's illness, and in his contacts with the hospital personnel did not appear disturbed. However, during his own therapy Alan told that at the time of Ben's hospitalization, he had become convinced that he possessed supernatural power. He believed that Ben would die unless he intervened in some magical way and he had felt that the daily visits were essential to keep his brother alive. In contrast to his former pattern of sporadic homosexual contacts with a variety of partners, Alan now established an intense and prolonged homosexual relationship in which he behaved as a wife to an older man. He found it difficult to maintain his usual level of functioning, lost his job, and subsisted on welfare payments. The tenuous adaptation to his twin's illness and their enforced separation lasted for almost a year until Ben refused to permit Alan to visit him. Alan later explained that he had taken his homosexual partner to meet his twin and suggested that Ben have an affair with this man. Ben became infuriated, denounced Alan, and told him to leave and never return. Within a few days, Alan became overtly psychotic and was hospitalized on the psychiatric ward of a general hospital but was little improved after several months when discharged. A friend persuaded him to enter another hospital located some distance from his home. Upon admission, Alan complained, "I am not sure who I am." He had hallucinations that people were calling him a homosexual, and he, too, believed that he could communicate with anyone by thought waves, and that everyone was reading his mind. He believed that he could have sexual intercourse with any woman he desired without physical contact. He considered himself on a higher plane than other people, which extended to the concrete delusional idea that he was not on earth but in outer space with a blond, blue-eyed wife. At times he believed that he was white, and, at other times, that people shunned him because he was black. He was frequently acutely disturbed during his first weeks in the hospital. He was placed on tranquilizing medication, and soon began to discuss his problems. Only a few points about his psychotherapy will be mentioned.

During the first six months, Alan always used the pronoun "we" and discussed various events in terms of how they affected "us," with most of the material concerned with the twins' interaction as a unit with the environment. At the end of this period he began to use the pronoun "I" and concomitantly to explore some aspects of his relationship with his twin. Alan made substantial progress over the next year and began to make plans to leave the hospital. He was markedly uncertain of his ability to get along without Ben and worried that his twin might be unwilling to re-establish their former close relationship. He obtained an interesting job and worked at it while still living in the hospital. When he was offered a permanent position with the firm, he used his therapy hours to discuss the feasibility of accepting work in a city distant from Ben at the expense of separation from his twin. He discussed his subservience to Ben and to the twinship and appeared to be resolving some problems in these areas, but when pressed for a decision concerning the job, became acutely disorganized and delusional for several weeks. A few months later Alan began to press for discharge, and it developed that he felt that he must leave the hospital for he had now been hospitalized as long as his brother. In the ensuing few months as termination of hospital care was dealt with, the importance of being identical with his twin became increasingly evident. His plans for discharge and living outside the hospital were strikingly similar to those his brother had followed. The issue of separation from Ben was not resolved but settled by the compromise of living in the same city and working at a job as similar to his twin's as possible.

COMMENT

The possibility that these patients' schizophrenic psychoses were dependent upon a common genetic factor is not excluded because they are fraternal rather than identical twins; but the unusual concordance in time of onset, symptoms, duration, and the dynamic interrelationships cannot be readily attributed to hereditary factors.

These twins were raised as a unit in a manner usual only with identical twins, and maintained their syncytial existence in adult life to an unusual extent. Almost all of the phenomena that various investigators have emphasized as characteristic of identical twins who are reared as a unit are found in these brothers, aside from the effects of physical identity. We wish to discuss briefly their (1) complementarity, (2) joint identity, (3) inability to tolerate separation, (4) homosexuality, and to relate these problems to their symptomatology.

1. Role Complementarity.—In filling one place within the family and sharing the mother at the same time, twins often manage the inevitable rivalries and the ensuing hostilities by developing complementary roles. The complementarity can be reached in many ways, but usually one is more dominant and masculine, and the other more passive and feminine. Kolb (1960) states that in males, the twin identified with the father becomes dominant and masculine. The division of roles and functions tends to direct towards incomplete ego development in both twins. In this instance Alan was designated as resembling the mother, and Ben the father. Alan established a feminine identification, and, perhaps, because the mother had to be away at work when the children were small and died when they were still dependent, assumed a maternal role towards Ben. As they grew older the relationship became more of a wife-husband relationship. In contrast to the anticipated relationship between gender roles and dominance, Alan was more dominant and directive probably because of the pattern of their parents and because a mother is directive of a child. Yet, potential rivalry was diminished because in accord with their gender roles, Alan ceded Ben the prerogative of being the better student.

2. *Joint Identity*.—The formation of a joint identity in these fraternal twins was furthered by the mother's emphasis on their twinship, her attempt to diminish their differences as indicated by dressing them identically, and the tendency to regard them as a unit ("the twins") rather than as individuals. To these factors was added the twins' dependence upon one another when left alone at an early age while the mother worked and later after the mother's death. The mother's ambition for them as a unit which they jointly internalized as an abiding directive tended to differentiate and isolate them from their peers. As happens with identical twins, they appear to have depended upon one another for maintenance of direction—the superego was combined or the approbation of the twin partly replaced an internalized superego. As they shared life experiences, to an extent that could be surpassed only by Siamese twins, they could follow each other's mental associations. To any similarity in genetic constitution, a more apparent similarity of life experiences was added. Ego boundaries remained incomplete and tenuous. Each was responsive to the other's needs as well as his own. Alan habitually used the plural "we" during his first months in the hospital and was perplexed by the problem of "Who am I?" which had never confronted him before. The identity problem prior to his brother's rejection of him had been "Who are we?" even as they had always asked "What will we become?"

3. *Inability to Tolerate Separation*.—We know of only two threats to the twins' syncretistic existence. The first occurred

in graduate school when Alan became engaged to marry and was followed in short order by a sharp decline in their studies which led to a requested resignation from the school. The second was initiated when Ben became disturbed by the intensity of the relationship and the homosexual attraction. Ben became overtly psychotic, and Alan developed the delusional concern that Ben would die unless he visited him daily. Alan felt responsible for Ben's life—one might surmise as a reaction formation to repressed hostilities, but also as an outgrowth of his desperate need to preserve the twin who was an essential part of him. A third separation was contemplated when Alan was offered a permanent job that would require him to live in a different city than his twin. He could not work through the problem which disrupted his psychotherapy and led to an acute relapse into flagrant psychosis.

4. *Homosexuality.*—Little is known about homosexuality in twins in general, but according to virtually all reports, those twins studied because of psychotic or severe neurotic difficulties have had strong homosexual tendencies. The problem is being studied by Kolb (1960) and his associates (Mesnikoff et al., 1963). Little is known about Ben's homosexuality other than that he had one such experience during adolescence. Alan's reports about his twin's homosexuality cannot be considered reliable. It seems evident that for Ben, who was identified with the father and filling the male role, homosexuality was ego-alien and had to be repressed or rejected. The threat of homosexual involvement with his twin appears to have forced attempts at separation and may have precipitated his psychosis. Alan, who identified with his mother and behaved as the female, could integrate his homosexuality better. He appears to have experienced loneliness more intensely, perhaps because he was mothering his twin rather than being mothered following the pattern of treating another boy as he longed to be treated. It became evident during his psychotherapy that his homosexual partners were at the same time substitutes for his twin and a means of defending against his homosexual cravings for his twin. When Ben was hos-

pitalized, Alan started his only prolonged homosexual affair, seeking to find a needed substitute object. In suggesting that Ben have an affair with his own homosexual partner, Alan was attempting to institute a homosexual relationship with Ben through an intermediary: perhaps, as part of his idea that he must sustain Ben's life. It is analogous to the twins reported by Cronin (1933), who lived in a polyandrous relationship with the wife of one twin. Such attempts to create substitute twin relationships through homosexuality have been described and discussed in papers previously cited (Solomon and Bliss, 1956; Chapter XIII). In a sense, the effort to have a sexual relationship through an intermediary does not differ greatly from Alan's delusional idea that he could have sexual intercourse without physical contact. It is also of interest that during the initial phases of their psychoses, Alan heard people calling him a homosexual, whereas Ben thought people were accusing him of having an affair with a girl. Each was hallucinating what the other twin objected to, an extrojection that punished for seeking a relationship that would disrupt the twins' interdependence upon one another—the hallucinations serving to control drive impulses when the ego was ambivalent.

SUMMARY

A pair of fraternal twins who were raised as a unit and who maintained to an unusual degree the type of syncytial relationship usually found only among identical twins, were hospitalized with interrelated schizophrenic psychoses. Although genetically different, their life experiences were unusually similar, and their development and self-structures were such as have been described in identical twins—without adequate ego boundaries, with a joint identity, but sharing roles and functions according to male and female identifications, exclusion of object relationships external to the twinship, and an inability to tolerate separation; defective superego structure; and homosexual strivings toward the twin.

The occurrence of psychoses in fraternal twins that were as similar and interrelated as any reported in identical twins helps elucidate the dynamics of psychoses in identical twins.

POSTSCRIPT

As with the identical twins discussed in the preceding chapter, homosexuality and homosexual incest were major developmental problems for these fraternal twins reared as identical twins. Here the younger twin became psychotic first, but it is of interest that the older twin had ceded to him a slight superiority in school as well as in other matters. We surmise that when orphaned, the older twin took on the functions of the stronger parent, the mother, as well as her feminine nurturant functions toward his younger twin, and perhaps, continued to transmit her ambitions for him.

The actual or feared threat of the loss of the twin to a homosexual or heterosexual partner clearly formed a major trauma, and indeed, a precipitant of psychoses in these twins much as for the identical twin described in the preceding chapter. In contrast, however, the onset of the schizophrenic psychosis in the female identical twin mentioned in the postscript to the preceding chapter, may have been precipitated by the intrusion of her twin into her marriage, perhaps through seduction of her husband, that disrupted her lifelong efforts to be distinctive from her twin.

The study indicates, or at least suggests, that the nature of the twinship—how the twins relate to one another as well as the family environment—and not simply zygosity influences concordance rates for twins.

XV

The Limitations of Extrafamilial Socialization

(1964)

The topic of the child's socialization beyond the family is of considerable importance to studies of the etiology of schizophrenic conditions. Recognizing the autistic nature of the patients' thinking, their preoccupation with a fantasy world and a turning away from reality, various investigators have explored the potentiality that as children and adolescents they have been relatively isolated and deprived of companionship. Most such studies have focused on a single factor such as the number of potential playmates in the area, the remoteness of the home, the oversolicitude of parents that kept a child from socializing activities, etc. The problem transcends matters of physical isolation. A question that, in a sense, pervades all chapters of this book concerns how well life within the family prepares the child to relate to other children, other families, to the school world, and the eventual capacity to live independently of the family of origin. It involves overcoming early childhood egocentric and family-centered ways and concepts, to know how to find one's way in the larger society, to be able to relate to others and understand their verbal and nonverbal communications including what people mean by what they say and do not say, as well as whether they mean what they say.

Every person assimilates experiences into schemata, many or most of which are started in early childhood and groups or assimilates experiences into categories. Each culture divides its ways of experiencing life into somewhat different categories, which, in a sense, is what different cultures are about. However, each family tends to

Theodore Lidz, Alice R. Cornelison, and Stephen Fleck. This paper was first published in the original edition.
Ezra Vogel's aid in surveying and analyzing the material is greatly appreciated.

327

*categorize somewhat differently from other families, differences that
are overcome to a greater or lesser extent for each individual by
socialization with people from other families, as well as by schooling.
The task of overcoming the more or less idiosyncratic family meanings
and ways of relating becomes difficult, and sometimes almost impossible, if the family ways are highly aberrant and/or if extrafamilial
relations are minimal. In a pluralistic society, at least, it is important
and perhaps essential for people to understand how persons with
different belief systems assimilate the same events or experiences to
different schemata, for example, that neighbors from different ethnic
and religious backgrounds may interpret events very differently.
Thus, the following chapter relates closely to Chapter VII on the
transmission of irrationality, and is very important to the development
of our theory of schizophrenic disorders.*

Although the family is the major influence upon the
emerging personality of its offspring, other individuals,
groups, and institutions not only implement the family by
carrying out various socializing functions, and exert a corrective influence by modifying the family idiosyncrasies, but
the child's attainment of an identity and a firm integration
depends upon gradually increasing extrafamilial involvements. As Wynne et al. (1958) commented, "Certain of the
needs and expectations of family members cannot normally
be fulfilled within the nuclear family, necessitating a meaningful participation in the larger society, and parents normally anticipate and facilitate such expression of the growing
child's experiences beyond the nuclear family." The child
must be so raised within the family that he becomes capable
of emerging from it, and his movement beyond the confines
of the family should be progressively fostered and encouraged as he matures. We wish to focus attention upon the
incapacities of the families with schizophrenic offspring to
promote such essential expansion of the child's horizons.

The influences of the extrafamilial world upon the child's
developing personality are, of course, legion. We wish, however, to draw attention to a few that interrelate closely with

the family processes. As G. H. Mead (1934) pointed out, the "self" forms in response to the attitudes of others, but these "others" must include more than the family members. After the child has found his place, role, and identity within the family, he begins to be a representative of his family. He has two names, a first name that places him within the family and a surname that defines him as a family member in relation to the remainder of society, and both contribute to his identity. Most children learn a great deal by spending time with the families of their friends and their parents' friends: their own parents and their own families take on definition by the comparisons thus afforded; and the idiosyncrasies concerning roles, meanings, and expressions of affect that exist in all families are modified by such associations. The nature of the transition through the oedipal phase which sets its indelible stamp upon the personality involves extrafamilial attachments. Whereas frustration of the eroticized attachment to the mother permits the turning of energies and attention to peer groups and learning, the converse also applies: the withdrawal of cathexis from the mother is aided by involvement with peer groups and the channeling of energies outside the family. Childhood groups play a major role in transmitting age-appropriate roles, skills, mores, and knowledge. The child remains within one family throughout the years of his immaturity, but he repeatedly shifts from one childhood subculture of his society to another, becoming apprentice, member, and then teacher in each, before moving on to repeat the cycle in a more advanced group. The peer group affords a background of shared experiences and value systems, common expectations, and ease of communication with others. Within such groups a child learns to fit into a society of peers, and finds himself evaluated and learns to evaluate himself on the basis of different attributes than those that gain approval or censure within the family. "Chum" relationships, as H. S. Sullivan (1946-1947) emphasized, are critical during latency and early adolescence. Having a "chum" contributes to the child's gaining a firm identity as a member of his sex; decreases his feelings of isolation when separating from his family; supplies an "alter ego" that helps withstand and modify both superego and id pressures; lessens feelings of unworthiness that sexual and aggressive impulses can foster; permits the sharing of problems that arise in relating to adults, etc.

The adolescent revolt against parental authority which is often essential in overcoming dependence strivings may be possible only when conformity to peer group standards supplies a stabilizing influence; and often the first moves toward intimacy with the opposite sex occur with the support and protective restraint afforded by the presence of other couples. The achievement of independence and identity as a mature adult depends not only upon the proper internalization of parental directives, but also upon the modification and alteration of the superego and ego ideals through the internalization of attributes of other objects and their ways of living.

Now, the extrafamilial socialization of schizophrenic patients has received some scrutiny in studies of the importance of social isolation in the etiology of schizophrenia, a consideration raised by Faris in 1934. Faris later attributed the isolation of the child who becomes schizophrenic to parental oversolicitude which promoted isolation from all but the intimates within the family and then led to "persecution, discrimination, or exclusion by children outside the family," and eventually to the child's withdrawal from a hopeless goal and the development of a "seclusive personality that is characteristic of schizophrenia" (Faris, 1944). Kohn and Clausen (1955) found that about one third of the forty-five schizophrenic patients they studied in contrast to only 4 per cent of the controls had been isolates at the ages of thirteen or fourteen. As two thirds of the patients seemed to have socialized reasonably well in early adolescence, isolation could not be considered to be a necessary precursor of schizophrenia. Further, they found "no evidence that the patients classified as isolates had different experiences in respect to

availability of playmates, childhood illness, residential mo-
bility, or parental restriction upon their activities or choice
of friends. They were not kept from social participation."
These investigators wonder why Faris seized upon isolation
as a crucial factor, since the questions of why the child was
rebuffed in the first place, and why he reacted so extremely,
seem more pertinent. An interpretation which they consider
more in harmony with their findings is "that as a result of
inadequacies in their social relationships both within and outside the family, certain individuals come to feel that they do
not belong . . . that is, they become alienated from their
peers. Under severe enough conditions, alienation may
lead . . . to isolation. But it need not. . . ." Isolation indicates
that the "individual's interpersonal difficulties [are] so great
[that he is] no longer capable of functioning in interpersonal
relations . . . how he got that way is not a question of social
isolation per se" (Kohn and Clausen, 1955).

We would agree that social isolation is a resultant of the
individual's interpersonal difficulties, but, as we have noted,
the isolation or alienation will, in turn, augment developmental problems. We must note, however, that Kohn and
Clausen's way of judging social isolation was rather inadequate, because the problem is far more complicated than the
presence or absence of fiends in early adolescence; moreover,
their judgments were based upon relatively meagre retrospective information.

The adequacy of a child's socialization within the family
cannot readily be separated from his extrafamilial socialization. The child's ease of movement beyond the family depends upon having a secure base from which he can venture
forth, the parents' abilities to foster autonomy, how well the
enculturation within the family prepares for living in the
society in which it exists, and the nature of the linkages of
the family to the outside world. The serious deficiencies of
the intrafamilial environments in which schizophrenic patients grow up have now been amply documented by ourselves and others. Children whose interpersonal relationships

and socialization processes within the family are deviant will have difficulties in relating to peers, teachers, and other adults. Playmates, for example, are apt to be ill at ease with a child whose behavior and ways of communicating are unpredictable and even exclude him from group participation. Many of the mothers foster separation anxiety either because of their difficulties in cathecting the children or because they project their own insecurities about caring for the child onto the child: serious school phobias are relatively common in children who later become schizophrenic. We wish, however, to turn from the handicaps imposed by faulty and eccentric intrafamilial nurturance and socialization to examine the many problems that arise from the family's alienation—the deficiencies of these families in relating as a group and as individuals to the extrafamilial environment and of fitting into the societal milieu.

Wynne and his coworkers (1958) noted that in some such families, "when there is a continual effort . . . to maintain pseudomutuality, the family members try to act as if the family could be a truly self-sufficient social system with a completely encircling boundary." This is one of many types of situations found within these families that created a barrier to the child's extrafamilial socialization. The divergent personalities, interests, and backgrounds of some of the spouses as well as intense conflicts between them made it difficult for some couples to have friends who were congenial to both. In some, the paranoid distrust of one or both spouses led to open discouragement of friendships. Some families were more or less isolated by cultural or social class incompatibilities with other families in the environs. Eccentricities and emotional disturbances of parents interfered with making or maintaining friends. As we did not study the community reactions to these families, we cannot examine the problem of how the community may have excluded these families from its social life. However, it seems very likely that other families and community groups may well have tended to withdraw from them because of these parents' eccentricities, deviant beliefs and mores, tendencies to be intrusive and enveloping, and because of a general difficulty in feeling at ease when associating with them. Attachments of some of these parents to their own families of origin were intense, and although such connections provided the children with associations beyond the nuclear family, they were of limited value because of the shared value systems of the extended family, and the intensely dependent attachment of one parent or the other to their relatives.

The various reasons for the relative social isolation of these families are, in a sense, outward extensions of the same factors that create the intrafamilial problems. We shall consider the impediments to forming relationships to other individuals, families, and groups created by (1) the psychopathology and idiosyncrasies of one or both parents; (2) the incompatibilities of the parents; (3) cultural and social factors. We shall then illustrate how the convergence of several factors in a family can create serious blocks to a child's opportunities for socializing.

THE PSYCHOPATHOLOGY OF PARENTS

The personality problems of one or both parents created difficulties for all of these families in several ways. People tended to withdraw from these parents because of their more or less unacceptable behavior, or simply because they found it difficult or unpleasant to maintain a relationship. Some parents sought to remain aloof and keep the family aloof because of paranoid feelings. Other family members avoided close relationships with outsiders because of shame over the peculiarities or inadequacies of the disturbed parent.

To establish and maintain a comfortable relationship, if not a friendship, most persons expect the other to be able to communicate meaningfully, to find a "distance" appropriate to the relationship, to behave sufficiently in accord with established mores to permit comprehension of their actions, and to be consistent enough to permit expectations to be realized. As over half of the patients had at least one parent who was schizophrenic or clearly paranoid, and still other parents were "near-schizophrenic" or "psychotic" characters who do not decompensate but confuse and perplex those with whom they live, it seems evident that such parents would have difficulty in forming firm relationships. Even psychiatrists and social workers found it difficult to remain with Mr. Newberg for an hour, listening to his incessant and driven talk and trying to follow his scattered concepts and descriptions of his "harebrained" inventions. He mistook friendly and polite interest in one of his schemes for serious commitment, and avoidance seemed the simplest way to escape involvement. Mrs. Benjamin, though pleasant enough much of the time, would speak in scattered fashion when under stress and provoke feelings of profound frustration by asking questions and then interrupting the start of any response with another question. Mrs. Newcomb seemed to believe that if someone disagreed with any of her unacceptable ideas, she could not have been understood and would rephrase and repeat the same idea.

The inability of a number of these parents to relate at a "proper distance" was very apparent. An overfamiliarity, particularly on the part of some fathers, caused people to be guarded with them. Mr. Thomas, a professor of education, told even the gas station attendants in the rural town in which the family lived about his wife's body odors and failures to maintain proper feminine hygiene. Mr. Benjamin would discuss his son's mental illness and hospitalization with strangers. Mr. Nussbaum repeatedly became involved in the personal affairs of his female clients, much beyond what was appropriate for his business, and in a similar vein repeatedly sought to involve the social worker in discussions of her life, and offered advice about situations that derived largely from his fantasies about her. When, for example, the social worker took the patient for a day's visit to the Nussbaum's home, Mr. Nussbaum made a number of "off-color" jests disregarding his wife's signals and displeasure and his daughter's embarrassment. When the Nussbaums learned that the worker could not see them for one week, they both erroneously assumed that she would be on vacation. They argued as to where she should spend the vacation and ultimately agreed that she should visit in their city and that she could stay in their daughter's room—neglecting their daughter's feelings about being displaced as well as remaining oblivious to the untoward familiarity they were displaying. When Mrs. Nebb's twin sons had difficulties soon after entering kindergarten, she visited to ferret out the cause, and soon took over the class from the astonished teacher in order to demonstrate how her sons should be drawn into the activities. We gained the impression that similar imperviousness to reactions to her intrusion into social groups led to her exclusion from them.

A number of parents, on the other hand, were "distant" setting a barrier of detachment between themselves and others. Even the two mothers whom we considered the most normal and clear thinking, Mrs. Lamb and Mrs. Newberg, conveyed an aloofness that was difficult to define, but which was apparent to acquaintances as well as to our staff. Further, undue intrusiveness is not incompatible with "detachment" because such intrusive parents are characteristically impervious to the individuality of others.

Paranoid distrust of outsiders not only fostered the isolation of some families, but also was taught directly to the children. Mrs. Schwartz who dominated the lives of her four sons and her passive and chronically depressed husband believed that her family was subjected to persecution similar to that which she had experienced in Poland during her childhood when relatives had been killed in pogroms. Mr. Grau explicitly warned his daughters against trusting any outsiders. He was particularly suspicious of Catholics, and forbade his daughters to go with their mother to church and later to date Catholic boys. Mr. Reading similarly distrusted outsiders, fearing that what people learned about the family would be used against them, and he specifically ordered his wife not to join the church sewing circle or any other social

organization. Both Mr. and Mrs. Dolfuss shared and conveyed to their children the belief that neighbors would not
wish to associate with them because they were Austrian and
enemy aliens during World War I. While there may have
been some truth in this belief many years ago, it seems unlikely that the community retained such attitudes. Mrs.
Narab, an overtly schizophrenic mother, believed that her
sons were in danger because of hatred for the ethnic group
to which they belonged.

Covert distrust was pronounced in the Lerner family where
family matters were concealed assiduously. The efforts to
hide the true state of the family finances and Mr. Lerner's
career failure required stringent limitations of social contacts.
Later, the disgrace of the daughter's mental illness had to be
hidden even more thoroughly because of the blow to Mrs.
Lerner's self-esteem. These attitudes not only served to isolate the family but also implied to the patient that failure or
weakness left a person extremely vulnerable. Such implicit
attitudes dominated many family transactions even though
the Lerners would deny having them.

Embarrassment and shame over the peculiarities of a parent or the family's way of life interfered with the formation
of friendships. Children are apt to feel ashamed of their
parents at some periods in their lives even under favorable
circumstances. In some of these families there were understandable reasons for a child to feel embarrassed. The
Thomas girls could not be but reluctant to have friends meet
their unkempt and confused schizophrenic mother whose
good qualities were not superficially apparent. Once, after
Mrs. Thomas visited her daughters at a fashionable boarding
school, a friend asked whether she was the family cook. The
situation was aggravated because Mr. Thomas expressed his
disgust with his wife but left his daughters in her care while
he found reasons to remain far from home much of the time.
The Grau girls would be embarrassed whenever they brought
a new acquaintance home because the parents, locked in a
struggle over the girls' religion, would cross-examine the

person about religion: if Protestant, Mrs. Grau showed her disapproval; if Catholic, Mr. Grau might make disparaging remarks. A number of other parents or parental couples could cause their children considerable embarrassment by their intrusiveness as well as because of their eccentricities or untoward behavior. Although the Lambs were almost unique in this series in having a very active social life, their son had ample reason to become embarrassed by his father's behavior: Mr. Lamb regularly disrupted social gatherings by his boisterous drunkenness, and was probably tolerated because of his wife and his business position; at the time his son became adolescent an affair with a neighbor created a scandal. When the Lambs entertained, he habitually insisted in a latently hostile manner that his shy and embarrassed son display his vocal talents to the guests.

PARENTAL INCOMPATIBILITIES

In order to form and keep friends and community relationships a couple must have some shared interests and tastes. In many cases the lack of any such common elements was striking. When, as in many of these families, their interests were in conflict, it became difficult to form friendships as a unit. We can somewhat arbitrarily group these problems under three headings: (1) incompatible interests and tastes; (2) inabilities of the spouses to relinquish attachments to their families of origin; (3) ethnic, religious, and social class discrepancies. However, the problem often could not be clearly separated out into these categories, for in many families serious emotional difficulties and conflicts between the spouses prevented bridging the gaps between them.

The Lerners each formed friendships or acquaintances in their careers which they did not or could not share because of their divergent interests and ideals. Mr. Lerner was a corporate attorney impressed by big industry and industrialists with whom he maintained business contacts and superficial friendships, whereas Mrs. Lerner was a social worker interested in social issues. Mr. Lerner was a conservative reactionary, whereas Mrs. Lerner tended to associate with and admire liberals. Their close relationships based on personal needs could be threatened by a mingling of their respective friends and associates. Further, after Mr. Lerner's professional failure, Mrs. Lerner could maintain the myth of having an eminently successful husband more easily if her socializing did not include her husband and entertaining at home.

The Robbs were even more clearly split by different political and social interests. Mrs. Robb came from a conservative Philadelphia "Main Line" family and felt at ease only among an exclusive social set, and she wished to raise her children as members of her group. Her husband had markedly liberal political tendencies which he tended to flaunt among her Republican friends. Although superficially the discrepancy might seem to involve differences in social status, in actuality, Mr. Robb also stemmed from an upper-class family against which he was in permanent revolt. Although Mrs. Robb sought to fit in with her husband's friends, she had difficulty in concealing her antipathy for them and her uneasiness with them. She knew that she continued to have marked anti-Semitic feelings despite her efforts to overcome them, and she resented her husband's insistence on spending several summer vacations together with the family of a Jewish colleague. Although her children belonged to the segment of society included in the social register, they were partly alienated from it because of their father's refusal to comply with its customs, and his contemptuous attitude toward many of its members.

Mr. and Mrs. Nussbaum had very different tastes and interests, and when their respective families became antagonistic, as will be discussed below, they had little in common and perhaps sought to hurt each other by attacking the other's family. Mrs. Nussbaum objected strenuously to his "gangster" friends and refused to go out with such shady characters. There seems to have been good reason for her complaints, and it is not at all clear why Mr. Nussbaum wished to go with these people since he was not engaged in activities that were legally questionable.

The Readings were divided because Mr. Reading liked to associate with groups of men in convivial fashion, but opposed his wife's desires to become a member of the proper social set in the town in which they lived. He not only refused to participate in entertaining and being entertained but kept his wife from belonging to any groups.

The inabilities of one or both spouses to separate from their natal families and transfer their central attachment and interest to their marital homes interfered with the attainment of a shared way of life in seven of the seventeen families and created very serious difficulties in four. Of course, to a greater or lesser extent the inability of the spouses to form a stable marital coalition contributed to the continuing dependence on relatives for emotional support and companionship.

Mrs. Nussbaum came from a very close-knit and large family. Mr. Nussbaum was dependent upon and loyal to his oldest brother who had supported him and paid his way through college. The Nussbaum marriage involved the close friendship between the two extended families. A few years after the marriage, Mrs. Nussbaum's family accused Mr. Nussbaum's oldest brother of business dealings that led to the suicide of Mrs. Nussbaum's father. A lasting feud ensued, and both spouses remained loyal to their kin, resenting the other's loyalty. Mrs. Nussbaum continued to spend much of her time with her relatives who tended to exclude her husband from any of their family activities. For a time, some common socialization continued because Mr. Nussbaum was in business and friendly with the husband of Mrs. Nussbaum's favorite sister. Then, the brothers-in-law quarreled, broke up the partnership, and refused to visit one another. Mrs. Nussbaum who gained little satisfaction from her marriage needed her sister and continued to socialize with her.

The Newbergs both retained strong ties to their parental homes, and the absence of any relationships between the two families greatly limited shared social activities for the spouses. Because Mrs. Newberg refused to leave the block on which her three sisters lived, her husband had to spend four hours each day traveling to and from work. Mr. Newberg spent one or two evenings each week with his mother and stopped off to see her en route home on still other evenings, but his wife did not feel welcome at her mother-in-law's. Mrs. Newberg was continuing, in a sense, to live within her parental family—in the same apartment house with her mother and two of her married sisters, and her extended family remained the center of her life. She discouraged her sons from playing with children other than their cousins. The Forel family was caught in a similar situation created by the spouses' attachments to their respective families. Mrs. Forel had also refused to leave the proximity of her parents and sisters for many years, and when eventually she did, she became alcoholic and extremely hostile to her husband. Yet in both the Nussbaum and Forel situations, attachments to the extended families modified the nuclear family eccentricities for the older children, whereas the youngest children who became schizophrenic were deprived of close relationships with grandparents, aunts, and uncles.

In this series, ethnic, religious, and social class discrepancies between spouses were not prominent; notable differences existed in only four of the seventeen families and they were a major source of difficulty in the case of only two couples. The serious blocks to forming social relationships caused by the religious differences between the Graus have been amply discussed. In addition, Mr. Grau came from a well-to-do Midwestern German farm family, whereas Mrs. Grau came from a lower-middle-class urban family that probably was just emerging from lower-class immigrant status. In any event, the Graus' concepts of marital roles, family life, and child rearing were divergent, and Mr. Grau's paranoid suspiciousness and jealousies accentuated the difficulties. Although Mr. and Mrs. Narab were nominally of the same ethnic and religious backgrounds, in actuality they came from totally different backgrounds. Mrs. Narab came from a wealthy Americanized family in which the father had pointedly turned away from the background of his ancestors. Mrs. Narab in seeking an identity married a scholar from abroad and sought to fit into his culture, but their interests were only superficially similar and their backgrounds were totally different. Mr. Thomas was a self-made man who acquired status through his education, whereas his wife was a schizophrenic heiress. Perhaps his drive for status made his wife intolerable to him, but in general the social discrepancy did not seem an important factor. Mrs. Nebb came from a poor family in a remote mountain community and married an orphan from an upper- or upper-middle-class background. Here, too, the significance of the class difference was difficult to evaluate because of Mrs. Nebb's serious emotional instability. However, Mrs. Nebb's social ambitions kept her associating in circles in which her ineptness made her an outsider.

SOCIAL AND CULTURAL FACTORS

A variety of social and cultural factors that served to separate or alienate the family as a whole from the community requires discussion. Neither geographic isolation of the family nor frequent changes of residence were prominent factors in this series of families. The Newcomb children were effectively isolated but more because of their mother's psychopathology than because of the relatively isolated area in which they lived. To cope with her anxieties about their safety, she had kept them in a fenced-in yard when they were young, and as she was too anxious to learn to drive a car, she could not take them to play with other children. The Thomas family moved several times, and the last move was to a remote country home, perhaps because Mr. Thomas wished to remove his schizophrenic wife from circulation. The influences with which we are concerned here are not so readily classified.

The Schwartz children were not only taught to be suspicious of neighbors by their paranoid mother, but the family continued to live behind its store in a slum neighborhood even after becoming reasonably prosperous. Mrs. Schwartz had high aspirations for her four sons and struggled to gain sufficient wealth to educate them to become professional men and scholars. The boys increasingly felt like outsiders in associating with neighborhood boys and later went to Ivy League colleges very poorly prepared to make friendships or to participate in any social life. The Thomas family, before moving to a remote estate, had lived in a slum area because of the father's settlement house activities. The children were urged to associate with neighborhood playmates; at the same time they were taught to feel superior to them. When they were sent away to school, Mrs. Thomas kept shifting them from one school to another because of her concerns about the adequacies of the schools. The Dolfuss family lived as expatriate nobility in a Boston suburb feeling both superior to their neighbors and unaccepted because they were "Austrian." Their way of life differed markedly from that of the community to an extent that must have made them objects of curiosity as well as creating difficulties for the children in learning to associate with peers. A uniformed chauffeur transported the children to and from school. The home life was extremely formal, the children spending scheduled hours with their parents. Mrs. Dolfuss, in dinner dress, together with her carefully groomed children, greeted Mr. Dolfuss at the door each evening. The two children's closest relationships were with the nursemaid and the butler in a manner somewhat reminiscent of *The Turn of the Screw* until the nurse was discharged upon the advice of the boy's schoolteachers, because he had not been taught many rudiments of self-care. In addition, the family's aberrant belief system set them apart from others: they belonged to a minute esoteric religious sect, and the family members considered Mr. Dolfuss to be a reincarnation of an Asiatic divinity.

The Narab family had problems other than those created by the mother's paranoid fears, but they are difficult to describe briefly. Mrs. Narab who had married a foreign member of her ethnic group had gone to live in his native land. She felt herself an outsider unaccepted by her husband's family and friends. When the country was threatened by the Nazi invasion, the family returned to the United States. Her family had lost its wealth, and the sons were sent to public school in New York, although they were unable to speak English; there they thought themselves unwanted and in danger because of their religion and foreign origins.

As has been noted, the social life of the Readings was limited by Mr. Reading's suspiciousness as well as the absence of interests shared by the spouses. The situation was further aggravated just as the daughters entered adolescence. Because Mrs. Reading had informed her husband's mother of his marital infidelity, Mr. Reading took revenge by selling their home in the best neighborhood in town and moving the family into a two-family house in a much less desirable neighborhood. He was striking a blow at his wife's social ambitions and her concern that her daughters associate only with "proper" companions. The move not only heightened the marital schism but seriously impeded the maintenance of friendships. The Benjamins, when the children were small, moved to a suburb in which Mrs. Benjamin had grown up and had a number of friends. However, they may not have been accepted readily because of Mr. Benjamin's rather crude behavior and his difficulties in knowing how to find and maintain proper distance. Still, a critical factor in their failure to make or maintain friends arose because Mr. Benjamin, in his usual impulsive way, had bought a very large house which they could not afford and then could not furnish for about ten years. As they could not invite people into a sparsely furnished home, they could not entertain and therefore could not accept invitations.

Although the impediments to extrafamilial socialization of the children in these families have been grouped under various headings for clarity in presentation, it is evident from these brief illustrations that the problems within each family created several such difficulties in relating to the community and to other families. Thus, as has been noted, the Thomas family lived for a time in a slum area where the children were differentiated from peer groups by their wealth and social position; then the family moved to a relatively isolated area; the mother being schizophrenic was incapable of forming friendships for the family, and the father estranged people by inappropriate confidences and intrusions; the children were shifted from school to school because of the mother's insecurities; the father remained away from home for extended periods; the parents had few if any interests in common; the children had realistic reasons to feel ashamed of their mother's appearance and peculiarities; whereas the family belonged to the social elite because of the mother's background, the mother was too disorganized to participate in social activities; the father was occupied with establishing his own position among people of wealth and prestige, which meant using his wife's wealth but excluding his wife from contacts with his acquaintances.

The children who grow up in these families are not only poorly prepared within the family to become integrated individuals capable of adjusting within society—as we have described in other chapters—but are also further handicapped because the family provides limited access to the extrafamilial world. We are not suggesting that "social isolation" is the cause of schizophrenia, but that it is important to recognize that these patients as children and adolescents were more or less isolated—not always in the sense of physical isolation as much as in having been relatively alienated or estranged. Such limitation of extrafamilial socialization in turn creates serious impediments to integrated development.

POSTSCRIPT

A somewhat different way of propounding the problem follows Edwin Hutchins' (1980) emphasis upon how much our transactions depend on inferences derived from a common cultural code, or, in a sense, on the innumerable cultural codes that we learn as we grow up. We are herein commenting that schizophrenics not only grow up in families with cultural codes, or schemata, that are sufficiently divergent from those of the larger social system but the relative social isolation of these families limits or even prevents the children's correction of these codes. In addition, aberrant ways of experiencing and communicating learned in the family may make it difficult for others to understand or feel at ease with these children, and on the other hand, leave these offspring prone to misunderstand others and have difficulties in establishing meaningful relationships beyond their own families. The chapter has documented a multiplicity of reasons why and how the families of schizophrenics make it difficult for their offspring to form friendships and fit themselves into the extrafamilial world.

XVI

Measuring Disordered Styles of Thinking in the Parents of Schizophrenic Patients on the Object Sorting Test

Part I

(1965)

Very early in our study of the families of schizophrenic patients we started the psychological testing of all family members, using intelligence tests, Rorschachs, and TATs. We considered that on a theoretical basis if the schizophrenic development of an offspring was largely a matter of aberrant personality development, fairly specific personality disturbances of parents might be found from their projective tests. The analysis of the projective tests of an entire family, and the interrelations of the tests of the various family members and the comparisons with controls presented inordinate difficulties. Several psychologists on our team failed to develop a suitable methodology, but insisted that the tests of these families differed greatly from the tests of "normal" control families. Indeed, even a relatively inexperienced projective tester (TL) could note that with normal families, the tests enabled one to gain a surprisingly clear impression of how the family members related to each other, whereas the responses in the test protocols of members of schizophrenic families were frequently so amorphous, diffuse, and constricted and often so peculiar that a reasonable grasp of the family transactions could not be gained from them. But how to measure these responses and the relationships between the responses of the family members?

The problem was largely overcome by the intervention of Margaret

Cynthia Wild, Margaret Singer, Bernice Rosman, Judith Ricci, and Theodore Lidz. This article first appeared in the original edition.

Singer, who, as a prelude to the studies of projective tests of parents that she carried out with Lyman Wynne, worked with the material we had collected. She not only correctly identified parents of schizophrenic patients, sketched characteristics of some patients from the parents' protocols with surprising accuracy, but also matched parents to patients from the protocols without error. It became apparent that Wynne and Singer had found some of the solutions we were seeking, and we have deleted several papers concerned with our less successful efforts from this edition.

However, we had in the meantime become engaged in a related project. McConaghy (1959) had published a paper which claimed that using Lovibond's (1953) scoring method for the Object Sorting Test, he had found that when he tested the parents of ten schizophrenic patients, each of whom had a "high" Lovibond score, 60 percent of the parents in contrast to 9 percent of the controls had a high score, and at least one parent of each schizophrenic had a high score. McConaghy suggested that if the thought disorder rather than the presence of schizophrenia were considered, his studies indicated a dominant genetic factor in the etiology of schizophrenia. As we had documented the presence of "irrational" thinking or communicating in a very high proportion of the parents in our study (Chapter VII), we considered it imperative to replicate McConaghy's study. What had seemed a simple task became very complicated as the scores of our subjects differed markedly from his; but after exchanging protocols with Lovibond, matters were finally straightened out. Lovibond had found in his more recent work that 20 percent rather than 9 percent of controls had high (7 or higher) scores. It also became apparent that scores were affected markedly by intelligence and education that limited the usefulness of the test. The results showed that the test differentiated the mothers of patients from the mothers of controls at a significant level, but not the fathers. However, the parents of schizophrenics, particularly the mothers, clearly had greater problems than control parents in conceptual thinking and categorization. The usefulness and problems of the Lovibond scoring system are presented elsewhere (Lidz et al., 1963; Rosman et al., 1964) and can be found in the first edition of this book. What is of specific importance here in that the studies confirmed our prior observation (Chapter VII) that the thought disorders of schizophrenic patients had notable precursors in the prior generation, but whether this was due to a genetic influence, as McConaghy believed, or to intrafamilial environmental influences could not be determined.

Although the Lovibond scoring method yielded results of limited value, the protocols provided a clear impression that the parents of schizophrenic patients differed markedly from others in the way in which they responded to the test procedures. As the Object Sorting Test is easier to give or to objectify than projective tests, Wild and Singer adapted the Singer-Wynne criteria of disordered styles of thinking and communicating on projective tests into a means of scoring such disorders for the Object Sorting Test. The procedure, the criteria used, and the rather striking results are provided in the following chapter.

In Chapter VII attention was drawn to the distorted, irrational modes of thinking and communicating that characterize the family environments of schizophrenic patients. Intensive clinical study of the families of fifteen such patients suggested the hypothesis that "these persons are prone to withdraw through altering their internal representations of reality because they have been reared amidst irrationality and intrafamilial systems of communication that distort or deny instrumentally valid interpretations of the environment." Wynne and Singer (1963a, 1963b; Singer and Wynne, 1965a, 1965b) working with projective tests, provided further evidence that family forms and styles of thinking and communicating are related to thought disorder in the offspring. McConaghy (1959) and Lidz et al. (1963; Rosman et al., 1964) reported that the parents of schizophrenic patients show significantly more evidence of thought disorder than control groups on the Object Sorting Test, a test of conceptual thinking. Thus, there is a good deal of clinical and experimental evidence to suggest that patients' parents manifest disturbed styles of thinking and communicating.

The present study was undertaken to see if the criteria developed by Singer (Wynne and Singer, 1963a, 1963b) that seemed to differentiate parents of patients from control subjects on projective tests could be applied to the brief, easily administered Object Sorting Test. Another purpose of this study was to determine whether or not her criteria of fragmentation and blurring of attention and meaning could be specified and objectified, so that the protocols could be scored reliably along these dimensions.

DESCRIPTION OF THE TEST

The test is administered according to Rapaport's instructions. The subject is confronted with thirty-three common objects such as tableware, smoking items, and toy objects. The test is divided into two sections. In the first section, the subject is presented with an object and is asked to place with it all of the other objects that belong with it. After he has completed the sort, he is asked, "Why do all of these belong together?" This procedure is carried out with seven different objects in turn. In the second part the examiner presents the subject with twelve different groupings of the objects in succession, each grouping having some different characteristic in common; that is, they are all tools, all red, all smoking materials, etc. Each time the subject is asked, "Why do all of these belong together?" The subject's verbal responses are recorded verbatim.

PROCEDURE

In connection with the study seeking to replicate McConaghy's (1959) experiment, which we discussed in the preface to this chapter, protocols had been collected from sixty-two subjects. They included twenty parents (ten couples) of schizophrenic inpatients who showed a thought disorder both clinically and on projective tests. The control group consisted of forty-two parents (twenty-one couples), all paid volunteers, unselected except to determine insofar as possible that neither they nor their children had been clinically psychotic.

To see whether Singer's criteria for differentiating the

parents of patients from control subjects on projective tests could be applied to the Object Sorting Test, she was sent protocols of ten patient-parent couples and fifteen control couples (fifty subjects in all). Aware only of the husband-wife pairings, she correctly identified twenty out of twenty-five (80 percent) of the couples as parents of schizophrenics or of normal offspring. Singer also included comments on each protocol, stating why she had attributed it to a patient parent or control parent. This discrimination seemed successful enough to continue investigating whether Singer's criteria could be objectified into a quantifiable scoring system that others could use with adequate reliability. Accordingly, her comments were used to make up a scoring manual, derived from Sample I. The manual, summarized below, is based on Singer's impression that the parents of schizophrenic patients show disturbances in their handling of attention and meaning, manifested in fragmented and blurred cognitive styles of attending to and interpreting objects in their environment.[1]

SCORING MANUAL

A. INABILITY TO MAINTAIN A CONSISTENT TASK SET

1. *Fragmentation of Attention*

a. *Intrusions*: Introduction of extraneous topics, ideas, or behavior that interferes with the testing. Subjects may ask the examiner personal questions, get off on some tangent describing personal experience, or get up and walk around the room.

b. *Shifts of Contexts of Reference*: Subject has a piecemeal approach to the objects within one sort, seeming to shift fluidly from one frame of reference to another, as from

---

[1]During the study, the manual was revised several times. While the specific behavioral manifestations scored remained the same, this present version is somewhat different from the original in terms of organizing and categorizing these manifestations under general headings and represents our latest thinking on which clusters of behavior seem to belong together. Further work will probably lead to more refinement and modifications of the manual.

concrete to abstract or from affective to physical aspects of the stimuli, seeming unable to maintain a consistent set. For instance, when confronted with the red objects on Part II, a subject says: "Only insofar as this [red eraser] might relate to eradicating anything that might be written. Or you could light the paper [red paper circle] with the matches [red match book]. The ball [red rubber ball] has no relation to the others—other than that they're both rubber-eraser and ball."

c. *References to Previous Sorts*: In the middle of responding to one item, subject starts talking about a previous sort.

d. *"Forgetting" of Test Structure*: For example, after a subject has completed Part I and most of Part II, he asks, "Am I supposed to classify them?"

e. *Overexactness and Quibbling*: Subject is meticulous in making a sort to a peculiar or bizarre degree. For instance, when presented with the rubber items, a subject says, "I assume the cigar is rubber [toy cigar]. Still have a little metal on the sink-stopper [its handle], paper on the wrapper of the cigar, and abrasives in the eraser."

2. *Inability to Maintain the Role of a Subject Being Tested*

a. *Controlling Behavior*: Subject wants to introduce other objects into the test or takes over the tester's role. For example, on Part II, a subject comments, "You haven't done cylinders—I'm waiting for cylinders" or adds another object to the grouping the examiner has placed before him.

b. *Imposition of Structure*: Subject attempts to impose his own structure on the test and may badger, lecture, or criticize the examiner for not following his own idea of the test structure. Or he seems to project his own idea of the test structure onto the examiner. For instance, when presented with the rubber ball on Part I, a subject says, "I already put that with the rubber. I got to put it with something—you're not satisfied leaving it with the toys?"

3. *Negativism*

Subject does not accept the basic assumption of the test that there is some reason why the objects belong together, especially on Part II. He actively and emphatically states that the objects do not belong together. For example, when asked why a grouping of round objects belong together, a subject says, "Who says they do!"

B. BLURRING OF MEANING

Subject gives several alternative responses, including the correct one, but the correct answer does not seem to "click," and subject goes on to give another answer or gives the right one with an air of extreme uncertainty or qualification. He does not let any response stand. Nor does he add any evaluative remarks about which of his responses he considers better than the others. Meaning is blurred, and in various ways closure is never achieved. For instance, on Part I, a subject puts the red ball with the red paper circle, saying, "Both reddish and round and otherwise I don't see any real connection with the other things."

C. PECULIARS

1. *Peculiar Verbalizations*

Subject uses stilted, artificial language that seems to represent extreme distance from the objects, like calling the smoking equipment "long and narrow surfaces in the smoking line." Or personal concerns appear to intrude in a strange manner, as when a subject says that the bell and ball are "not really close—about third cousins." Extreme forms of peculiar verbalizations are clang associations or neologisms.

2. *Imprecise Referents*

Vague statements about the group of objects that could refer to almost any sort. For example, a subject puts the silverware together because "they're all coordinated," or "you use them together."

A score of 1 is given for each manifestation of the above categories, so that one response can receive multiple scores. A subject's total score consists of the sum of scores assigned throughout the protocol.

The manual makes it clear that verbatim recording is essential for this scoring system. Utilizing the manual, two trained clinical psychologists, one of whom had not been involved in devising the manual, scored the sixty-two protocols with a reliability of .66 (Pearson r). A median test performed with the averaged scores of the two raters showed a significant difference between the control and patient-parent groups ($X^2 = 15.61$, p < .0005, one tail). These results seemed promising enough to warrant further investigation. When 121 more protocols had been collected in connection with the study described in Lidz et al. (1963) and Rosman et al. (1964), these were scored blindly by the same two scorers with a reliability of .91. As a further check on reliability, thirty new protocols obtained from the National Institute of Mental Health were scored by a third trained clinical psychologist, who had had no previous contact with the study, with a reliability of .84 with one of the original scorers.[2] These findings seem to demonstrate that Singer's criteria of fragmentation and blurring of attention and meaning can be objectified and applied to the Object Sorting Test with adequate interscorer reliability.

RESULTS

Findings were first examined with a total sample of 193 subjects including 78 patient parents (thirty-nine couples) and 115 control parents (forty-nine couples, with seventeen additional fathers and mothers).[3] The groups were matched on education, but not on age, the patient parents being approximately seven years older. Although the results showed striking group differences on these measures, significant correlations were found between scores and both education and

[2]We are grateful to Dr. Lyman Wynne for his cooperation and to Mrs. Peggy Toohey for her work in making these protocols available to us. We also thank Dr. Dorothy Ciarlo for her help in doing the scoring.

[3]This sample is the same as that described in Lidz et al., 1963; Rosman et al., 1964, except for the omission of five patient-parent couples whose protocols were not recorded verbatim and for the inclusion of ten patient-parent couples recently obtained from NIMH. The patient parents had at least one hospitalized offspring with a clear-cut clinical diagnosis of schizophrenia, and the control parents were all paid volunteers whose children had never been clinically psychotic as far as could be ascertained.

age. In the patient-parent group, the correlation between score and education was $-.38$ (p $< .01$) and in the control group $-.11$ (ns). The correlation between score and age in the former group was $+.15$ (ns) and in the latter group $+.24$ (p $< .02$). Furthermore, there were significant correlations between education and age in both groups. These correlations, as well as the lack of matching on age, made it impossible to use the total sample to determine the effectiveness of scores in discriminating the patient parent from the control group independent of the effects of age and education.

Therefore, 93 subjects, drawn from the total population of 133, were carefully matched on education and age. Mothers and fathers were separately matched on these variables. Except for the matching criteria, the sample was randomly selected. The final sample consists of 44 patient parents (nineteen couples and six individuals) and 49 control parents (seventeen couples and fifteen individuals). The sample characteristics are presented in Table I. It shows that the patient-parent and control groups are well matched on age and ed-

TABLE I

CHARACTERISTICS OF MATCHED SAMPLE

Patient Parents vs. Control Parents

	Range	Mean	t	P
Patient Parents (N = 44)				
Age	39-66	50.11	.66	ns
Years Education	4-21	13.16	.25	ns
Control Parents (N = 49)				
Age	41-65	49.45		
Years Education	8-20	13.37		

Combined Fathers vs. Combined Mothers

Total Fathers (N = 42)				
Age	39-66	51.05	2.34	$< .05$
Years Education	4-21	13.29	.34	ns
Total Mothers (N = 51)				
Age	41-64	48.71		
Years Education	6-20	13.00		

ucation. While fathers and mothers are well matched on education, fathers are significantly older than mothers (t = 2.34, p. < .05, two tails).

Table II presents the number of *individual* patient parents and control parents with scores above and below the over-all group median of 3.25. It can be seen that more patient parents have scores above the median than control parents (X^2 = 16.55, p < .0005, one tail).

Two methods were used to analyze the results in terms of *couples* (nineteen patient parent and seventeen control couples).

Table III presents the number of patient-parents and control couples with scores above the over-all median for both spouses, for one spouse, and for neither spouse. It shows

TABLE II

COMPARISON OF SINGER SCORES FOR PATIENT-PARENT AND CONTROL GROUPS

	Number of Scores Above the Median	Number of Scores Below the Median
Over-all Median = 3.25		
Patient Parents	33 (75%)	11 (25%)
Median = 6.75		
Control Parents	15 (31%)	34 (69%)
Median = 1.75		

$$X^2 = 16.55, p < .0005 \quad (1 \text{ tail})$$

TABLE III

NUMBER OF PATIENT-PARENT AND CONTROL COUPLES WHERE BOTH SPOUSES HAVE HIGH OR LOW SINGER SCORES OR ONE SPOUSE HAS A HIGH SINGER SCORE

	Both Parents Above the Median	One Parent Above, One Below the Median	Both Parents Below the Median
Over-all Median = 3.25			
Patient-Parent Couples	11 (58%)	5 (26%)	3 (16%)
Control Couples	2 (12%)	8 (47%)	7 (41%)

$$X^2 = 8.43, p < .02 \quad (2 \text{ tails})$$

that the scores significantly differentiate patient-parent from control couples ($X^2 = 8.43$, p < .02, two tails). Fifty-eight per cent of the patient-parent couples both have high scores in contrast to 12 per cent of the control couples.

Table IV presents the results for couples when the mother's and father's scores are added together. This method of analysis also shows a significant difference between the two groups of parents ($X^2 = 11.15$, p < .0005, one tail). parent and control groups are discriminated better when the parents are treated as couples and their scores summed than when they are treated as individuals. There is no marked difference in the patient-parent group, where 75 per cent of *individuals* and 79 per cent of *couples* have high scores. But in the control group, 69 per cent of *individuals* have low scores in contrast to 82 per cent of *couples*.

Table V presents the comparisons of patient fathers with control fathers and patient mothers with control mothers. Since fathers and mothers were matched separately on age and education, the analyses were performed in terms of the fathers' and mothers' group medians (3.75 and 2.75 respectively) rather than the median for the total sample. Table V shows that more patients' fathers have scores above the median than control fathers ($X^2 = 4.68$, p < .025, one tail), and more patients' mothers have scores above the median than control mothers ($X^2 = 17.05$, p < .0005, one tail). While the

TABLE IV

NUMBER OF PATIENT-PARENT AND CONTROL COUPLES WHERE MOTHER'S AND FATHER'S ADDED SCORES ARE HIGH AND LOW

	Number of Scores Above the Median	Number of Scores Below the Median
Over-all Median = 6.75		
Patient Parents	15 (79%)	4 (21%)
Median = 12.25		
Control Parents	3 (18%)	14 (82%)
Median = 4.25		

$$X^2 = 11.15, \ p < .0005, \ (1 \ \text{tail})$$

TABLE V

COMPARISON OF MOTHERS' AND FATHERS' SINGER SCORES

	Number of Scores Above the Median	Number of Scores Below the Median
Fathers' over-all median = 3.75		
Patients' fathers	15 (71%)	6 (29%)
Median = 6.75		
Control fathers	7 (33%)	14 (67%)
Median = 3.25		

$$X^2 = 4.68, \ p < .025 \quad (1 \ \text{tail})$$

Mothers' over-all median = 2.75		
Patients' mothers	20 (87%)	3 (13%)
Median = 6.75		
Control mothers	7 (25%)	21 (75%)
Median = 1.75		

$$X^2 = 17.05, \ p < .0005 \quad (1 \ \text{tail})$$

fathers' overall median is higher than the mothers' median, further analyses show that fathers do not differ from mothers significantly in either the patient-parent or control group. However, it can be seen that the scores differentiate mothers somewhat better than fathers.

DISCUSSION

These results demonstrate that the criteria of disturbance in the focusing of attention and blurring of meaning that Singer used to distinguish the parents of schizophrenic patients from control parents on projective tests can be objectified, scored reliably, and applied to the Object Sorting Test. They also seem to show that these scores are affected by age and education. The tendency for scores to increase as years of education decrease does not seem surprising, since subjects with less education would be apt to show more evidence of disturbance on a test of concept formation that would challenge their intellectual ability. Similarly, Rosman et al. (1964) in a study including 173 of the subjects from this sample found that education had a strong effect on Lovibond's

(1953) measure of thought disorder, so that it differentiated patient from control parents only at higher educational levels. Although an increase of scores with age was not anticipated, since Lovibond's measure of thought disorder showed a negligible relationship to age, this finding does not seem surprising. Such criteria as inability to maintain a consistent task set and giving irrelevant verbalizations appear likely to be associated with age. For example, Singer (1963) found that in a sample of normal, healthy men, aged over sixty-five, one segment classed as showing a "senile quality" in clinically rated behavior exhibited less task-oriented and more rambling verbal behavior on tests than "nonsenile quality" subjects. Of course, the results pertaining to education and age could reflect particular sampling characteristics, and more work needs to be done with subjects of different age and educational levels to clarify the relationship of these variables to scores. Clearly, in further studies groups should be matched on education and age.

However, the results from the forty-four patient parents and forty-nine control parents closely matched on education and age appear to demonstrate that the groups differ significantly on the measures independent of the effects of these variables. Furthermore, the two groups of parents are discriminated when they are treated either as individuals or as couples. The first analysis of couples seems to show that the scores discriminate patient-parent from control couples when a criterion of both parents having high or low scores is used. Fifty-eight per cent of patient-parent couples both have high scores in contrast to only 12 per cent of control couples, and 41 per cent of control couples both have low scores in contrast to only 16 per cent of patient-parent couples. However, if one parent has a high score, the groups are not discriminated, for 47 per cent of control couples and 26 per cent of patient-parent couples have one high-scoring spouse. When the scoring unit for couples is the sum of the mother's and father's scores, the summed scores discriminate patient-parent from control *couples* better than patient-parent from control *indi-*

viduals. Comparison of Tables II and IV shows that the improvement is more apparent in the control group; and scrutiny of the data indicates that of ten control couples with at least one moderately high-scoring spouse (score of 3.0-6.0) nine have a low-scoring partner (score of under 3.0). This observation suggests that a healthier parent may offset the effect of the sicker one, so that the family style of communication is not seriously disturbed. Scrutiny of the data also shows that the summed scores of eight patient-parent couples (42 per cent) are higher than those obtained by *any* control couple. These findings seem particularly meaningful, since Wynne and Singer (1963a) stress that disturbed communication is a function of the interaction between patient-parent couples, rather than the pathology of each individual parent. However, it remains to be seen whether scores of the Object Sorting Test will discriminate between parents of schizophrenics and parents of other psychiatric patients.

The discriminative value of this scoring system seems to be relatively independent of sex of parent, a variable that has been shown to affect other measures of thought disorder on the Object Sorting Test. For example, Rosman et al. (1964) found that Lovibond's measure of thought disorder distinguished patients' mothers from control mothers, while patients' fathers were not differentiated from control fathers. Thus, the Singer measures, which seem to reflect disturbances in general style of test taking and communication, appear to pick up more pathological indicators in patients' fathers than a scoring system such as that used by Rosman, which is focused on specific manifestations of thought disorder in the conceptual sphere. For instance, a constricted, paranoid person may not reveal much evidence of thought disorder per se, but show striking negativism, controlling behavior, or projection of his own ideas of test structure. Although there is no difference between patient fathers and patient mothers, there is a tendency for control fathers to have higher scores than control mothers ($X^2 = 1.86$, $p < .20$, two tails). However, this finding could be attributed to the fathers' older age, rather than to greater incidence of pathology among fathers.

In sum, these findings suggest that this brief, easily administered test, scored according to Singer's criteria, has potential value as a screening device for selecting a high-risk population of parents who might have schizophrenic offspring or for further investigations of thought disorder.

The results presented in the preceding section indicate that criteria resembling those developed by Wynne and Singer (1963a, 1963b; Singer and Wynne, 1965a, 1965b) for distinguishing the parents of schizophrenics from control parents on projective tests could be objectified, scored reliably, and applied to the briefer Object Sorting Test. These findings pose at least two basic questions: (1) What is the significance of the Object Sorting Test scoring system in terms of the pathology it reflects in the parents of schizophrenic patients? (2) What is the impact of such parental pathology on their children? The purpose of this section is to suggest some implications of the findings in the light of these questions; first, by considering the actual transactions between patient parent and examiner around the test, and then by presenting some speculative, theoretical interpretations.

Singer and Wynne's transactional approach to testing and their major criteria for differentiating patient parents from control parents will be briefly summarized, since they provide a general framework for the following discussion.

SUMMARY OF SINGER AND WYNNE'S APPROACH TO TESTING AND CRITERIA FOR DIFFERENTIATING PARENTS OF SCHIZOPHRENICS FROM CONTROL PARENTS

Singer and Wynne consider that family *styles* of interacting and communicating are closely linked to disturbed thinking in the offspring. They view tests as:

Cynthia Wild: Implications of Disturbed Styles of Thinking Manifested on the Object Sorting Test by the Parents of Schizophrenic Patients. This first appeared in the original edition.

. . . a sample transaction between subject and tester, not simply as projections of intrapsychic problems. . . . The transaction between subject and tester provides a relatively standard way of sampling attention, thinking-communication, and relating. . . . Thus, the protocols can be used as a means of studying the same kind of stylistic aspects of thinking as have been observed in the clinical work with the families. . . .

Viewing and responding to the TAT and Rorschach cards corresponds to everyday situations in which two people see a series of different kinds of "reality," but because of their roles, one is the interpreter of the reality to the other. . . .

The parents [bring] to the testing situation the distinctive and enduring styles of behaving also found in their interpretive transactions with their children and with each other.

Further, we have assumed that styles of attending, perceiving, thinking, communicating, and relating used in family transactions are likely to have promoted the cognitive development of the offspring in certain directions, either by serving as models for identification or by eliciting complementary behaviors [Singer and Wynne, 1965a, p. 190].

Thus, since the focus is on the transaction between subject and tester around the test, it does not seem necessary to use specifically "projective" tests; briefer, more easily administered tasks, such as the Object Sorting Test, which involve continuous interaction between subject and tester would seem just as effective in picking up the behaviors Singer and Wynne use to differentiate the parents of schizophrenics from other parents.

Singer and Wynne work not only from the basic hypothesis that family transactional styles are related to cognitive development in the offspring; they assume that disturbed interpersonal relationships are reflected in cognitive disturbances as well. The *style* of the interaction is as important as the style of conceptualization; and even though a parent produces an adequate conceptual response, he may receive a score for the disruptive or blurred style with which it is given. Singer and Wynne focus on four major features of family interaction in differentiating schizophrenic families from others.[4] First, they find basic disturbances in the handling of attention and meaning in the parents of schizophrenics. If a family cannot even begin to focus attention selectively on shared percepts, ideas, or feelings, the possibility of meaningful communication developing is obliterated from the start. These parents seem unable to focus selectively on either external reality or internal states, which would lead to impairment of the child's capacity for selective attention, purposive behavior, or subjectively meaningful experience. In contrast, Singer and Wynne find that in neurotic families, attention is directed toward particular issues over a period of time.

A second major feature of family interaction that they use to differentiate schizophrenic from other families is erratic and inappropriate kinds of distance and closeness in making contact with both human and nonhuman aspects of the environment. These parents cannot maintain a proper cognitive or affective distance from objects or people; nor can they flexibly shift their distance appropriately as transactions develop. This behavior has been described as characteristic of interviews with patients' parents (Cornelison, 1960). Cognitively, on tests, for example, they may show sudden concrete literalness and switch quickly to vague, overgeneralized, syncretistic responses.

A third major criterion Singer and Wynne employ concerns a deep, underlying sense of pervasive meaninglessness, pointlessness, and emptiness to existence, possibly related to a fundamental hopelessness about ever achieving gratification through human contact. Cognitively, this sense of futility seems reflected in an inability to let any response stand, so that closure is never achieved, or to allow a concept to develop clearly and distinctly.

---

[4]Since the fourth feature—pseudomutuality and pseudohostility—does not seem so relevant to the Object Sorting Test scoring system as the other three features, it will not be discussed here.

IMPLICATIONS OF THE FINDINGS SUGGESTED BY THE
EXAMINERS' REACTIONS TO TRANSACTIONS WITH PATIENT
PARENTS IN THE TESTING SITUATION

Since the focus in the testing situation is on the transaction with the examiner around the test, one way of viewing the parental pathology reflected in the Object Sorting Test scoring system and its impact on their children is to consider the examiners' reactions while testing these parents. Therefore, some of the testers' impressions will be presented to illustrate more vividly how Singer and Wynne's three criteria of disturbed patterns of handling attention and meaning, inappropriate switches from distance to closeness, and a sense of pervasive pointlessness to existence were experienced.

Isolated examples do not really convey the total effect of a massing of such behavior. The examiners often felt drained and exhausted after only an hour or so of testing. Sometimes, it seemed as though the parents were spreading themselves in many different directions, so that it was grueling work to try to keep them within the bounds of the task to complete the testing. For instance, long, tangential, rambling speeches had to be cut short; efforts had to be made to get parents to sit down, as with one father who insisted on standing throughout the test; and parents' attempts to take over the testing had to be controlled. In terms of the scoring system developed for the Object Sorting Test, such behavior seems to reflect *Inability to Maintain a Consistent Task Set*, particularly disturbances in the handling of attention.

At the same time, the examiners often had to cope with what felt like a hammering barrage of disruptive questions that seemed to interfere with the task and with communication rather than promoting it. For example, parents would ask questions, interrupting the examiner right in the middle of the initial test instructions, inhibiting development of a meaningful transaction at the outset. Questions were often asked insistently and intrusively, as with a father who, when presented with the bell, asked: "This is what? A bell? Supposed to be, isn't it—what is it—a bicycle bell? What's *this* [red paper circle] supposed to be?" An hour of such questions is wearing, and the examiners received the impression that answering them as well as possible within the requirements of testing or saying, "It's up to you," had little if any effect. Control parents, on the other hand, seemed more able to adapt to the task, ceasing to ask questions after being told "It's up to you" several times. This impression of the patient parents seems related to Singer and Wynne's point about a lack of flexibility in shifting behavior appropriately as transactions develop. It can be imagined how hopeless the children of such parents must feel about ever communicating effectively or making their own needs known to elicit an appropriate parental response.

Pervasive, emphatic negativism also led the examiners to feel that they were beating their heads against a stone wall in trying to call forth any response other than "they *don't* belong together," which must be similar to what the child experiences in trying to get his needs met. Some parents remained as negative as that throughout the nineteen test items, leaving the examiners with feelings of futility and frustration about having made any meaningful communication around the testing situation.

An especially difficult sort of question for the examiners to handle involved the parents' self-engendered assumptions about the test structure, such as, "You mean sort them according to their use?" After being told that they could sort the objects in any way they liked, often they would repeat the same question on the next item, or proceed to sort every item in terms of the objects' use. Sometimes a parent became very angry at the tester for not having told him that his assumptions about the test were not true, even though the parent had not brought them out in the open. For instance, the same father who asked all the questions about the bell said that he saw nothing to go with the ball. When he was asked to try to find something, he said: "Even this stuff we used before?" He had apparently come to his own conclusion that he could not use any objects more than once. When he was told that he *could* use the objects over again, he said angrily, "Oh, you can! You should say so, you should say so if you know about that!" Here, a lack of separation from the tester is suggested in his use of "we" instead of "I" when he refers to "this stuff we used before" and in his assumption that the tester would know what was on his mind without his having to verbalize it.

Such behavior, coming under the scoring category of *Inability to Maintain the Role of a Subject Being Tested—Imposition of Structure*—seems to have more to do with the *transaction* between subject and tester than with cognitive style; and this style of transaction would appear to indicate a lack of clear separation from the examiner on the part of the patient parents. A response given by a patient's mother who was asked to sort objects with the toy pliers seems to provide an even more striking illustration of a blurring of boundaries between subject and tester. She said: "Again, you can go back to toys—or you can again go on. . . . Depends on how far you want to go. . . . If you add the screwdriver, you can add the lock—you could go further—it depends how far you want to go—how much you want to write." Not only does this mother never come to any resolution or closure; but she almost gives the impression that the examiner is taking the test in her constant use of "you" instead of "I" and in her saying that the sort depends on how much the examiner wants to write. After a time with such parents, testers became aware that they were held responsible for the parents' responses and imbued and suffused with the parents' thoughts and feelings, resulting in a confusion and lack of clarity about who was giving and who was taking the test and about whose thoughts and feelings were whose. It can be imagined how confusing it must be for the children of such parents never to know clearly the difference between "we," "you," and "I," or whether a thought or feeling originates from within parent or child. Constant transactions like these would be apt to lead to serious problems with self-differentiation in the child (Lidz and Lidz, 1952; Reichard and Tillman, 1950). Such behavior appears to verge on projection and would be apt to foster the development of projective mechanisms in the offspring.

Sudden personal questions were another disruptive behavior that made these parents difficult to test. These questions seem to reflect Singer and Wynne's criterion of sudden switches from tremendous distance and lack of communication to inappropriate, intrusive closeness. Such shifts would be likely to lead to even more serious impairment of the capacity to maintain proper distance in the child, possibly resulting in excessive withdrawal.

Another major difficulty in testing many of these parents was what seemed like the impossibility of ever getting a clear, definite, specific response to any item, leading to a sense of utter frustration and hopelessness in the tester about eliciting a direct, straightforward answer. This pervasive characteristic appears related to Singer and Wynne's criterion of blurring of meaning and lack of closure. Attention may never be clearly focused on the objects, so that any chance of meaning developing is removed from the outset; or if some meaning is achieved, it is not allowed to stand, but blurred or taken away. One basic requirement for meaning to develop would seem to be an initial identification of the objects; and patient parents often seemed unable to identify them, turning over even the basic responsibility of labeling to the tester. One father, given the red paper circle, said: "I don't know, I don't know what it is—and I don't know of anything to go with it. . . . You must have something to go with it? Depends what this is. You want me to imagine something that goes with it? I see nothing that goes with this little piece of paper—unless this eraser goes with it—or you want to put the matches on it?" Later, when asked if the red objects had any common characteristic, he replied: "Color, shades of red, but this [eraser] is pink. Color—color only." Although this father is capable of identifying the paper circle as "a little piece of paper" and can achieve the concept "red," he produces a feeling of frustration and an impression of slipperiness, for he never seems able to commit himself even to labeling a common, everyday object or to a relatively simple concept, never letting any meaning stand or allowing himself to be pinned down. It can be speculated that the child of such a parent would tend to grow up in a hazy, undifferentiated world—a condition that would lead to difficulty in learning to identify and specify common objects in the environment and to form stable concepts. Furthermore, if a parent is so vague and elusive in labeling everyday objects, like those in the test, he would be expected to have much more trouble with identifying more complex and subtle feelings or affect-laden concepts, such as love and hate.

The majority of patient parents were undoubtedly more anxious than the control parents in the testing situation and some of the scoring categories could be considered as anxiety indicators. However, the behavior rarely occurred in isolation, and there does not seem any reason to expect that this total constellation of pathology reflects anxiety only. For example, while anxiety could account for negativism and tangential speeches, it is difficult to see how it could produce a confusion between "we," "you," and "I," or a tendency to impose structure on the test.

In sum, the examiners' reactions to the patient parents' disturbances in the handling of attention and their negativism suggest the feelings of frustration and hopelessness their offspring must experience about the possibility of ever communicating their own needs effectively or having them met or of ever focusing on and sharing a meaningful experience with their parents. Such behavior would be apt to produce a sense of hopelessness about verbal communication serving as an aid to collaborative interaction and about the value of words as useful tools of problem solving. The parents' *Inability to Maintain the Role of Subjects Being Tested* seems to reflect a lack of clear separation from the examiner, resulting in uncertainty and confusion about whose thoughts and feelings are whose, which would be apt to lead to serious problems with establishing a distinct sense of self in the child. Similarly, sudden shifts from extreme distance to excessive closeness in the patient parents were experienced as disconcerting by the examiners in the relatively neutral testing situation and must seem much more inconsistent and confusing to a child constantly engaged in emotional transactions with such parents. Finally, the blurring of meaning and inability to let concepts or even labels for common objects stand would be apt to lead to a vague, hazy view of external reality and arouse feelings of frustration about ever achieving a subjectively significant experience as well.

Some Tentative Theoretical Implications of the Findings

Some more speculative views of the data have already been suggested in the previous section. The theoretical implications presented here are offered only as tentative ways of interpreting the findings, with the realization that they are open to further, alternative interpretations.

As indicated above, Singer and Wynne contribute the idea that disturbed interpersonal relations are reflected in disordered cognitive styles. One often-observed fundamental aspect of parental pathology to which they call attention is a lack of differentiation of self from the environment or a looseness and fluidity of ego boundaries, leading to serious impairments in both ways of relating to people and cognitive functioning. The Object Sorting Test scoring system appears to pick up a number of manifestations of boundary problems in the parents of schizophrenics. In fact, this test, requiring as it does a specification of the similarities and differences between common, everyday external objects, may be particularly sensitive to eliciting reflections of fundamental boundary difficulties both in cognitive styles and in transactions with the testers. Following Schachtel (1959), a case can be made for severe attention disturbances being related to diffuse, indefinite ego boundaries. A capacity for focused attention on external human and nonhuman objects and their particular attributes seems to imply an ability to separate oneself from the environment and to differentiate various aspects of it; and a capacity for focused attention on internal thoughts and feelings would seem to depend on a capacity to maintain mental representations of external objects over time, to separate one's own thoughts and feelings from those of other people, and to distinguish between various kinds of internal states. Otherwise, as in the infant, attention will be global, diffuse, and unselective. It can also be hypothesized that such attention disturbances would lead to an inability to exclude irrelevant aspects of the internal and external environments or to distinguish their separate aspects with any degree of clarity.

The scoring categories of *Controlling Behavior and Imposition of Structure* onto the testing situation, with a greater or lesser apparent loss of distinction between who is giving and who is taking the test, also can be considered as indications of fluid boundaries, leading to confusion between what is inside and what is outside the self. Sudden shifts from excessive closeness to excessive distance could also be seen as reflecting serious boundary problems. The schizophrenic's parent seems almost to become the tester at times, imbuing both tester and test with his own thoughts and feelings, making them over in his own image, so that they no longer have an objective existence as a person and task apart from the parent's internal state.

In addition to differentiation of self from objects, another related requirement for sustained focal attention would seem to be sufficient alleviation of internal need states, so that environmental objects can emerge distinctly and neutrally, independent of personal wishes and desires, and reality can be objectively perceived (Schachtel, 1959). Often, the patient parents' Object Sorting Test performance appears to show an inability to perceive an object apart from their own needs. Some parents seem completely unable to view the objects separate from their *use* in providing immediate gratification. Such parents sometimes give the impression of being in a continual state of "emergency," experiencing a desperate sense of primitive deprivation with respect to issues of basic survival, such as heat and warmth, emptiness and being full, food and shelter. For example, one mother answered almost every test item in terms of how she would *use* the items in an emergency. To a sorting of silverware, she said: "Because if you have a fork, you need a spoon and a knife when you set the table. . . . And if you don't have a knife and fork, you use your hands." Then, to the bell, with which she sorted the tools, she said: "Well, since I'm not a mechanic and if I planned to put this on, I'd have to have one of these [tools]. . . . This [hammer] . . . wouldn't have to use it probably—in an emergency maybe I might need it. If I was going downstairs to my tool chest, I'd take it to save myself a trip to go back." Her lack of neutral detachment from the objects and inability to attend freely to their properties apart from her own needs are evident in these responses. Furthermore, if her own needs color even this relatively neutral area of functioning, it could be surmised that they would have a greater influence on emotional transactions, making it impossible for her to perceive her children's needs apart from her own.

In sum, the attention disturbances that Singer uses as a major criterion for differentiating the parents of schizophrenic patients from other parents could be related to primitive difficulties in separating self from nonself and experiencing the world as separate from internal need states. The often-observed fluidity of boundaries between generations and of sexual identity in schizophrenics' families (Lidz, 1963b) seem like further reflections of problems with self-definition. The *Inability to Maintain the Role of a Subject Being Tested* also could represent problems in keeping a distinct separation between subject and tester and confusion about what is inside the parent and what is outside in reality. This fluidity of boundaries would be likely to lead to vagueness and lack of clarity about how inanimate objects differ from one another, how people differ from one another, how inanimate objects differ from people, and how internal thoughts and feelings differ from one another and from the thoughts and feelings of other people. Singer and Wynne's second major criterion for distinguishing the parents of schizophrenics—inappropriate shifts from extreme closeness to extreme distance—also can be seen as reflecting difficulties in maintaining consistent ego boundaries. At times the boundary is too loose, resulting in intrusive closeness; and at other times, the boundaries are too tight, leading to extreme distance.

If boundary problems are a crucial aspect of the pathology of schizophrenics' parents, what impact might such difficulties have on their children? Generally, these boundary problems would be likely to interfere severely with a child's capacity to establish a separate identity, with resulting impairment of cognitive skills and capacity for developing mutual relationships. At early stages, if a mother has trouble separating herself from her baby and responds to him primarily in terms of her own needs, his own internal states will never be clearly differentiated and labeled if they are not responded to at the time they are experienced, and his needs will not be clearly distinguished from his mother's. Such a mother would be likely to have difficulty empathizing with her baby's experience and with understanding the cues he gives out apart from her own impulses and feelings (Bruch and Palombo, 1961). If the father shows similar boundary problems, the child will have even less chance of learning to separate himself from others as a distinct individual and to label clearly and differentiate objects in the environment. He will also have trouble learning that appropriate instrumental action on his part can effectively alter external reality.

A capacity for sustained, mutual relationships with other people could probably not develop in such a family atmosphere, where the purpose of the child's existence is to meet his parents' needs, so that he cannot experience himself as a person in his own right. The ability to form satisfying human relationships would seem to require a distinct sense of self as a prerequisite, for lack of self-differentiation means that closeness brings the danger of merging, annihilation, and nothingness, as well as the feeling of living in and through another person to serve that person's needs. Such symbiotic relationships also would seem to produce a fear that the parents will die or be destroyed if the patient separates himself from them, a fear that is not without realistic foundation (Lidz and Lidz, 1952).

Singer and Wynne's third major criterion for identifying the families of schizophrenics—a basic sense of pointlessness and meaninglessness, related to a cognitive inability to ever let any concept fully emerge or stand once it has emerged—would also be apt to have a profound effect on a child. As these authors point out, the sense of futility and hopelessness that these parents show should be differentiated from depression where, despite sadness and despondency, real interactions occur between people. These patient parents seem to show a more schizoid sense of inner emptiness, deadness, and isolation. A child growing up with parents holding such a despondent and pessimistic attitude toward human contact certainly would not feel encouraged to search for relationships outside the family, especially if he could not find meaningful contacts within it.

A final crucial question that should be raised is: How do the patients' parents in the sample, few if any of whom had ever been hospitalized, differ from the patients themselves? As has been pointed out, the parents often seem able to label objects correctly or come up with adequate conceptualizations, which they then proceed to blur. The children in such a family, however, might grow up without learning to label concepts and objects adequately, since the parents never let any meaning stand. This deficiency could interfere markedly with learning to employ words as carriers of concepts, an ability that seems essential for adequate ego functioning and for directing the self into the future. This *transactional* aspect of the scoring system may be what makes it more effective in picking up disturbed parental *styles* of interpreting the environment, which could lead to more serious *thought disorders* and deficient reality testing in their children.

POSTSCRIPT

The second section of the article by Dr. Wild helped sharpen our thinking about how the disordered styles of parental communication were related to the conflictful and distorted family environments they created. The failures of one or both parents to have established adequate self-boundaries could be related to the egocentricity that leads them to confuse their needs, impulses, and wishes with those of their children, or of their spouses and to be impervious to the feelings and perceptions of others; particularly others who share their lives. Focusing primarily upon the parents' boundary problems, the article insightfully relates such difficulties to attention disturbances, to failure to differentiate what arises within and without the individual, self from nonself, to object constancy and "self-constancy"; and how, as we have discussed elsewhere, the confusions between self and nonself impair category formation; to projection of impulses and wishes, and chronic misunderstandings of what others seek to convey. The potential effects of such parental difficulties upon their offspring are indicated and the broader implications are left for the reader to contemplate and ponder. They are discussed further in Chapter XIX where the relationship between diffuse self-boundaries, object constancy, and Piagetian egocentricity is presented in the formulation of a theory of schizophrenic disorders.

XVII

The Influence of Family Studies on the Treatment of Schizophrenic Disorders

(1969)

Nowhere in medicine has it been so apparent that the hypotheses held concerning the nature and etiology of a condition influence treatment as in the case of schizophrenic disorders. Belief in demonic possession led to exorcisms and burnings. The conviction that these patients suffered from a somatic disorder was, in large measure, responsible for the relegation of generations of patients to neglect in custodial institutions. The hypothesis, accepted as fact, that the brain or its metabolism was at fault provoked the damaging of countless brains by insulin, metrazol, electric shock, lobotomy, and currently by the excessive use of neuroleptic medication. Jung's and E. Bleuler's beliefs that the psychological disturbances they described were secondary to a toxic disorder, and Freud's idea that the schizophrenic patient's narcissistic fixation and regression made a transference relationship impossible convinced psychoanalysts that these patients were beyond their approach. Indeed, when Sullivan, Fromm-Reichmann, and Hill demonstrated that a therapeutic relationship that could turn into a transference could be established, many other analysts were skeptical and even de-

Theodore Lidz: The Influence of family studies on the treatment of schizophrenia. *Psychiatry*, Vol. 32, 1969, pp. 237-251. Copyright © 1969, The William Alanson White Psychiatric Foundation, Inc. The paper was presented on November 15, 1968 as the Twelfth Annual Frieda Fromm-Reichmann Memorial Lecture under the auspices of the Washington School of Psychiatry. This version has been modified somewhat from the original lecture and publication.

rogatory because the fact ran counter to accepted tenets. The theory that schizophrenic reactions, as the most profound regressions, are due to fixations during the oral phase, led to the focus on maternal rejection during infancy—a period beyond conscious recollection; this orientation has led some therapists to believe that supplying the nurture and love the patient lacked during infancy forms the cornerstone of treatment.

It is essential to have hypotheses to guide therapy, but science progresses when hypotheses are based upon ascertained data rather than primarily upon theoretic assumptions. For many years we have been engaged in an intensive scrutiny of the family settings in which schizophrenic patients had grown up. We started from the clinical observation that schizophrenic patients seemed always to have emerged from seriously disturbed families; and from the hypothesis that because the foundations of language and thought are laid down within the family, the thought disorder that forms the distinctive feature of schizophrenia might well be related to these disturbed family environments. We hoped to find something specific within the radius of the family circle that was related to the etiology of schizophrenia; but the global nature of the family pathology created difficulties. Something was seriously amiss with each aspect of the family and its transactions that we examined. Whereas some of the mothers had been unable properly to invest the patient as an infant, others had serious difficulties in establishing boundaries between themselves and the children who became schizophrenic. Most but not all of the mothers were strange if not seriously disturbed, but the fathers just as frequently displayed severe psychopathology. Many of the families were rent by serious schisms between the parents, but others were distorted by a skewed parental relationship in which an apparent harmony or pseudomutuality was maintained because the aberrant ideas and ways of child rearing of one parent were not countered by the passive spouse. The failures of parents to maintain boundaries between generations and to adhere to their gender-linked roles led to incestuous problems, gender identity confusions, and homosexual tendencies in both parents and offspring. The peculiarities of communication and the distortions of reality within the family fostered a proclivity toward irrationality in the children. The extrafamilial socialization of the child had been impeded by a variety of asocial influences in these families. The serious problems found in virtually all areas in all of these families had started prior to the birth of the patient and were continuing when the patient became overtly psychotic in adolescence or early adult life. We described our findings as objectively as we could; and many others have published similar findings and amplified them. When the protocols of family studies carried out in Bethesda (Bowen, 1957, 1960; Bowen et al., 1959; Wynne, Day et al., 1957; Wynne, Ryckoff et al., 1958), in Paris (Delay et al., 1957, 1960, 1962), in Finland (Alanen, 1958, 1960a, 1960b), or in Palo Alto (Bateson et al., 1958; Jackson, 1958; Jackson and Weakland, 1959) are reviewed, they reveal essentially the same difficulties, even though sometimes differing in emphasis concerning what is considered most salient. It had become apparent by now that whatever else may enter into the genesis of schizophrenia, the family problems have major pertinence (Lidz, 1967).

Focusing upon the etiology and understanding of schizophrenic reactions, I have written relatively little about their treatment in recent years. However, our explorations of the families were carried out in a therapeutic setting and included analytically oriented therapy of the patients. In looking back over the past twenty years I realize that my own treatment of schizophrenic patients, and that of some of my colleagues as well, has been profoundly influenced by the data and the conceptualization derived from these studies. I shall discuss some of these influences and effects.

The first consequence that I wish to note may seem almost trivial but I believe it has had great therapeutic moment. It is the assurance the therapist can have that he will find ample and tangible material for psychotherapeutic work. He can set aside concerns that he is confronted by some mysterious ailment of metabolic origin and that he is struggling with useless epiphenomena, doubts fostered by the weight of tradition and bolstered by the constant flow of articles announcing the discovery of some new metabolic defect, none of which is subsequently verified—doubts to which the therapist may be vulnerable because of the discouraging turns that are an inevitable part of the work with schizophrenic patients. He can also feel assured that the problems are not beyond the reach of a psychotherapeutic approach, or that they may only become accessible after prolonged analysis. Assurance is essential because the therapist must arouse glimmers of hope in a person who has abandoned hope of coping with the world and those who people it; and the schizophrenic patient is unusually sensitive to pretense of conviction.

Further, the therapist can feel assured that the material he needs to establish a meaningful relationship is not cryptic, for some guides are usually fairly obvious to one who can but observe and hear them.

Let us consider a seventeen-year-old high school student whom I saw on the day I wrote these paragraphs. He had been flown to the hospital from a preparatory school where he had started behaving strangely, expressing delusions and talking almost incoherently. When I asked what brought him to the hospital, he responded, "My mother." "Your mother?" I asked. "My mother is a witch!—A seductive witch—No, she's a wonderful person—She won't let me do anything I want—No one is good enough for me—She controls me and my father is a weak man who does what she wants—He's a strong man—He was a West Pointer—He beat the hell out of me when I was little." He slipped back and forth, talking of the preparatory school and the nursery school he had once attended, but through it ran themes of ambivalence to his two unhappy parents and their conflicts, and his inability to be free from his mother's needs and demands. Yet, not so many years ago much of what he said about his witch mother, who seduced and controlled, would have been disregarded as but a reflection of his schizophrenic illness.

Even when the patient is out of contact, highly pertinent directives may be inadvertently provided by the parents.

For example, a college girl was admitted to the hospital after having been removed from a train bewildered and acutely delusional. I interviewed her parents when they arrived. In terms of the history alone, the girl's desperate condition sounded much like a bolt out of the blue. She had been a fine student who was interested in writing, somewhat shy but sociable and well liked by her friends and roommates. However, the session itself was replete with material familiar to those who work with parents of schizophrenic patients. The mother did all of the talking, while the father, a wealthy art dealer, remained silent. When I directed remarks at him, I gained a response from his wife. Even when I turned my back on the mother and pointedly placed a question to the father, she intruded before he completed a sentence. It was difficult to learn much about the patient for the mother told about herself, her Pilgrim ancestry, and her ambitions as a writer. When I finally interrupted and asked about the daughter's college career and her interests, I learned that the girl's whole life revolved about becoming a novelist; she had a passion for Virginia Woolf. The mother became enthusiastic; she prayed that her daughter would become another Virginia Woolf. I hesitated, and then commented, "But Virginia Woolf had psychotic episodes and committed suicide." The mother did not hesitate when she replied, "It would be worth it."

I could form a working hypothesis that in this family the parents' marriage was skewed, with the mother dominating the family transactions, preempting roles usually filled by the husband and unable properly to fill the maternal expressive-affectional role, at least toward this daughter. The father, no matter how competent in his career, did not occupy much of the masculine, instrumental role in the family. The mother's interest in the patient was egocentric, seeking to raise a daughter who would carry out her own frustrated ambitions, and she was likely to be intrusive but impervious to the girl's own desires and needs. The girl probably felt accepted only insofar as she could salvage her mother's own frustrated ambitions.

While making rounds some weeks later I noted several novels by Virginia Woolf in the patient's room and asked about them. She replied in a flat voice, "Mother sent them—she has a thing about Virginia Woolf." Over the next months the patient talked of her despair over her inadequacies as a writer, her desires for a marriage in which she could help a husband assert himself, and her resentments over her obligation to live out her mother's aspirations for her. I had some difficulty in believing that she was complying to the extent of becoming psychotic like Virginia Woolf, which proved a serious error, a fatal error. When the patient emerged from her psychosis, her mother insisted she continue her treatment on the West Coast where they lived. At home, caught up in her mother's control, she relapsed, and then followed the fate foisted upon her by committing suicide.

The therapist cannot only feel secure that meaningful material for psychotherapy will be available, but he can anticipate the nature of the problems upon which the therapeutic transactions will usually focus. As I have noted, difficulties exist in virtually all aspects of the family transactions throughout the patient's life, and we have set down our findings elsewhere. I would now like to extrapolate from this abundant material those difficulties that I currently believe are essentially schizophrenogenic.

When we began our studies, we considered that the patient's dependency and symbiotic needs followed upon the mother's inability to establish boundaries between herself and her child (Lidz and Lidz, 1952). Needing the patient to complete her own life, often to live out the life that was closed to her because she was a woman, she failed to differentiate her own needs and feelings from those of her offspring, who then could not develop as a separate individual. His energies and attention went primarily into giving meaning to his mother's life and supporting her tenuous emotional equilibrium, rather than into his own development. The child could not clearly distinguish his needs, feelings, and wishes from those of his mother. I believe that these observations, which had also been made by Reichard and Tillman (1950) and which were elaborated by Hill (1955), were on the right track. However, it is not always the mother's inability to differentiate from the child that leads to the patient's failure properly to establish boundaries between himself and others and attain a distinct identity. The father may be the prime source of such difficulties, particularly with daughters, or with sons when the father has strong homosexual tendencies (Raybin, 1969; Chapter X). Then, too, when the parents' marriage is markedly schismatic, the child may be caught in the conflict so that his major investment lies in seeking to bridge the gap between the parents, perhaps even by serving as a scapegoat upon whom the burden of the parental difficulties can be placed. The result is much the same in that his own emergence as a person is thwarted and sacrificed to preserve one or both parents. He is prematurely burdened by a task that stifles his development. Study reveals that one parent—or both—is profoundly egocentric; that is to say, the parent is seriously handicapped in being able to understand others only in terms of his own life. Not only is the child understood merely as an extension of the parent's existence, but the spouse is also treated egocentrically; and events are perceived only in terms of the parent's life and needs, and are often distorted to fit into an extremely egocentric view of the world. Now, whereas the parent is limited, at least he or she has an egocentric orientation and strives to preserve his integration. The patient, however, is not as fortunate, for his orientation is mother-centered or parent-centered; he views the world according to the parent's feelings, needs, and defenses, and lives to protect the persons from whom he has not properly differentiated (Lidz, 1973).

Fortunately, this statement of the situation is something of an exaggeration. Most patients who become schizophrenic in late adolescence or adult life have been able to try to differentiate and live their own lives, but because they are poorly prepared to understand others and to relate to them, they become enmeshed in difficulties and give up. Successful regression is impossible, for it leads back to dependency upon the engulfing parent, who arouses homicidal impulses or provokes incestuous fears. The questions of how the patient solves this dilemma and where he seeks refuge lead us to consider the thought disorder that forms the essence of schizophrenia.

As various investigators have pointed out, the patient's foundations in the meaning system and logic of his culture had been faulty. My colleagues and I described the transmission of irrationality within the family because of the parents' proclivities to distort reality in order to maintain their own precarious emotional equilibria. Commonly patients had been placed in a "double bind" (Bateson et al., 1956) in seeking to fill a parent's mutually exclusive demands in order to feel loved or accepted; or had become perplexed about the utility of verbal communication because of the discrepancies between what parents said and what they conveyed by their behavior, or because of "the mystification" (Laing, 1962), in their contradictory communications. As Wynne and Singer (1963a, 1963b; Singer and Wynne, 1965a, 1965b) have amply demonstrated, there is a strange amorphous or fragmented quality in the parents' communications. The patient who is parent-centered tends to perceive in terms of a parent's needs rather than in terms of how perception and communication help him master his environment and how others in his community perceive and understand. Those patients who had been caught between irreconcilable parents try to maintain irreconcilable versions of the world that can only be brought together and resolved paralogically.

There is another aspect of the problem of the schizophrenic thought disorder that is difficult to explain succinctly. In order to perceive, think, or communicate, one must divide the ceaseless flow of experience into categories. By and large the vocabulary of a language is a catalogue of the categories a culture uses in dividing experience. In learning the language the child learns what his society considers essential or useful in understanding the world, and also what can be neglected and what must be ignored. This division of experience into categories requires the separation of what is actually a continuity. Experience is continuous—categories are discrete. Each culture teaches its members to ignore what would blur boundaries between essential categories. A fundamental step in establishing categories that must occur in each child's life concerns the differentiation of the self from the non-self. Every culture places a taboo on things that had been self and become non-self, such as secretions and excretions (Leach, 1966); and upon fusions of the self and the mother, as in nursing and the oedipal ties; and also upon other blurrings of essential divisions, such as the attributes of the two sexes. In persons who become schizophrenic, such boundaries have never been clearly established—between the self and the mother, between what is masculine and feminine—and these failures affect subsequent category formation and conceptualization. It is in the hiatus, in the nebulous region that lies between categories that the schizophrenic finds refuge. Often he returns to fantasies of a vague union with the mother in which boundaries are obliterated, a union that is now sexualized in a polymorphous perverse manner; and to a state where he is neither clearly male nor female, and where the burdens of being an individual self have vanished (Lidz, 1968). Others, perhaps less able to regress in this fashion, but still with poor boundaries between the self and others, attribute their own impulses to others in what we term projection, or seek to control forbidden impulses by extrojecting poorly internalized parental prohibitions as hallucinations and delusions.

I believe that this explication of what I currently consider to be the crux of the schizophrenic situation provides the therapist with guidelines through the maze of data and the perplexing contradictions of the patient's communication and behavior; it permits the therapist to gain and retain perspective despite the booby traps that the patient can so adroitly set for him, and despite the inevitable flights from reinvolvement with the world and the unreliable, egocentric individuals who people it.

The therapist can know that the basic therapeutic task lies in releasing the patient from the bondage of completing a parent's life or of bridging the divisiveness between his parents, and in enabling the patient to become a person in his own right, investing his energies in his own development rather than remaining tied to the problems of the preceding generation. The therapist persistently fosters the patient's latent desires for individuation that he has given up as hopeless, and counters his fears of rejection and abandonment if he asserts his own needs and desires and his terror that self-assertion and expression of his ambivalent hostilities will destroy his parents. The patient must become capable of perceiving his parents, their behavior, and the interpersonal environment differently from the way his parents need to see these matters and from the way his parents require him to see them, and he must learn to trust his own feelings and perceptions.

Now, such therapeutic tasks require an approach that differs in many ways from conventional psychoanalytically oriented therapy. Many analysts who are interested in schizophrenic patients become discouraged because of attempts to remain as classically analytic as possible, in part because they are uncomfortable without the techniques with which they became familiar in work with neurotic patients, but also because they have not adequately considered the differences in the nature of these conditions. Most, if not all, psychoanalysts who treat schizophrenic patients with reasonable success have greatly modified psychoanalytic techniques, often developing approaches that are psychoanalytic only in being genetic-dynamic, in utilizing certain psychoanalytic insights, and in fostering the patient to take as much initiative as seems feasible at any given time. Free association, for a person who is already flooded by extraneous associations and primary process material, must be replaced with means of guiding the patient into clearer conceptualizations and the use of common modes of communication. Thus, waiting and long silences have little use; the patient is weaned from his autistic world and idiosyncratic communication by the therapist's ability to hear what the patient seeks to express even as he seeks to conceal in terms of metaphor and cryptic associations. We wish him to regain the filtering function of categories and cohesive conceptualizations rather than remain in the nebulous realm of egocentric ruminations. Lessening the perceptual contact by placing the patient on the couch, increases feelings of vulnerability as well as fostering delusions based on transference to the therapist of a parent's incestuous behavior. In general, we are seeking to strengthen ego functions rather than have the patient set them aside for the purpose of associating freely. I am reminded that James Joyce is reputed to have asked Carl Jung, "Why is it that I write whatever associations come into my mind, and I'm considered a great novelist, but because my daughter talks that way she's called schizophrenic?" "It is the difference," Jung answered, "between diving and drowning." In a similar vein we do not foster anxiety to achieve proper therapeutic movement for anxiety lowers the stimulus barrier and is apt to disorganize further; nor do we challenge and analyze distortions arising from mechanisms of defense of the ego as much as the distortions imposed by the parents' needs to defend their own tenuous egos. We seek to imbue in the patient trust in his own feelings and ideas while we question those that are essentially his parents' feelings and perceptions offered as his own. The patient is apt to test repeatedly the therapist's ability to differentiate between the two. Our knowledge of the common dilemmas and life situations of schizophrenic patients, knowledge gained from direct family studies, has particular importance in permitting us to be alert to what the patient is saying in his strange ways. The schizophrenic must come to trust verbal communication, and he does so by learning that the therapist listens to what the patient says and means what he says, but is not imposing his ideas upon the patient. Thus, the therapist does not interpret so much as seek clarification of nebulous material from the patient. Then, too, whereas a therapist commonly questions why a neurotic patient blames his parents, and interprets in terms of distortions created by oedipal conflicts, he encourages the schizophrenic patient to express feelings about parents even if those feelings contain projective elements—for only then can the patient begin to sort out his confusions about his parents and properly question their attitudes and demands.

The schizophrenic patient develops a relationship to his therapist when he can trust, and he trusts when he feels understood and when he begins to dare believe that the therapist will not use him or abandon him because he is understood. But the therapeutic relationship is long a tenuous thread before it becomes a means of reliving and reevaluating childhood experiences. Indeed, it is likely to start as an anaclitic relationship in which the patient seeks omnipotent and omniscient care from the therapist. The patient is incapable of ambivalence, and the therapist is subject to "splitting"; he is either "good" when bestowing and caring or "bad" when denying or when he fails to understand. The therapist is all too readily misunderstood, and it takes a long time until the patient learns that he can feel both affection and hostility toward the same person depending on the circumstances, and until then a real transference relationship cannot develop. The relationship is also fraught with the actual dangers of the patient's childhood intrafamilial relationships. A therapist's interest, concern, care, and affection are apt to be equated with parents' intrusiveness and envelopment, and with their imperviousness to the patient's own needs and feelings. In brief, a major requirement for the therapist concerns the ability to care and refuse to give up while not needing the patient or his devotion. The therapist seeks to convey that even though he wants very much for the patient to improve and will go a long way and make personal sacrifices to foster such improvement, he pursues this goal neither for the parents' sake nor because of his own need for a therapeutic success.

Then, too, because the patient has learned to disregard what is said, the unspoken signals are of great importance. "I long ago learned to stop listening and note how mother was feeling," said one young woman. Much has been written about the schizophrenic patient's intuitive capacities. They have learned to base their interactions with parents on indications and to become skilled in responding to feelings. However, despite such abilities or because such abilities are based upon relationships with peculiar parents, schizophrenic patients often misinterpret. Similarly, it is often difficult to know what a remark will mean to the patient, who can plunge into inchoate blackness of despair because of an imagined rebuff. It is important to counter a patient's tendency to consider the therapist as omniscient, for errors and misunderstandings are bound to occur; and many schizophrenic patients have learned that they must accept the parent's views or be rebuffed. The relationship can also be threatened by the common practice of considering as projections the patient's concerns that the therapist will seduce, or that the therapist wishes to be rid of him. A woman who seems to believe firmly that her analysis will lead to an affair with her analyst may be projecting her wishes to some extent, but, basically, she is transferring to the therapist her hope and fear that if she shows affection, he will seduce her, even as her father had started masturbating her when she became pubescent.

As many schizophrenic patients were raised by parents who had vacillated between intrusive closeness and inattentive withdrawal into their own fantasies or problems, establishing a proper working distance in therapy presents difficulties. A patient's feelings that I was withdrawn in some sessions and oppressively intrusive in others depended upon inadvertent changes of two or three inches in the customary placement of her chair. In general, schizophrenic patients have been burned by having been seduced into involvement with their engulfing parents, and because of the pain have renounced forever hopes of any meaningful relationships. They are wary and must be wary. When they find their resistances to the therapist melting they are very likely to flee . . . flee the hospital, flee into panic, or flee into withdrawn states. The therapist who has properly been encouraged by the developing relationship can become profoundly discouraged and even give up or fall back on a primary reliance on neuroleptics. This is a critical moment in treatment that must be anticipated even though it does not always occur. Now the therapist is being tested and if he persists and surmounts the rebuff, therapeutic movement can gain momentum, for a less tentative relationship will follow.

I have, perhaps, dwelt too long on how certain core problems in establishing and maintaining a useful therapeutic relationship gain meaning in the light of the family studies. Knowledge of the types of settings from which schizophrenic patients emerge provides guidance in many other ways. I shall offer a few examples rather than endeavor to be comprehensive.

Let us consider the common preoccupations of schizophrenic patients with homosexuality and with fears of undergoing a change of gender. An appreciation of the parents' confused gender identities and failures to maintain the gender-linked roles provides a therapeutic approach that is more useful than ideas about innate bisexuality. A firm sexual identity forms a foundation of a stable ego identity. In these families a child does not have a suitable model for identification in the parent of the same sex, whose worth is further undercut by the parent of the opposite sex whose love the child seeks. Sometimes the parents have virtually reversed gender roles and in other cases a parent's homosexual tendencies are apparent. A schizophrenic youth with many effeminate traits and homosexual and masochistic preoccupations had an alcoholic father who had been an eminent football player. The father was contemptuous of his effete, artistic son, whereas the mother had fostered his esthetic development, conveying the idea that he must not become like his crass father. Eventually, the youth began to speak of his notions that his father had homosexual tendencies. They were not projections. His mother abreacted with a social worker the anguish she had experienced when her husband had admitted that his attraction to athletics involved his fascination with nude male bodies, and when his impotence and his intense attachment to a fellow athlete had marred the early years of their marriage. The homosexual concerns of the patient could be approached meaningfully in terms of his perceptions of his father, who represented the type of man attractive to his mother, and in terms of the unacceptability of masculinity when it meant the callousness he and his mother had experienced from his father—and later through attention to his unresolved identification with his mother.

Fears of incest, which create panic because the patient fears proximity to the parent he needs, are not simply regressions and projections but reflect both the parents' own incestuous tendencies and the pathological family structure. A young man who had brought a girl friend into the home to sleep with him after his father left his mother was incoherent when hospitalized, but his mother begged, "You must cure him—he is all of my life—when he started to become sick I slept with him just like man and wife." A young woman who had been hospitalized because of her confusion and public promiscuity had her genitalia examined by her physician father each time she returned home from a date to make certain she was still a virgin.

We learn, too, that not all of the poor habits and sloppiness of the patient are evidence of schizophrenic dilapidation; some are reflections of the failure of parents to inculcate basic social behavior and essential adaptive techniques. A young male patient befriended a schizophrenic young woman and took her out to dinner. He reported to his psychiatrist that he could not continue the friendship for he could scarcely eat because of his disgust with the girl's sloppiness. She not only spilled food all over herself but blew her nose in the napkin. When the matter was broached with the young woman, she wanted to know what was wrong—her father, an eminent professor, blew his nose in his napkin. Another young woman always appeared untidy, and the nurses observed that she did not know how to put her nylons on properly nor how to adjust her brassiere. At the age of twenty-six she would not go to buy a properly fitting bra; she did not know how, for her mother had always brought them home for her. Such lack of education concerning social amenities can, in turn, interfere with socialization with peers, from whom the adolescent must learn so much about interpersonal relationships. We have come to appreciate that many schizophrenic patients require guidance in techniques of living and need group experiences which promote interchange about personal behavior to supplement or offset the intrafamilial experiences.

Along similar lines, the patient's thought disorder requires specific attention. It is not simply a regression or an intrusion of autistic primary process material, but a complex resultant of the parents' amorphous or fragmented styles of communicating, of poor training in categorizing, of having been taught paranoid mistrust within the home, of the paralogical thinking that results from trying to elude the "double bind," of thinking irrationally to suit the parents' egocentric needs. The topic is too large to pursue here. However, a major function of the special high school for adolescents in the Yale Psychiatric Institute lies in providing a type of instruction that counters the schizophrenic patient's overinclusive thinking and enhances focal attention and clear conceptualization. The therapist can promote such changes by fostering clear boundaries between the patient and others, and by clarifying conflicting feelings and attitudes. Increasingly, however, I have focused specifically on freeing the patient from the need to distort his perceptions and meanings to fit into his parents' aberrant version of the world. It is a difficult passage, but when accomplished, the patient is out of the mire and on more solid ground.

Conjoint family therapy when used as an adjunct to individual therapy can be particularly helpful. In the family sessions the patient may be unable to avoid realizing that one or both of his parents distort reality to their own needs, that they will reject the patient if he challenges their defenses, and that their remarks are untrustworthy. The patient may have become capable of assessing what his parents say through his experiences in therapeutic groups where participants challenge others and comment on defensive maneuvers. The patient finds it easier to cope with the actual parent with a therapist present than with the parent as a malignant introject. The woman who had not known how to purchase a brassiere had made little progress until conjoint family sessions were started. She had considered her mother as a perfect woman who had long sacrificed herself to keep the family solvent after the father had become depressed and ineffectual. In the family sessions, whenever the patient sought to discuss problems in the home that had troubled her childhood and adolescence, the mother consistently shifted to talking about the patient's difficulties as a child, intimating that no parent could have been successful with an inherently disturbed child. Yet, at other times, she would insist that the patient had been a normal but highly gifted child. With but slight help from the therapist, the inconsistencies came into focus. Then, in a crucial session, the patient saw her mother in a new light. The mother persistently asked to have the patient at home for a weekend, but in these meetings it became apparent that whenever the patient could make the trip, the mother found the occasion unsuitable. Eventually, the visit home could not be sidestepped. During the subsequent session the father criticized the patient for various trivial shortcomings during the weekend. The patient finally said that although it had been good to be home she would have enjoyed it more if her father had not nagged so much. The mother immediately snapped, "Your father never nags." The patient was silent, but later remarked, "You know, Mother, I am just realizing that I often feel ill at ease with you." To this the mother replied, "If you are, you are the only person I know who is." The bind had been placed, but it was too apparent. There was no argument, no blow-up, but the patient now began to express her own feelings and her own ideas.

The priority I have given to discussing how knowledge of the patient's family milieu can serve to guide psychotherapy does not indicate a disinterest in direct work with the family. Indeed, I believe that neglect of the family has been a major cause of therapeutic failure. Particularly with youthful patients efforts must be made to modify parental attitudes toward the patient as well as the patient's attitudes toward his parents. All too often when a patient is hospitalized a member of the staff elicits a history from the parents, notes that they are difficult or even troublesome, and lets them know that they have handed over their offspring to competent surrogates. Of course, it seems simpler if the staff can focus on the patient without the family's interference—but the family problems cannot be avoided through avoidance of the family. The opposite extreme—of hospitalizing the family with the patient, as carried out experimentally by Bowen and his colleagues (1957)—does not permit the patient the disengagement that is a major purpose of hospitalization.

If the parents were not difficult or peculiar, it is unlikely that the patient would be schizophrenic, but this does not mean that they are not intensely involved with their child, whose hospitalization is one of the unhappiest experiences in their lives. They require support lest one of them or the marriage collapse under the strain. They also need to face the family problems rather than believe that their child's illness is the major source of their unhappiness and difficulties. Commonly, therapists who know that months or years of intensive work will be required with a patient, somehow expect the parents to change simply because they are told to do so.

The premature removal of the youthful schizophrenic patient just as a good therapeutic relationship is being established is often a major frustration in hospital treatment (Fleck et al., 1957). The parents are likely to remove their child for several reasons. The mother cannot believe that her son or daughter can survive without her, a concern that earlier had caused the school phobia from which many of these patients had suffered, and which had blocked their socialization with peers. Only a person who has worked with such mothers after their children have been hospitalized can appreciate the almost unbearable anxiety they suffer. The mother must control the treatment because no one can understand or really care for her unique child. The parent may also dread the patient's growing attachment to the therapist, experiencing it as total abandonment. Then, when as part of his improvement the patient displays hostility to the parents, they know that he has become sicker and find reasons to remove him from the hospital. If the staff members have been hostile to the parents or have neglected them, they can more readily believe that the hospital is turning the patient against them. Such crises must be anticipated and headed off. When someone on the staff understands the parents' problems, keeps them informed, and works with them to modify their concerns about the patient and their fears of losing their offspring, they are less likely to disrupt the therapy.

The removal of the patient from the family commonly creates a familial crisis. The difficulties with the patient had served to mask the incompatibilities of the parents; or the mother becomes anxious and depressed, deprived of the major focus of her life; or recriminations flare into the open, with each parent blaming the other for their child's illness; or another child now feels the brunt of the family difficulties. The hospital cannot fully shelter the patient from the aggravated family problems. Sometimes, the family establishes a new equilibrium without the patient, particularly when the parents have been excluded from the hospital. The family closes ranks, leaving no room for the patient, and despite protests to the contrary, will resist resuming any responsibility for him—a common cause of abandonment of patients in state hospitals.

Stanton and Schwartz (1954) made a major contribution to the understanding of the treatment process when they pointed out that flare-ups of disorganized behavior often occurred in response to disagreements among the staff members about the patient. The patient had become sensitized by being the focal point of the family schisms and sometimes had been a master at provoking them in his role as a scapegoat for parental conflicts. In the hospital he is apt to be sensitive to the expressed or covert disagreements about him between parents, or between parents and staff, or among staff, and caught between his loyalties, he covers the situation by regressive behavior. It is worth a great deal of effort to try to unite the parents concerning the need for hospitalization and the plan of treatment, even if they cannot agree about anything else. Neglect of the parents, hostile exclusion of them, or condescension toward them often lead to aggravation of the patient's condition even though the psychiatrist may believe that the patient needs protection from their malignant influence.

Indeed, it has now become apparent—how had it been overlooked?—that the acute onset of many schizophrenic reactions, or the exacerbation that leads to hospitalization, follows upon the patient's being placed in an insoluble bind by his parents' impending separation. The patient is pulled in two directions by the competing parents—a condition reflected in the ideation of the catatonic excitement or stupor. A few days ago I listened to an interview with a graduate student who had suffered several catatonic episodes. She told of her delusions during the first episode, when she believed that everyone in the world loved her but she was responsible for their well being. At the time, her parents had finally decided to end their unhappy marriage. Both used the patient, their oldest child, as a confidant and sought her as an ally. Her mother told the patient that she feared the father would seduce the patient's pubescent sister, with whom he frequently slept. The father confided that the mother was a lesbian and a menace to the three daughters.

When one realizes that an acutely disturbed patient is responding to an approaching break-up of his parents' marriage in which he is torn between them or knows that he will be left irrevocably tied to the task of salvaging a parent's life, one can accomplish considerable therapeutic work even when the patient is inaccessible. A sixteen-year-old youth was admitted in an extreme state of excitation, believing that an atom bomb had destroyed the city, that he alone remained alive, and that no one else was real. During the several months during which he remained out of contact, it was possible to modify his parents' relationship so that they no longer planned to separate. At first, the mother, who claimed she had only remained with her highly eccentric husband for the children's sake, had become even more determined to leave him, blaming him for their son's psychosis. However, as discussions continued, she realized that they had both been at fault: Their marriage had never led to a proper family life because both were pathologically tied to their families of origin, each of which undercut the worth of the other. The patient, who had long sought to bridge this schism, had become terrified at the prospect of being the mother's major support in the absence of his grandiose father. Receiving emotional support from the hospital staff during the crisis, the parents stopped blaming one another and began to face their shortcomings as spouses and parents. They supported one another sufficiently to give up their stranglehold on their son and later to accept the advice to send their son to a preparatory school. Their difficulties were far from resolved—the father's severe pathology precluded any easy solution—but they managed to have their son remain away from home and from further involvement in their problems.

At present the current flows strongly in the direction of

brief hospitalization for schizophrenic patients lest the hospital foster regression or increased withdrawal from socialization. A hospital that is a therapeutic community does not promote regression but provides a retreat from living situations that have overwhelmed the patient, and fosters the socializing experiences with peers he had lacked at home. The pathology of the family is extensive and can be changed only under fortunate circumstances and with prolonged and intensive therapeutic work with the family. It forms a pathogenic environment, particularly for the patient who has become sensitized to it. Even after a prolonged hospital stay, it is usually unwise for the patient to return to his family. It requires considerable work with the parents as well as the patient to make such separation possible, but it is often vital for any definitive and lasting change in the patient's life.

We would like to believe that we can alter the family transactions and modify the parents' attitudes sufficiently to permit the patient to return to more normal ways and resume his development. This is the goal of conjoint family therapy, which some psychiatrists now believe is the treatment of choice for schizophrenic patients. Undoing the influences that had been throttling or distorting the patient's development throughout his formative years is scarcely possible without intensive psychotherapeutic work with the patient. It is a very different matter from eliciting changes in the family when the child is still very young. Moreover, the parents are no longer youthful and their personalities and patterns of interaction are set. Still it is worth the effort for when inroads are made, changes in the family are followed by significant changes in the patient. Although conjoint family therapy has much to offer in clarifying family problems to the family members, and can open the way for profound changes in attitudes, my own experience leads me to doubt its effectiveness as the sole approach rather than as part of a more total program of treatment for both the patient and the family. Another highly useful form of family therapy is carried out in open-ended parents' groups. In these groups parents not only relate to others with similar problems and can together try to work out some solutions, but also may be able to see in others what they had been unable to see in themselves.

I have sought to present some of the influences upon the treatment of schizophrenic patients that have been emerging with the realization that these patients have grown up in seriously disturbed and distorting family environments, and with our increasing knowledge of what these families are like and just how they have failed to provide certain requisites for the patient's integrated development. I have considered some of the ways in which such knowledge provides directives for psychotherapy with the patient, and also for effecting changes in the family situation, in the parents' relationships with each other, and in their attitudes toward the patient. Techniques utilized will vary, and should vary, according to the personality and training of the therapist as well as being suited to the specific patient; but I believe that certain fundamentals are basic to all approaches: these have to do with the therapist's ways of relating to a patient who has become hopeless and befuddled because of his parents' needs, self-deceptions, and inability to regard and respect the patient as a discrete individual with needs and feelings of his own. What counts in tempting the patient from withdrawn disillusionment and idiosyncratic ways of understanding the world is openness—a willingness to examine the patient's experiences, appreciating their validity as ways of experiencing, and his desperate need to try to find some meaning in his chaotic family environment; to avoid the temptation to seem omniscient and to respect the patient's individuality and wish to guide his own life; to be able to counter his despair by conveying that life can be meaningful and worth living. For some therapists the way to establish such relatedness is very simply to become involved in learning from and with the patient, and rather than "treating" him to explore a life together with the patient. We cannot always change the family situation and we cannot often change it profoundly. We must seek to make it possible for the patient to escape from it into a different way of living rather than into irrationality and delusion. Occasionally, the patient gains sufficient independence, rationality, and perspective to appreciate that his parents had been so deprived in their own childhoods, so caught up in a net created by their parents' difficulties, that they could not have been different than they were, and that he, the patient, cannot salvage their lives for them, but rather has all he can do to make something of his own and break the pathological chain that has extended from generation to generation. Then, the ambivalent animosities toward his parents and his fears of them can dissolve into compassion for them. It was such compassionate resolution that Tennessee Williams sought in writing *The Glass Menagerie* long after he had fled his home and that Eugene O'Neill strove to work out in the series of plays that culminated in *Long Day's Journey into Night*. The patient is unlikely to achieve such understanding if the therapist regards parents as villains and feels hostile to them, rather than grasping the tragedy of the parents' lives even as he seeks to understand and empathize with the patient.

POSTSCRIPT

Although the chapter has sought primarily to convey how knowledge of the family environment in which the patient grew up can provide direction for the psychotherapist, it seems useful to add brief comments concerning predicaments arising from some current concepts of schizophrenic disorders.

Because of the traditional teachings about the bland affect of schizophrenic patients, therapists may become confused when the patient becomes depressed, and change the diagnosis to Schizoaffective in keeping with the DSM III attitude that schizophrenia and schizoaffective conditions are discrete illnesses. The therapist may then resort to antidepressive agents or lithium to counter the affective illness. Becoming depressed is a common occurrence when the patient starts to recover. The patient begins to face the reality of his or her cardinal relationships and experiences despair. Indeed, a major difficulty in the psychotherapy of schizophrenic patients is to have the patient become willing to face and reexperience the hopelessness, helplessness, and despair over the family situation. Depression, particularly anaclitic depression, must be anticipated when the patient leaves the hospital or when treatment is terminated, for the sense of helpless neediness recurs, but it can be a transitory regression if essential temporary support is provided.

It is also essential to recognize during the current epoch of reliance on neuroleptic medications, that little effective psychotherapy can be carried out when the patient's mental and affective capacities are stultified by large doses of drugs. Neuroleptics can be very useful in diminishing agitation, delusions, and hallucinations and lessen the difficulties in forming a therapeutic relationship; but high dosages cover over, rarely resolve problems, and diminish the patient's motivation by countering affect. It may be useful to consider that neuroleptic medication should be titrated according to the therapeutic relationship, and when necessary increased to help patients during episodes of particular stress. The practice of trying a different combination of medications each time the patient becomes upset can further impede psychotherapy by conveying the impression to the patient that drugs control whereas the patient cannot be expected to have self-control and that improvement rests on medication rather than on solving the problems that have confronted the patient.[1]

---

[1] A related but later presentation of the author's therapeutic orientation can be found in *The Origin and Treatment of Schizophrenic Disorders* (Lidz, 1973) and a more recent discussion of the critical aspects of the therapy of schizophrenic patients in "Curative Factors in the Psychotherapy of Schizophrenic Disorders" (Lidz and Lidz, 1982).

XVIII

Some Observations on the Nature and Value of Psychotherapy with Schizophrenic Patients

(1980)

Although the following chapter is not directly related to our re-search on the families of schizophrenic patients, it reflects many of the insights gained from the studies. It is included primarily because it conveys a fundamental requirement of intensive psychotherapy with schizophrenic patients that was not made explicit in preceding chap-ters; namely, the extent of the commitment required of therapists—a readiness to experience considerable concern, inconvenience, and even some disturbance of their own lives; and at the same time the ability to establish boundaries between the patient and the therapist.

Medical practitioners, meaning physicians during the scientific era as much as during the prescientific millennia, have always drawn inferences from more or less impressionistic therapeutic effects upon the nature of causation or etiology. Equally often, an etiological theory, once formulated, has led to therapeutic prescription, or even, in the case of schizophrenia, to therapeutic nihilism. The history of the treatment of schizophrenics is replete with enthusiastic therapeutic endeavors, sometimes based on very erroneous premises, such as the alleged mutual exclusion of epilepsy and schizophre-

Stephen Fleck: Some Observations on the Nature and Value of Psychotherapy with Schizophrenic Patients. *The Psychotherapy of Schizophrenia.* J. S. Strauss, M. Bowers, T. W. Downey, S. Fleck, and I. Levine, eds. Copyright © 1980. Plenum Medical Book Co., New York. This paper was presented at the conference on the Psychotherapy of Schizophrenia held in honor of Ruth W. and Theodore Lidz on April 9 and 10, 1979 in New Haven, CT.

nia, which led to convulsive treatments, therapies which then led to other etiological credos (Bleuler, 1978b; Jackson, 1973; von Medina, 1937; Sakhel, 1936). Psychotherapy, effective as it can be with schizophrenics, is no exception to such *post hoc propter hoc* etiological hypothesizing. We know that the pathogenic mechanisms in psychological development and in familial behaviors which we can identify during psychotherapeutic work are basic, but we do not know if they are the only, *sine qua non* etiological factors. They, or some chromosomal aberration, may or may not be the first level in a spiral of abnormalities, but this is as uncertain as is the position or role of abnormal dopamine activity in such a developmental spiral culminating in schizophrenic manifestations.

What is overridingly important is that chemical measures affect certain symptoms and behaviors in particular, often those that can prohibit the patient's even sitting for any length of time; but that, with or without medication, schizophrenics can also be treated psychologically, and that all of them, especially young ones, require psychosocial treatments, psychoeducational guidance, and rehabilitation and even socialization.

In contrast to these relatively technical measures, dyadic psychotherapy is primarily the use of self—all of one's self—on behalf of another person. This includes those aspects of one's person with which one would rather not be acquainted. In psychotherapeutic work with schizophrenics in particular, attention to these more archaic facets within ourselves may be as important as our cognitive selves (i.e., our knowledge of theories or facts about personality development and structure, about the biology of schizophrenia, and the chemistry of neurotransmitter systems).

Using oneself in this total way on behalf of another, specifically a schizophrenic person, is anxiety-provoking as well as unbelievably fatiguing. Yet, without such total investment of oneself, I do not consider the psychotherapy of schizophrenics a valid endeavor, especially for therapy evaluation purposes, even though other so-called psychotherapeutic measures, like behavioral techniques, especially in groups, and sociotherapy, are also important, as already indicated. Yet, when colleagues like Elvin Semrad and Otto Will, and others speak of psychotherapy of schizophrenics, I believe, indeed, I know, that it is this total psychoemotional involvement of one person with another that most of them have in mind (Fromm-Reichmann, 1939; Gunderson, 1978; Hill, 1955; Sechehaye, 1951; Semrad et al., 1952; Will, 1975). Other writings and discussions of psychotherapy of schizophrenia, including some studies in which some of these same colleagues have participated, like the remarkable research at the Massachusetts Mental Health Center under Grinspoon (1972), or studies done by May (1968) on the West Coast, do not conform to the model of therapy as I have defined it (Fleck, 1978). There is currently also a tendency to define psychotherapy negatively (i.e., everything that is not somatic or drug treatment is called psychotherapeutic). Psychotherapy with severely disturbed schizophrenics cannot usually be accomplished in two sessions a week, or incident to dispensing medications, although the frequency of encounters is by and large less important than is the nature of the mutual investment in exploring the difficulties both the patient and the therapist experience in their encounters (Semrad et al., 1952; Will, 1975).

Some years ago a forty-six-year-old professional married woman, the mother of several children, was referred to me by an older colleague with the mandate to get her back into the hospital. She had been first diagnosed as schizophrenic more than five years earlier and had been hospitalized much of the time since then. She had received insulin and electric shock treatments but had remitted for only several months at a time. She had been out of the hospital for about a year at the time of referral and had worked during part of that time effectively in psychotherapy with a colleague, until a month before the referral when she again became psychotic for reasons she nor her therapist could understand or work out together. She was then seen by still another colleague, who, after a couple of sessions, rejected her, she felt, and she was referred to me. Although blatantly psychotic and a considerable burden to her family, she adamantly refused to return to any hospital—a stand which I could respect and I therefore proceeded to explore with her how she could live at home, and, for the time being come to see me for therapy every day. She was willing to see me, but not every day, although she gave in on that point and we quickly established a working relationship, with subsidence of her overt psychotic symptoms. However, after a few weeks, she failed to keep her appointment and over the phone refused to return or tell me why she would not return. During a second phone call that day, she agreed to come and discuss her decision not to continue in treatment with me. When she came, she was sullen and silent. During the previous two sessions, she had expressed wishes to be close to me. Once I focused on these expressions, specifically on her fantasy that she would like to be down at the beach with me skipping along in the sand and holding hands, she suddenly glared at me and said, "Yes, and you put your hand in your pocket." I acknowledged that I might have done so, although I was not aware of it, and that her interpretation that I rejected her wish was correct insofar as I wished to work with her and could not do so skipping along at the beach, holding hands or not. At this she brightened up and we continued treatment for several years.

I will return to some other facets of her treatment later to illustrate further how difficult it can be to fathom and encompass the total process and interchanges. The therapist cannot afford to be lax in awareness of himself, his actions, or his own needs and defenses.

Our more systematic understanding of such personal investment and interpersonal engagement began with Freud, who not only taught us about unconscious mechanisms, but discovered and elucidated transference and countertransference. Yet Freud's clinical interpretations, psychological theories, and analysis of transference phenomena remained circumscribed, with a focus on personality development and structure—a focus on defenses (against instinctual drives) in particular, which led him to believe that schizophrenics, whose defenses are not well structured, fail to establish transferences, let alone develop transference neuroses that are a focal element in traditional psychoanalysis (Freud, 1940).

Others, however, accepted the necessity and found ways to widen the scope of therapeutic relatedness. Among such psychoanalytic pioneers were Sullivan (1925-26, 1931-32), Fromm-Reichmann (1939), Sechehaye (1951), Simmel (1937), and Hill (1955)—all of whom dared tread where Jung, in a sense, gave up to proceed systematically, although he continued treating schizophrenics. Some of our generation, including Elvin Semrad, are a sort of second generation of schizophrenia therapists, following on Sullivan and Fromm-Reichmann and Hill and others already a third generation. It needs to be understood that psychotherapy with schizophrenics is a limited field, and those who engage in it need one another for mutual reassurance and reaffirmation in this work, which is arduous, lonely, often painful, upsetting, and always uncertain. There is no cookbook, as Otto Will (1975) has said.

Some of the most difficult and painful events, sessions with schizophrenic patients and also some severe borderline patients, concern the unspeakable sadness and forlornness these patients can exude, by which the therapist certainly will be affected and may feel engulfed. I say "unspeakable," and mean it quite literally, because this sadness relates to preverbal experiences and a sense of helplessness and hopelessness, which one can observe at least partially in Monica's apathetic turning away, demonstrated so cogently by Engel (1962). Unfortunately, I, for one, have never been able to pinpoint with patients retrospectively just what particular conditions or maternal neglect patterns did occur so early in life. Inconsistency in mothering is very probably one factor, seen later in transformation as the need–fear dilemma described so well by Burnham and his co-workers (1967). The intense need for attachment leads to desires for fearsome overcloseness, which drives the patient to a stance of negativistic mute sullenness, to paranoid constructs, or, worse still, to aggressive action. We can fathom this experience from the data on imperviousness and intrusiveness of many mothers of schizophrenic patients that we and others have gathered. But it is not clear to me what particular interactional elements may be missing in either the mother or the infant, or both, that imprint the infant with this lasting terror of such a forlorn state, often elaborated later on into a sense of worthlessness and unlovability and also connected with a crucial developmental deficiency or failure in acquiring object constancy. Without the acquisition of object constancy, cognitive development is hampered too, especially in the sense of persistent egocentricity, as pointed out by Lidz (1973).

It is these core problems from which schizophrenic patients suffer which have tremendous implication for the therapeutic process, although I hasten to add that I do not mean to invalidate other important psychodynamic aberrations in personality development and structure. Among these, the deviations leading to and imbedded in faulty linguistic development are particularly important (Wynne, 1972). However, the basic problem of forlornness also constitutes a potent force in the evolution of therapeutic relationships. It makes for the tremendous intensity with which such patients relate and attach themselves to therapists, and for the patient's demandingness and longing for symbiotic union with the therapist, which are as intense as they are unfulfillable. These longings lead in turn to fantasies of dismemberment on the part of the patient, fears of fragmentation of him- or herself or of the therapist when separation occurs or threatens. Such intense relationships between therapist and patient are indeed different from the neurotic patient's transference (Freud, 1940; Chapter 11).

I do not need to elaborate on the vicissitudes of trust these patients experience, trusting in a magical way one moment, and finding the therapist totally untrustworthy the next. Furthermore, when patients feel underattended or insufficiently loved, they also easily resort to distortions and paranoidal constructs. For instance, if a therapist repeats a phrase of the patient's, such as, "I must be defective," the patient on the next day or even within the same hour may claim it to be the therapist's judgment about the patient, leading to agony for the patient, negativistic, incensed distancing in the next hour or beyond it, and perplexity for the therapist.

Serious and dangerous destructive behavior can ensue from such "misunderstandings," the quotes being there because these impasses are not amenable to the usual corrective statements about misunderstandings between people. The patient referred to above had such an hour with me about two and one-half years after we started working together and again I could not discover what had gone awry between us. She let me know only that she felt desperate and was convinced that I did not give a hoot about her, but gave me no indication what particular event, omission or commission on my part had led to this conviction. The patient had by then returned to her professional work and there were a number of people we knew in common. My conjecture that she had received some unwelcome or disturbing information about me in this way was denied. The next hour I saw another patient, but was aware that the first patient had gone to the bathroom and had not left the suite. This concerned me enough that I interrupted the hour with the second patient and went to the bathroom, where I found her almost unconscious. She had taken a large amount of barbiturates, and fortunately could be rushed to a nearby hospital where she was saved by dialysis and eventually recovered completely. I found out later that this nadir experience occurred after she had learned that my wife and I were giving a party to which she had not been invited (there had never been any social contact). I can add that this also led to a clarification of the impasse she had reached with the previous therapist, who, indeed, had become friendly with her and included her in social activities which made her eventually feel rejected by him, which led to renewed psychotic disorganization.

We worked for another fifteen months, at which time both of us moved to different parts of the country. The patient undertook further professional training and for the past twenty years has functioned superbly as a teacher, and has established much improved relationships with her children. She also entered more formal analysis with a senior colleague, which went well even though I had recommended against formal analysis for her. She has remained well and asymptomatic. During the first several years, she would touch base with me rather regularly through a phone call or note, but now only occasionally. I emphasize this because one of the aspects of psychotherapy with schizophrenics is very important—it rarely ends completely. Somehow such patients remain attached, and although they no longer need any direct contact for long periods of time, they may need it every so often when it may be quite crucial for them. One could conjecture that their capacity for achieving object constancy remains weak, and needs shoring up once in a while.

It is important to emphasize that most follow-up studies of schizophrenics, no matter how they were treated, are "stills" instead of subsequent life histories. The latter are difficult to come by unless the outcome is poor, leading to the familiar data on chronicity and recurrent hospitalizations. Indeed, this is often viewed as the natural history of the "disease," because data on these patients are so readily gathered. Not so with recovered patients, who are usually reticent to make themselves available for meaningful follow-up studies, except for the contacts with their former therapists to which I have referred. But generally, data on patients who do well remain scattered and epidemiologically unavailable. Meaningful follow-up data constitute the importance of Bleuler's (1978a & b) work based on personal contacts spanning twenty-five years, presenting a very different natural course than one finds in most textbooks.

Unlike recovered addicts, former schizophrenic patients are reticent about declaring themselves. Green (1964) is an exception, but patients who have recovered and are successful in life cannot be reported on without their consent, and may even be readily identifiable by others. Recently I saw a woman fifteen years after several years' hospitalization at another institution which is also devoted to psychotherapy of schizophrenic patients. Like some of our "graduates" from the Yale Psychiatric Institute, successful or not, she was very negative and resentful about her hospital experiences, and was just then incensed at what she considered the hospital's clumsy and intrusive follow-up research. She, too, had done well since discharge, had weathered surgery for a malignancy, but also had maintained quite regular contact with her therapist through the years. She was referred to me because of her continued need for support following her surgery though still essentially asymptomatic. She was working and had successfully managed her move to new surroundings.

An ex-patient's single follow-up contact with a stranger, often consisting of completing a schedule of symptoms and behaviors, cannot result in meaningful information about personal growth and change processes which follow years of intimate work in a special relationship between two people. Epidemiological surveys are important to establish indices of cognitive and social functioning (Brown et al., 1972). They cannot provide data of how corrective changes came about in a person, any more than anybody can quickly and easily ascertain what relationships or experiences with a significant other, family member, teacher, or friend made for growth and significant change within oneself.

The importance of *effective* psychotherapy with schizophrenics is not in its extent, since obviously not many patients compared to the huge number of schizophrenics in the world can be treated this way. Its importance lies in the fact that it is possible to help some of the most severely psychotic people help themselves and rejoin our world effectively, indicating thereby that there is enough plasticity in both personality malformation and whatever neurochemical systems may be involved to change toward more conventional patterns and interactional responses. Psychotherapy may be a clumsy and costly way to effect changes in the neurochemical substrate, or even in the miscarried development of psychosocial structures and behavior patterns, but it demonstrates that no matter what and how severe the pathology may be, living as a member of the human race can be achieved.

In addition to demonstrating the plasticity of all these structures, treating such patients is a crucial learning experience for psychotherapists. The qualities a therapist must bring to and cultivate for this work encompass, among others, tolerance for ambiguity and anxiety, and tenacity in keeping oneself involved even when fatigued or bored. Furthermore, the theistic ambitions which many of us harbor are more likely to hinder than help the process and evaporate soon in the face of the effort required to help these patients. Therapists must evolve a mix of empathetic collaboration and curiosity, of cognitive-interpretive activity and guidance, which will be different with each patient. Some, but not all, psychotherapists must learn how to sit with, respond to, and interact beneficially with these psychotic patients, with and without the help of chemicals, because there is much to be learned in this therapeutic process about the nature of being, and, more important, of becoming human.

This experience is important not only for those of us who become therapists primarily, but also for administrators or leaders of psychiatric institutions and services. Without the experience of living, so to speak, with psychotic patients, program directors will likely not address the needs of these patients effectively and compassionately. Furthermore, it is essential knowledge if we are ever going to prevent this crippling condition. I believe we have made progress in this direction, not so much through psychotherapy *per se*, but by having been led through our psychotherapeutic experiences to family studies. It is possible now in a gross, albeit yet incomplete way, to state what the essential ingredients of familial inputs into human development are, and this is one of the most promising leads to pursue for understanding and eventually preventing schizophrenia as a deficiency disease in psychosocial nurturance and enculturation (Alanen, 1966; Fleck, 1975; Lewis et al., 1976; Lidz, 1973).

There is the question of how much it costs to treat a schizophrenic person. It is the wrong question, no matter how insistently our third-party payers or medical-cost watchers ask it. How much does it cost *not* to treat a disturbed person optimally? What price human misery—the patient's, his or her family's, not to mention the price society pays, not only in dollars, but also by living with the guilty knowledge of ignoring the professed principle that we are our brother's or sister's keeper? As long as we believe in and strive toward the idea that the individual counts—that the search for well-being and full development is for everybody, we cannot honestly abrogate or forego the best forms of help we know, inadequate as present knowledge may be.

Schizophrenia or mental ill health in general is not the only medical condition where we fall short in providing adequate care and services, and where our knowledge is only partial; but psychosis happens to be our specialty, and it is our duty to advocate optimal treatment for our patients, and optimal education for our colleagues-to-be. Until we discover differently, psychotherapy with schizophrenics not only offers some patients hope for real life, but also constitutes one of the major research opportunities for the study of this condition, and for the study of the human condition and of the human condition gone awry.

POSTSCRIPT

It is apparent enough that the problems of schizophrenic disorders will not be solved through the arduous task of individual psychotherapy or family psychotherapy. However, it is through the knowledge gained from intensive psychotherapy together with studies of the family environments that we can gain an understanding of the development, interpersonal and intrapsychic problems of schizophrenic patients that can guide prophylactic efforts as well as more generally applicable therapeutic endeavors. Then, too, as the chapter reem- phasizes, studies of schizophrenic patients provide a unique approach to understanding the human condition.

XIX

A Sketch of a Theory of Schizophrenic Disorders

(1973)

A sixteen-year-old girl was admitted to the Yale Psychiatric Institute after she had chopped up the living room furniture with an axe and left a note reading, "Mom and Dad, you're next" which she signed "Lizzie Borden."[1] Actually, she had become progressively more withdrawn during the preceding four years. Eventually she had refused to attend school and remained locked in her room for days at a time. Despite several suicidal attempts, she had been unable to convey her desperate need for help until she threatened to emulate Lizzie Borden who "took an axe and gave her mother forty whacks."

Her parents were about to end their chaotic marriage. Her mother had originally been married to the father's older brother, a highly capable man who had managed his family's large industrial empire. When he was killed in an airplane crash, his family persuaded his wife to marry his younger brother in order to preserve the integrity of the family for-

Theodore Lidz: "Family Studies and a Theory of Schizophrenia." This is a slightly amplified version of the Stanley R. Dean Award Lecture presented at the annual meeting of the American College of Psychiatrists in 1973 and published in *Annual Review of the Schizophrenic Syndrome*, Vol. 3, edited by R. Cancro. Copyright © 1974, Brunner/Mazel.

[1]Lizzie Borden was a young woman whose parents were found hacked to death with an axe. Although unproven, the murders were popularly attributed to Lizzie, and immortalized in the children's rope-skipping jingle:

Lizzie Borden took an axe
And gave her mother forty whacks.
When she saw what she had done,
She gave her father forty-one.

tune. The second brother turned out to be ineffectual and passive and soon became a severe alcoholic with paranoid tendencies. The mother felt that her life had become meaningless and she conveyed her hopelessness to her daughters. She focused her attention on the patient, expecting to gain gratification from the girl's accomplishments, but she could not understand the child nor hear her despair because she needed to believe that she had a perfect and happy child who would embellish her life and make it worthwhile.

Starting with this vignette from a case history, the paper seeks to present a sketch of a theory of schizophrenic disorders that has evolved from studies of the family settings from which schizophrenic patients emerge. It is not simply a "family theory" of schizophrenia. It is just as much an existential theory for it holds that the development of a schizophrenic disorder is a potentiality inherent to the human condition; and if we did not know the syndrome, we would have to search for it as an anticipated aberration of the process of personality development, much as one might search for a potential anomaly of embryonic unfolding. It is also a biological theory, or if you wish, a psychobiological theory, for it rests upon the recognition that the human is integrated at a symbolic level, dependent for adaptation on language and thought, and also upon the realization that the family, even though a social rather than a biological structure, is an essential concomitant of the human's biological makeup. The paper seeks to present a sketch of a comprehensive theory based upon observable data, and eschews positing potential, though still undetected, genetic and neurochemical factors. Such factors are not omitted through any conviction that they may not be significant, but rather because the sketch seeks to convey that the nature and etiology of schizophrenic disorders can be understood without them.

The following findings will serve as points of departure:

1. Schizophrenic patients suffer from serious disturbances of thought and communication. This is a matter of definition as the presence of a thought disorder is the critical attribute

of the category of psychiatric disorders we term "schizo-phrenic."

2. The schizophrenic patient's "self" boundaries are ten-uous, leading to confusions between what arises within the self and what outside of it, as well as to deficiencies in maintaining the integrity and differentiation of the self.

3. The patient's family of origin is always severely disturbed, as demonstrated by our own work and now confirmed by various other investigators (Alanen, 1958; Bowen, 1960; Delay et al., 1957, 1960, 1962; Wynne et al., 1958). Though it is hazardous to say "always," I know no reason not to do so. Those who deny this finding have not studied the patient's families intensively as well as the patient.

4. One parent, or both, has markedly disturbed ways of communicating (Bateson et al., 1956; Singer and Wynne, 1965a, 1965b; Solvberg and Blakar, 1975; Wynne and Singer, 1963a, 1963b; Chapters VII and XVI).

The basic concepts that give these observations pertinence are

(1) Psychoses are gross failures of ego functioning, which can be defined simply as the capacity to direct oneself into the future. Since the capacity to direct oneself, as well as to conceptualize a future, depends on symbolic functioning, serious distortions of symbolic functioning can lead to psychosis.

(2) Although infants are born with the capacity for symbolic functioning, they must learn their culture's language and ways of thinking as they grow up. The foundations for gaining this system of meanings and logic are established in the family. Distortions of communication within the family of origin can provide a child with a faulty or tenuous foundation in the culture's system of communicating and thinking.

(3) Schizophrenic disorders are also failures to achieve or to maintain an integrated personality. For infants to develop into integrated persons, the family—or some planned substitute for it—must nurture the children, foster their individuation, provide models for identification, afford a

framework for the structuring of their personalities, and provide for their basic socialization and enculturation.

(4) Pervasive family disturbances, including disturbances in intrafamilial communication, can impair both an offspring's symbolic development and ability to achieve and maintain a discrete and integrated personality and leave the child vulnerable to becoming schizophrenic.

We have in this volume described various disturbances in the family settings that give rise to schizophrenic offspring, and shall here only summarize certain of these findings that seem to have particular pertinence.

At a general and perhaps nonspecific level, all of these families had been seriously disturbed and distorted from before the patient was born through the time that the study was being conducted; that is, at least until the patient was an adolescent or young adult. Whatever aspect of the family transactions we studied, we usually found something seriously amiss. We were forced to move beyond the study of schizophrenic disorders to try to understand our findings through determining what the family must provide for its offspring in order to foster their adequate personality development—their integration as reasonably independent individuals by early adulthood. The scrutiny of these families led us to note influences that have been largely overlooked in developmental psychology, probably because the family is ubiquitous and therefore many of its vital functions for the child have been taken for granted rather than been made the focus of scientific scrutiny.

Stated as briefly as possible, we found it useful to consider the family's functions in child rearing under four, or perhaps five, categories (Lidz, 1963). These are (1) The parental nurturant functions, from the total care required by the neonate, through fostering differentiation from the mother to find his or her place as an individual in the family, to promoting the child's separation from the family at the end of adolescence—functions that are crucial to the child's emotional stability, emotional reactivity and security and are also important for cognitive development. (2) The influence of the dynamic organization of the family upon the structuring of the child's personality, providing an inner structure that can eventually replace the family structure as well as provide superego guidance; and, in particular, how the parents' abilities to achieve and maintain a parental coalition, the proper boundaries between the generations, and adhere to their respective sex-linked roles serve to channel the child's drives and provide a proper framework around which the child's personality can gain integration. The models for identification as well as superego development do not depend only upon the parents as individuals and how each relates to the child, but also upon the parents' relationships to one another. (3) Teaching the child both the basic social roles and institutions of the society, and their worth as guides in living and in furnishing motivations. (4) The transmission of the instrumental techniques of the culture, and, in particular, its language with its system of meanings and logic, including its ways of categorizing experiences, but also its mores and ethos. (5) Providing a basic parental model for identification.

The appreciation that the family in which the schizophrenic patient grows up has failed to provide adequately any of these requisites for a child's integrated personality development shifts the focus away from the early mother-infant relationship alone, or, indeed, from any specific traumatic occurrence or period in the child's life, and requires us to take into account the enduring panphasic difficulties that existed throughout the patient's formative years.

Although the findings that the families had failed in a global way to provide the requisites for a child's integrated development are pertinent to the etiology of schizophrenia, the appearance of schizophrenia does not depend upon these global disturbances and deficiencies alone, but upon more specific distorting influences to be delineated, that provide guidance for our therapeutic efforts.

We have tended to divide these families into two types, the skewed and the schismatic, but an overlap between these paradigms occurs rather frequently. The skewed pattern is found more often in families with schizophrenic sons than daughters. Here, the focus of attention is apt to be drawn to the so-called "schizophrenogenic" mother, a woman who is extremely intrusive into her child's life but impervious to the child's needs and feelings as a separate individual. However, the father is also important because he is often unable to counter his wife's strange ideas of raising children and because he provides a poor model for identification to his son, either acting as another child or being intensely rivalrous with his son for his wife's affection and attention. Although the mother is usually unable to be close and maternal to her son as an infant, she soon becomes overprotective and engulfing, and is unable to believe the child can survive without her constant concern and supervision. She cannot establish clear boundaries between herself and her son and fails to differentiate her own anxieties, needs, and feelings from those of the child. Feeling incomplete and unfulfilled as a woman, she conveys to her son that her life would be empty and meaningless without him. The boy grows up feeling that it is his duty to complete his mother's life, and that leaving her would be tantamount to killing her, but also that he cannot get along without her, continuing his early childhood beliefs in the omniscient and omnipotent powers of a mother. Still, he eventually realizes that she opposes any movement toward autonomy from her. His initial identification with his mother is not supplanted by an adequate identification with his father, and without firm boundaries he may fear that closeness can lead to incestuous involvement with her. Yet any move toward independence or even a failure to repress hostile components of his ambivalence is experienced as paramount to killing her. A daughter may remain undifferentiated from the mother, anaclitically needy and with strong homosexual longings and unable to shift and make an attachment to her father. Whatever the father's makeup —passive, alcoholic, psychotic—he is ineffectual in the home and usually disdained by the mother who thus conveys to her son that he must grow up to be different from the father to please her and complete her life. In these families, the mother's, but sometimes the father's, emotional balance is so precarious that she can retain her equilibrium only by distorting her perception of events to the way she needs them to be; and she requires other members of the family to distort matters according to her needs. As the father does not counter these ways, the family becomes an unreal place into which children must fit or feel rejected. The child's own feelings and perceptions are invalidated, and the world that the child should come to know, and even the value of his own emotions as a guide to relating to others, are denied.

The schismatic pattern more commonly forms the background of female patients. There is open antagonism between the parents with each spouse undercutting the worth of the other, and competing for the loyalty of the child, seeking an ally in the intrafamilial strife. The mother who has little self-esteem and is very insecure as a mother is constantly derogated by her husband who has little use for women. Some of the fathers who are insecure as men sought wives who would docilely cater to their wishes and support their narcissistic needs. The husband takes dissent by his wife as hostile rebelliousness. The mother, often a poorly organized woman, cannot hold her own against a dominating husband who is often grandiose if not actually paranoid. She conveys a feeling of the meaninglessness or hopelessness of life. She, too, seeks to be overprotective of her daughter, but cannot convey any maternal warmth. Her overprotection has a negative, and even, an inimical quality (Alanen, 1958). In these families the fathers are as disturbed as the mothers, and often more so because of their paranoid tendencies, even though they may function rather effectively outside of the family. When the father's rigid and unrealistic expectations are not met by his wife, he may become seductive toward a daughter in a way that verges on being incestuous, seeking to use her to fill the admiring role his wife is unable or unwilling to occupy. In some cases, however, the father seems pushed into a mothering and rather seductive relationship to the daughter because of the mother's apathy or aversion toward the child. The daughter's developmental process becomes very complicated because in her efforts to gain her father's affection she must seek to become someone very different from her mother. A son in such families does not feel capable of satisfying the expectations of the grandiose father, particularly when the mother conveys he must not become like the father, and his primary task seems to be to make the mother happy despite the father's neglect or disparagement of her. Commonly the child, whether a girl or a boy, finds that trying to please either parent provokes rejection and rebuff by the other. It is a situation in which a child may accept the role of scapegoat, acting in a manner that seems to cause the family schism and thus masking the parents' incompatibilities. In so doing, the child sacrifices his own developmental needs to preserve the family.

Although the schismatic and skewed configurations may seem very different, they have certain characteristics in common. These are: the use of the child to complete a parent's life, or to maintain the parents' marriage, which interferes with the child's development of self-boundaries; the failure of the parent of the same sex as the child to provide an acceptable model for identification, together with the devaluation of this parent by the spouse; the disruptions of the boundaries between the two generations which lead to incestuous tendencies, faulty oedipal resolution, and confusions between parent and child functions; the parents' failures to adhere to their respective gender-linked roles; the parents' inability to permit and even less to help the child to manage increasingly on his own; the feelings of emptiness or hopelessness about life conveyed by one or both parents; and the disturbances in verbal and nonverbal communication that pervade family transactions.

It now seems firmly established that although an insufficient cause in itself, a child will rarely, if ever, become schizophrenic unless the intrafamilial communication is markedly disordered. My colleagues and I (Chapter VII) described how these parents distort their perceptions of experiences to preserve their own tenuous emotional balance which creates a strange family setting into which the children must fit themselves or feel rejected. The child's perceptions of events and feelings are distorted or invalidated to fit the parents' needs. Bateson, Jackson et al. (1956) first focused attention on how the developing child is constantly placed in cognitive doublebinds; that is, he is given mutually contradictory messages accompanied by the covert threat of rejection if he does not carry out one message, but also if he does not carry out the contradictory one. He is, so to speak, damned if he does, and damned if he doesn't. One such situation that is common and sweeping is that the mother conveys to her son that he must become a great person to be acceptable to her, but at the same time he must never become independent of her. In schismatic families, the child is caught between the opposing directives of his two parents that leads to a split in his inner directives. Wynne and Singer (1963a, 1963b; Singer and Wynne, 1965a, 1965b) have drawn our attention to the amorphous and fragmented styles of communication of these parents that interfere with the child's ability to maintain the focal attention essential for learning language and to communicate coherently. Further, the parents do not let clear concepts stand but create a milieu filled with inconsistencies, contradictory meanings, and the denial of what should be obvious. There are many ways in which the intrafamilial transactions and communication interfere with the child gaining a coherent grounding in the culture's system of meanings and logic, confuse his grasp of the world, and leave him despairing about making sense out of events and relationships.

Having provided this brief sketch of the types of family settings in which the schizophrenic patients develop and which impede the development of a coherent and stable identity, let us now turn to examine the nature and origins of the schizophrenic thought disorder, and how it relates both to the patient's faulty training in the culture's system of meanings and logic and also to the failure of the family setting to foster the patient's autonomy or individuation with clear boundaries between the self and a parent. As it is the pervasive disorder of thought and language, usually including delusional thinking that distinguishes schizophrenic disorders, a theory of schizophrenia must explain the thought disorder.[2]

The schizophrenic thought disorder has been defined in many ways. Schizophrenic reactions are a type of withdrawal from social interaction, and the thought disorder can be considered as a specifically schizophrenic means of withdrawal into fantasy, of finding explanations and guidance from delusions and hallucinations, and by breaking through the confines set by the meanings and logic of the culture; or, one might consider that because interpersonal relationships depend so greatly upon a shared system of meanings, disruptions of the linguistic system are isolating. Everyone is delimited by the meanings and logic of his culture, but without them relationships beyond infantile dependency —collaborative interaction with others—are not possible and self-direction is greatly impaired. Schizophrenic patients escape from irreconcilable conflict, unbearable hopelessness and despair, and an unbearable sense of emptiness by breaking through these confines to find some living space and self-esteem by using their own idiosyncratic meanings and reasoning, but in so doing impair their ego functioning and ability to collaborate with others.

When Eugen Bleuler (1911) focused attention on the central position of the schizophrenic thought disorder, he described it as a derailment of associations. Various investigators have considered the same phenomena as manifestations of deficiencies in forming categories; and I have noted elsewhere that category formation serves as a means of filtering

[2]The classification of "schizophrenia without thought disorder" is a paradox and indicates inadequate study and understanding of the patient, or the strange idea that delusions are not disorders of thought.

out extraneous associations (Lidz, 1968). Norman Cameron's (1938) designation of schizophrenic thinking as "overinclusive" is a highly useful way of describing what happens with the breakdown in categorizing. What has been overlooked is that the overinclusiveness is primarily egocentric, in Piaget's usage of the term. The patient typically believes that what others do or say centers on him, even when it is totally extraneous to him, as in ideas and delusions of reference and persecutory delusional systems; or, he believes that his actions, thoughts, or feelings have influence on others, and even magically affect the inanimate universe. The schizophrenic patient, in brief, believes that he is the focal point of events that are, in actuality, fortuitous or coincidental to his life. At one pole, the paranoid patient perceives that some person or organization of persons is seeking to thwart or injure him; and at the other pole, the catatonic patient remains immobile because he is the fulcrum of the universe, or because any movement he makes can have devastating consequences to the world. Indeed, we are finding evidence that the patient becomes manifestly psychotic when he begins to order his world in such egocentric ways, frantically finding direction from contingent events (Bowers, 1974); and with remission, the egocentric overinclusiveness ceases, or, at least, diminishes markedly. The schizophrenic is also egocentric in other ways. He tends to distort reality to his own needs and point of view, and he often fails to recognize that others do not view matters and understand them as he does.

Now, one of our basic findings about the parents of schizophrenic patients is that one or both parents is profoundly egocentric. Many of the characteristics noted in parents of schizophrenic patients, such as their intrusiveness into their child's life but imperviousness to his feelings; their inabilities to differentiate their own needs and feelings from their child's, or to grasp that the child views situations differently than they do, or to believe that the child can manage anything without them; the use of the child to complete their own lives, etc. have been attributed to the parent's failure to establish proper boundaries between the self and the child. However, such parental difficulties in forming boundaries are almost synonymous with parental egocentricity; and parents' eccentric ways of thinking and communicating are also often a type of egocentricity.

The parent's egocentricity usually differs from the patient's. It is often, though not always, most clearly manifest in relationships with family members and, particularly, in the parent-child relationships, and concerns the inability to recognize that the other person has different feelings, needs, and ways of experiencing than the self. The egocentric parent, thus, cannot properly accommodate to the child and his needs, but rather the child's needs and perceptions are sacrificed and distorted to meet the parent's needs, requiring the immature child to fit himself to the parent's orientation—to see the world as the parent needs to have him see it to help preserve the parent's tenuous equilibrium. In the skewed family, the egocentricity of one parent is not countered by the other; in the schismatic family, two egocentric parents cannot understand or empathize with each other.

The patient, having ever needed to adapt himself to the parent's needs, is alert to the needs and feelings of others and may be unduly sensitive to them in contrast to the parent. Thus, the egocentricities of the parent and child are reciprocal in that the patient's egocentricity is in many ways parent centered; and whereas they serve to protect the parent's emotional balance, they leave the patient vulnerable because he is directed by the parent's needs rather than investing his energies and attention in his own development. The patient comes to believe he can affect his parents profoundly by his own thoughts and feelings, and these feelings of being central to his parents' lives lead to feelings of being central and important to everyone, including God, whom the child models as an extension of his parents, as both Freud and Piaget have shown. And, on the other hand, the patient may transfer his parent's misunderstanding of him or a parent's aggression toward him onto others, a reason for delusion formation other than projection of his own impulses. Moreover, he fails to develop his own ego capacities, his abilities for self-direction, but continues to seek directives and cues from others—even to projecting both impulses and constraints.

To some degree, I have simply been changing the frame of reference of something that many clinicians and investigators have emphasized; namely, that schizophrenic patients have weak self-boundaries, and, therefore, confuse the self and objects, what is internal and external, and what is motivated from within and what from without. However, the weak boundaries are not due to an innate defect, or to some metabolic abnormality, but rather as we (Lidz and Lidz, 1952) noted some thirty years ago, the patient's failure to establish proper boundaries between the self and others derives from a parent's inability to form boundaries between the self and the patient. I am now pointing out that the patient's profound egocentricity would seem to derive from the parent's egocentricity. The change of the frame of reference helps clarify the nature of many basic symptoms of schizophrenic disorders, and, particularly, the nature of the cognitive disturbance.

It is essential to realize that the failure to differentiate clearly between what is self and non-self that is so characteristic of schizophrenic patients is, as Piaget (1926) has described, also characteristic of the young child. It represents the egocentricity of the sensorimotor period and to some degree of the preoperational period of cognitive development. The infant gradually overcomes such egocentricities as he achieves object constancy and differentiates from the mother in the separation-individuation phase that Mahler (1968) has described. Overcoming this primitive egocentricity is vital to human development for many reasons, and specifically for cognitive development because no true category formation can occur unless the self can be excluded from a grouping or category. Developing beyond early erotized attachment to the mother, recognizing that the mother's life does not center completely on the child, is thus a final step in overcoming the primary egocentricity and enables the child to enter the stage of concrete operations in which he or she can begin to categorize—something that will be seriously impeded if the mother continues to confuse her feelings and needs with her child's.

I have been focusing attention on the relationship of the schizophrenic patient's faulty self-boundaries and the importance of the separation-individuation phase to cognitive development, but it is obvious that the person who becomes schizophrenic has not remained fixated at this primitive level of cognitive development: if he had never established boundaries between himself and his "object" world, his language usage and his emotional development would have been so profoundly affected that he would have remained autistic, or, at least, a symbiotic psychotic child (Mahler, 1968). Most, if not all, late adolescent and adult schizophrenics had been able to form concrete, if not also abstract, categories. However, because of the peculiar family environment in which they had been raised, and because of its irrationalities —including the requirement that they distort their own perceptions in accord with their parents' needs—their meaning system, their ways of categorizing experiences, are not firmly based in the culture's system of categorizing. They are not only more apt to categorize in idiosyncratic ways, perceiving the world less conventionally than others (even as do artistically creative persons), but, they are also left vulnerable to regress to thinking in complexes, or to precategorical, syncretic ways of thinking, particularly when they lose themselves in real or imaginary fusion experiences when seeking intimacy with someone outside of the family.

In order to understand the cognitive egocentric regressions typical of schizophrenic disorders, we must comprehend the egocentrisms of later developmental stages that Piaget (1929) has described. Piaget has emphasized that a child must overcome a different type of egocentricity as he moves through each stage of cognitive development. Egocentrism, for Piaget, means both the overestimation of the power of thought over objective recognition and also the distortion of reality to satisfy the point of view and the needs of the individual. Both are unconscious, essentially resulting from the failure to distinguish between the subjective and the objective. Egocentrism increases each time that the developmental process brings the child into a new and untried field of cognitive action—a new stage of cognitive functioning—and slowly subsides as the child masters the new field, only to reappear in a new form as the child moves into a new stage of development. The preoperational—or, in the psychoanalytic frame of reference, the preoedipal—child must come to differentiate his wish from reality, and words from the objects they represent; as well as largely overcome his "animism," his "artificialism" (the belief that all objects are created by men, or for men), his "participation" (the belief that his thoughts and actions influence or control nature), and other magical concepts of causality. In particular, the preoperational child cannot grasp that events can be fortuitous but rather believes that they always center on him. Such failures to differentiate the subjective and objective—to believe in the efficacy of the wish, to resort to fantasy solutions, to believe in animism, etc., are, of course, very common in schizophrenic patients. The child in the stage of concrete operations (which parallels the so-called latency period) gradually learns that persons in different places do not have the same view of an object as he has, and then, that others may not share his orientation. He begins to accommodate to the views of others and overcomes the misunderstandings that arise because he does not realize he must orient others to what he is talking about, and the distortions that occur because he cannot share the point of view of another, or even really grasp that other points of view exist. Failures to recognize that others perceive and feel differently from the self are, as we have noted, common among both schizophrenic patients and also their parents.

However, it is the egocentricity that arises early in adolescence that has more specific pertinence to the development of schizophrenic states. In the past, too much emphasis has been placed upon the events of very early childhood that established the fixation points and proclivities for regression, and too little upon the later developmental problems which, when not surmounted, create the dam—to follow one of Freud's analogies—that forces the regressive backing up of the developmental flow.

Some schizophrenic patients will never have moved completely beyond the stages of preoperational and concrete thinking, but many will move into more abstract conceptual thinking and then regress. The first group may be considered as "developmental" akin to "poor premorbid" or "process" schizophrenics, and the latter group as "regressive" akin to "good premorbid" or "reactive" schizophrenics. However, "developmental" and "regressive" are poles between which most patients are distributed rather than two separate types of schizophrenic disorders.

Schizophrenic patients usually move into mid- or late adolescence before regressing both cognitively and emotionally. They reach the developmental period when they are confronted by such psychosocial tasks as achieving independence from their families, formulating a life plan, gaining an ego identity, and a capacity for intimacy—tasks that trouble all adolescents. Those who become schizophrenic find these steps particularly difficult, if not impossible, because of the intrafamilial impediments to their development, including the limitations of their extrafamilial socialization brought about by the various peculiarities, beliefs, and fears of their parents (Chapter XV).

Adolescents also undergo a major transformation that has been disregarded in psychoanalytic developmental theory. Cognitively, they enter the stage of formal operations. They now become capable of reflective thinking, of thinking about thinking, and instead of simply proceeding from what is real to what is possible, as they did previously, they can now plan from the possible to the real, and in so doing, may become seduced by their capacities to be the master in the mental realm of the possible. The period contains the particular danger that youths can get lost in mental operations, fantasying potential futures for themselves and the world without becoming involved in the tangible measures required to make them become real. It is an expansive period of hopes and dreams, which, at first, is untempered by the need to prove the feasibility of an ideal, or to go through the tangible stages of convincing others and the laborious measures required to bring a plan to realization. As Inhelder and Piaget (1958) state, "The adolescent goes through a phase in which he attributes an unlimited power to his own thoughts so that the dream of a glorious future or of transforming the world through ideas (even if this idealism takes a materialistic form) seems to be not only fantasy but also an effective action which in itself modifies the empirical world. This is obviously a form of cognitive egocentrism."

It often takes years to overcome the egocentricity that appears with the onset of formal operations, to recognize that one's own ideals and points of view about social issues are never precisely those of others; that thinking things out for oneself is very different from convincing others and from working them out in the real world. It is a characteristic of youth to be carried away by the hypothetical possibilities, to formulate plans mentally, and go on to construct imagined brilliant outcomes, but the ability to do so contains a trap into which the vulnerable may fall. Adolescents who become schizophrenic overdo this reliance on imaginary solutions and gratifications and will even believe they are extraordinary persons with notable attainments because of them—an overevaluation that reflects the mother's grandiose ideas concerning her child—and may then paranoidally blame others for not recognizing their worth.

The egocentric aspects of formal operations are overcome through increasing socialization that brings the youth in contact with persons with different orientations and forces a reevaluation of his or her own concepts (Inhelder and Piaget, 1958). The process of decentering is aided by adolescents' endless discussions and arguments; by the joining and re-signing from various social movements that are so much a part of youth; but also by undertaking a real job in which accomplishment rather than imagined results is what counts; through starting upon a career which supplies tangible directives and role models around which the personality consolidates; and by becoming intimate with persons from other families, and accommodating to their different ways of relating and perceiving.

Sometimes the first indications that a youth may be in danger of becoming schizophrenic—when his future seems to hang in balance—may come when goals fail to jell and instead become more diffuse, and rather than moving toward accomplishment he remains in the realm of fantasied achievements. The various grave impediments to personality integration that result from growing up in a disturbed and confusing home now block the development of a coherent ego identity and the crucial emergence as an adult; and for some, the difficulties in socializing keep the youths from overcoming their egocentric overevaluation of their cognitive abilities. Such youths lack the inner structure to replace parental protection and guidance, and fears of being engulfed or the equivalence to incest panic when they seek intimacy with another. It is, however, not only the inadequacies and distorting influences in their earlier development that create difficulties; they are still caught up in concurrent difficulties with the same disturbed and disturbing parents who raised them. It is not just a matter of infantile and preoedipal fixations that distorted their subsequent development but the panphasic influences that affected them from birth through adolescence and the continuing oppressive and confusing characteristics of the current relationships with their most significant persons that interfere with forward movement, lead to despair, sometimes to terror and initiate regression. Of course, the onset of a schizophrenic disorder often comes later than adolescence or early adulthood, but in many such instances the patient had not actually mastered the essential tasks of adolescence, and if no longer caught up in problems with the family of origin, has transferred them to those who had become the significant persons in their lives; and in others, a relationship that permitted the adult to maintain a precarious balance for some years had been lost or undermined, as when the death of a parent or the parents' divorce changes the cardinal relationships profoundly.

As part of his inability to move through adolescence, the youth who becomes schizophrenic fails to decenter cognitively. Feeling hopeless about the future and permeated by despair of ever becoming a person in his own right—the youth develops more elaborate fantasy solutions and regresses cognitively as well as emotionally. Poorly grounded in reality testing, and with tenuous boundaries between the self and others, he finds a way out of his real developmental dilemma by falling back to childhood forms of egocentric cognition. All egocentrism, whatever the specific type and from whatever stage of development, is bound together by the common characteristic of reliance upon the "omnipotence of thought." The schizophrenic can again give precedence to wish over reality, to belief in parental omnipotence, and the efficacy of the magic of the wish. Desperately seeking meaning and direction that seem hidden from him but obvious to others, everything takes on heightened relevance and becomes personally meaningful. He finds that every fortuitous occurrence applies to him as he again believes himself central to all that happens (Bowers, 1974). To some degree he will regress even more profoundly and, like the early preoedipal child, confuse the self and non-self and what arises within him and what comes from outside of him. The results are far-reaching and devastating. The categorizations he had developed are now seriously impaired, and with the filtering function of categories lost, inappropriate associations intrude and derail thought and communication. The process, when the onset is acute, is augmented by anxiety and panic for with stimulation of the sympathetic nervous system and an outpouring of epinephrin, the physiologic filtering of input by the reticular activating system is lowered. According to the individual and the situation, thinking becomes preconceptual, or even syncretic and metonymic, permitting the patient to connect anything that is spatially or temporally contiguous and thus further justify his egocentric distortions.

The breakdown of proper category formation has another potential consequence, as I have explained elsewhere (Lidz, 1968). Various authorities have noted that the formation of boundaries between the self and non-self is basic to all category formation. Experience is continuous, whereas categories are discrete, so that boundaries must be established between categories by repressing what lies between them, starting with what is self and what is not self, and what is inside and what outside the self—to start with, the fusions between child and mother such as nursing at the breast, and later fantasies of fusion in sexual relations, as well as taboos on excretions and secretions that were part of the self, but become non-self (Leach, 1966). We may also posit a similar fundamental need to place taboos upon, or repress, whatever might confuse the categories of parent and child, and of male and female. These are precisely the areas in which parents of schizophrenics are apt to fail to foster essential repression. With the regression to egocentric thinking and the disruption of categorical thinking, the schizophrenic may be particularly vulnerable to preoccupation with material that lies between categories—with an intercategorical realm concerned with fusions of the self and mother, with polymorphous perverse fantasies concerning orifices and genitals, with cannibalistic impulses, with dreamlike notions of being of the opposite sex, and other such material that is eliminated from awareness as a child grows up, and normatively can have little conscious representation and for which no clear-cut categorizations exist. It is in this intecategory world that some schizophrenic patients spend much of their time; a world which we, as therapists, find very difficult to penetrate and about which we have but fragmentary glimpses, but which erupts into their talk and their associations as if from another world. It is not just the eruption of his internalized version of reality that is somewhat akin to ours, but more of a nether world, a world that is antipodal, composed of what we have learned even to keep out of most of our fantasies and, perhaps, even out of our dreams, but which were not so repressed but kept near consciousness because of the nature of the family transactions. Still, no matter how profound the regression, the schizophrenic patient is not an infant or even a child, and much of what he had acquired cognitively remains available to him, and limits the extent of the cognitive disorder. Further, what he had acquired is not, or need not be, permanently lost.

It is not a way open to all but only to those whose foundations in reality testing, in the culture's system of meanings and logic, are weak or faulty. Although it may seem a tempting way of resolving problems, it is usually filled with the terror of persecution and patients often struggle to escape, and not all persons who become schizophrenic remain so.[3] However, the condition can readily consolidate as delusional beliefs expand to explain the perplexing world in which the patient had been raised and in which he lives, to "rationalize" failure, and to find some gratification through retreat into fantasy. The psychotic state can continue because the patient no longer tests the validity of his ideas by their instrumental utility or by how they foster collaboration with others.

This article has not sought to account for the entire range of schizophrenic thought disorders. It will be apparent that paranoid delusions and hallucinations are also concerned with boundary problems and egocentric cognition, in which the patient projects his own feelings and impulses onto others, but it is erroneous to consider all hallucinations and delusions as projections of unacceptable impulses and wishes.

---

[3]Currently many psychiatrists do not realize that prior to the introduction of neuroleptics, a third of schizophrenic patients recovered if they received reasonable psychiatric care (see, for example Terry and Rennie [1938]); and that many chronic schizophrenics become reasonably well as they grow older (Ciompi and Muller, 1976; M. Bleuler, 1978a,b).

Some are a defense against yielding to such impulsions by the projection of threats of punishment; that is, superego dictates that seem powerless when intrapsychic are projected onto the environment. Another source of delusion formation lies in the axiomatic acceptance of the parents' teachings. Thus, when a young schizophrenic said, "The one thing of which I can be certain is that my mother loves me," it became apparent that he would have to distort much of his experience, for his mother's acceptance of him depended upon several important qualifications which he could not possibly meet. Then, too, some paranoid delusions, such as Schreber's delusions that Dr. Flechsig, a father figure, was persecuting him (Freud, 1911) are transferences of a parent's malevolence onto others, and properly speaking, are not projections. The flooding of egocentric referential ideas that accompanies the bewilderment and panic at the outset of the psychosis becomes unbearable and a delusional explanation of the dilemma can bring surcease from the unbearable tension and is grasped tenaciously. When the situation is no longer acute, the schizophrenic can often think competently except in areas that confuse and create emotional turmoil. The question is not whether the schizophrenic is capable of conceptual thinking, but rather under what circumstances his ability to categorize breaks down, or what leads to egocentric cognitive regression as well as libidinal regression.

The confused language of chronic schizophrenic patients may have other origins. Social isolation may increase the tendency to talk in terms that only the patient can understand. Commonly, chronic patients use vague and idiosyncratic language as a means of self-protection, to respond and still hide what the patient feels or means. Lorenz (1961; 1963) has described three types of schizophrenic linguistic defenses: ambiguity, literality, and stereotypy. Because the speech that utilizes such linguistic defenses is often concrete, it has often been taken to mean that the patient cannot think abstractly, but careful attention to the patient's production may reveal a capacity for very subtle abstraction.

This sketch has not entered upon all of the ramifications of the theory, or upon all that it can explain, but has been sufficient, we believe, to bring coherence to the basic phenomenology of schizophrenic disorders together with the findings of family studies about the patient's developmental settings. The theory explains why persons who become schizophrenic are particularly vulnerable because the family in which they grew up failed to provide the requisites for the integrated development of the child, and specifically because parental egocentricity interfered with boundary formation between parent and child and distorted the intrafamilial communication. It focuses attention on the vulnerability of the adolescent to disorganization and regression because of the cognitive egocentricity that comes with the start of conceptual thinking and leads away from reality to fantasy solutions as well as because adolescence is the time when personality integration must jell. Unable to surmount the developmental tasks of adolescence and lacking inner structure, the schizophrenic patient regresses to earlier egocentric, overinclusive types of thinking, which, in turn, leads to a breakdown in categorical thinking and the intrusion of primitive intercategorical material, as well as withdrawal into a delusional fantasy world and to profound regression in a search for childlike dependency. It may also permit us to understand the various gradations of severity and chronicity and the admixtures of manifestations with affective, hypochondriacal, sociopathic, and obsessive disorders. It becomes apparent that some individuals will become psychotic at an early age and become chronic because they have never achieved any semblance of integration as an independent person, whereas others regress after attaining some more mature personality capabilities and cognitive functioning and are not as seriously or, necessarily, as permanently impaired. Further, if we understand that many of the various disturbances of cognition commonly observed in schizophrenic patients are regressions to various types of egocentric cognition found in all children and adolescents, we need not believe that they are caused by some brain dysfunction and may even realize that, perhaps, they cannot be; but rather result from gross disturbances in personality development that derive from growing up in a particular type of disturbed family setting in which there are serious communicative disturbances.

POSTSCRIPT

We find that the chapter in seeking to achieve clarity has made too sharp a distinction between skewed and schismatic families. The family, as noted elsewhere in the book, may be an admixture of the two types, or shift from being schismatic to skewed with changed circumstances. Occasionally the father may be the intrusive and over-possessive, so-called "schizophrenogenic" parent, with the mother too distant or troubled to counter the relationship her husband has established with a child.

Once again, we wish to emphasize that with the few exceptions we have noted, the parents have sought to do the best they could for their children, but their own serious personality problems interfered. When one appreciates the serious disturbances of the parents and the problems that existed in their families of origin, the investigator or therapist realizes very clearly that the parents cannot be blamed, any more than they might be blamed for transmitting faulty genes or a susceptible neurophysiologic makeup.

XX

Beyond Schizophrenia

(1984)

The studies we have reported in this volume have had a profound influence on the conceptualization of schizophrenic disorders and their therapy; and have been a major influence in the consideration of the importance of the family in psychiatric disorders and in the development of family therapy. Our efforts to comprehend the material required explorations of the functions of the family that led to examination and apprehension of the fundamental and inordinately complex role of language in human adaptation and integration. We wish in this final chapter to leave schizophrenia and comment on some of the implications of the studies for psychodynamic theories of personality development and psychiatry in general.

Perhaps the most important offshoot of our studies has to do with the resolution of the old conflict concerning the biological and cultural determinants of personality that has created schisms not only in psychiatry but throughout the behavioral sciences. Recognition of the critical role of the family in human development does not lead to an abandonment of a biological orientation in favor of an environmental or cultural approach. To the contrary, appreciation of the critical importance of language to the evolution of the human species leads to the recognition that the family is a necessary concomitant of the human biological makeup, and that those who ignore the importance of a culture and the family to a person's development and functioning cannot properly comprehend the human biological endowment.

Any basic psychology of personality development and maldevelopment must recognize that the human has a different method of adaptation and survival than any other organism. The evolution of Homo sapiens rested upon the selecting out of mutations that increased the capacity for using tools, and particularly that tool of tools, language. The acquisition of symbolic capacities has permitted persons to fragment past experiences and project converging strands through the transitory present to an imagined future, and to imaginatively try out actions without committing the self or others to the irrevocable consequences of actions. Such capacities released humans from motivation by drives and conditioning alone and humans could be motivated by future goals and thus become capable of ego functioning. Although the human physiological makeup, like that of all living organisms, is suited to a relatively limited physical environment, humans could increasingly modify the environment to their needs, and because they could communicate what they learned to others and across generations, learning became cumulative, and peoples developed cultures—different ways of living together in different localities. To live in very different physical and social environments, they had to assimilate the necessary adaptive techniques from those who raised them.

Unless we appreciate that humans have a dual endowment—a genetic inheritance that is born into them and a cultural heritage into which they are born and which they must assimilate from those who rear them, we can never understand human development or maldevelopment correctly. Homo sapiens has been defined in many ways—as the tool-bearing animal, the talking animal, the thinking animal, and even as the clothed animal—but more critically Homo sapiens is the species that cannot develop into a person or even survive without assimilating a culture. This fact is vital to a viable science of personality development and must form the foundation of any scientific psychiatry.

Human infants, most malleable of all animals, do not develop into integrated individuals simply as a concomitant of their physical maturation including the growth and maturation of their brains. They must assimilate and learn a great deal during their long years of immaturity from those who raise them. The complex process is carried out to a great extent by the family, or some planned substitute for it, which conveys, often unknowingly, the fundamentals that children must acquire as the parents nurture and protect the child and provide a shelter within and against the remainder of society. Indeed, even though the family is a social rather than a biological structure, it is an essential correlate of the human's biological makeup and any attempt to understand the child's development without due consideration of the family in which it takes place is bound to error, for it eliminates an essential of the developmental process.

A major outgrowth of our studies has been this realization that in order for infants to develop into persons, indeed, even to survive, they require considerable input from those who raise them in addition to nurturant care and adequate stimulation. We have in the various chapters in this book as well as elsewhere (Lidz, 1963a, 1979) sought to designate what children require from their families to move through the various developmental stages to become properly independent with an "ego identity" and a capacity for intimacy by the end of adolescence or as young adults. Any thorough presentation of our current and still changing understanding of such requisites would be very lengthy and involved, and we shall here simply designate the general tasks of the family as we have divided them into five or six categories.

The essential parental nurturance must change in accord with the child's developing capacities—from the total care required by the newborn through gradually rescinding erotized ties and forming increasingly clear boundaries to promoting the offspring's capacities to separate from the family by the end of adolescence. The developing personality not only requires stimulation but also delimitation of drives and structuring which relates to the dynamic organization of the family. The interaction and organization of the family is abetted by the two parents forming a coalition with reciprocally interrelating roles, and the adherence of parents to the boundaries between generations and their respective sex-linked roles that are reasonably compatible with the society in which the family exists. The fulfillment of such conditions helps assure the child's adequate oedipal transition and achievement of a proper sexual identity as well as providing a reasonably conflict-free area within the family into which the child can develop. The family socializes the child through conveying roles appropriate to age and sex and by providing knowledge of the basic institutions of the society and of their worth, in part through the manner in which the parents fill their parental roles, relate maritally and behave in other institutional contexts. The value of being a man or woman, or of marriage as a way of gaining satisfaction and security, etc., depends on how the parents relate to each other as well as on the individual models they provide. Superego development derives from internalization of directives and models of two parents, and internalized conflict and splits in ego development can reflect efforts to relate to irreconcilable parental figures. The parents serve as prime models for identification and as basic love objects, and their worth as such depends not only on the individual parent but on how the parents relate to one another. As we have already noted, a critical function of the family is to convey the basic instrumental techniques of the culture and particularly a firm foundation of the society's language with its meanings and syntax that are needed for clear cognition and the capacities to interrelate with others, and indeed, upon which most learning after infancy depends. The ability to think clearly, to test reality, to have the verbal tools necessary for directing the self depend upon tutelage within the family and the consistencies and styles of the parents' ways of communicating. Indeed, trust in the usefulness of verbal communication as a means of problem solving and of fostering interpersonal cooperation depends largely upon how language is used within the family.

It becomes apparent that the influence of parents upon children cannot be understood properly only through examining the interaction between a parent and a child. The nuclear family is a true small group in which the action of any member affects all, producing reactions, counteractions, and potential shifts in the family equilibrium. The intrafamilial influences must be understood transactionally; for example, the interaction between parents can affect the child profoundly; the relations between two siblings influence a third sibling, and through this third child, the way the parents relate to one another and to their other children, and all are or can be influenced by the relations of the family to other families or the relationship of any member to someone from another family.

The nuclear family as a small group has special characteristics of structure and function in addition to those of small groups in general that may best be understood systemically, through systems theory, with attention, as we have already noted, to the nature of the boundaries between generations, sexes, individuals, and the remainder of society; the leadership coalition and the attainment of reciprocal roles; the affectional aspects including the family atmosphere of competence, meaningfulness and hopefulness; as well as the clarity and meaningfulness of the intrafamilial verbal and nonverbal communications. All such matters have an enduring effect upon the family's offspring. Moreover, this group has to change as it progresses through the life cycle, and each point of transition requires readjustment and realignment. If the group as a whole or a member resists such progression, transition assumes crisis intensity and growth will be hampered—a potential for psychopathological fixation (Fleck, 1983).

A particularly significant concomitant of the transactional orientation that has emerged from family studies has been the attention given to cognitive as well as emotional or libidinal development. The many careful studies of linguistic and other aspects of cognitive development carried out by Piaget and others are being fitted into a psychodynamic framework to the benefit of both—and as an essential step toward achieving a comprehensive developmental theory. The influence upon dynamic developmental theories has already been profound. We can mention only a few significant areas. Recognition of the central role of language in ego functioning has required a reevaluation of the development of ego functions in line with the child's and adolescent's cognitive capacities. Kohlberg's (1964) studies of the relationships between cognitive and moral development make it obvious that superego controls are very limited at the age of five or six and that not until the child has turned into an adolescent can he properly grasp conventional morality. Another related consequence of the cognitive studies of severely disturbed persons has been the realization that the division of cognition into primary and secondary process thinking is inadequate, and as discussed in part in the preceding chapter, the capacities and limitations of each stage of cognitive development must be taken into account in understanding psychopathology.

The orientation we have been presenting challenges the psychoanalytic concept that the so-called choice of the neurosis, or more properly, of the psychopathological syndrome, derives from fixation at or regression to a particular phase of libidinal or psychosexual development. It seems very likely that a felicitous start in life in a stable and supportive family provides a resiliency to withstand or rebound from later emotional trauma, disappointments, and disillusionments that are an inevitable aspect of life. However, it becomes apparent that numerous sources of deviant personality development exist in addition to those deriving from arrested psychosexual development—and which, indeed, make such fixations more dynamically comprehensible than does a primary emphasis upon inborn predisposition or even upon the mother's ways of handling the child or of relating to the child during a given developmental phase.

Indeed, our studies of schizophrenic, delinquent, and addicted patients and their families showed that the intrafamilial problems that affected the patient were not limited to any particular developmental stage, but rather were panphasic. It seems likely that the early preoedipal and oedipal problems of the child and between a parent and child that have been emphasized in psychoanalytically oriented psychopathology are but an early indication of continuing or repetitive transactional difficulties.

Concepts of what leads to a specific type of psychopathology have been changing, though the changes have rarely been noted clearly. Some of the most telling and therapeutically useful contributions to personality development and psychopathology in recent decades have derived from paying attention to family configurations and styles of behavior, to habitual parental ways of interacting with a child rather than to specific trauma or to the interactions during a single phase, and to the internalization by the offspring of parental ways of perceiving, thinking, and communicating. Both Knight (1937) and Chassell (1938) described closely related family configurations that gave rise to "essential alcoholics"; Johnson and Szurek (1952) found that children's antisocial behavior was related to "superego lacunae" in one or both parents that provided unconscious directives to the child; Bruch (Bruch and Touraine, 1940) related eating disturbance to the mother's emotional needs derived from her childhood and the configuration of the family. However, it was only through the studies of schizophrenic families that attention was clearly directed to the importance of the family transactions to the type of psychiatric disorder a person develops (Bateson et al., 1956; Lidz and Fleck, 1965; Singer and Wynne, 1965a, 1965b; Wynne and Singer, 1963a, 1963b; Chapters I, V, VII). The parents' styles of thinking, communicating, and behaving create an environment as well as a set of directives which children assimilate and to which they react. One might ask, for example, if obsessional neuroses may be a matter of being raised by obsessive parents who incidentally would be apt to use rigid bowel training, but even more important, if they would also foster ambivalence, stubbornness, shame, undoing, isolation, and reaction formation as means of handling anxiety; and if hypochondriacal parents do not inculcate a retreat from anxiety into bodily complaints, etc. Stierlin (1978) has directed attention to the importance of a continuing family pattern that influences parents' attitudes at the time the adolescent separates from the family, and leads to "binding," "delegating," or prematurely "expelling" modes that profoundly affect the adolescent's future life style.

The ramifications of a family systems orientation for personality development, psychopathology, and psychotherapy are many, and we have here been only attempting to convey the implications. In order to indicate the scope of the expansion and reorganization of psychoanalytic theory and psychopathology that appears to be required, we shall briefly consider problems of sexual identity. Whether a person is a male or a female is probably the most important determinant of personality characteristics, and security of sexual identity is of critical moment to harmonious personality development. We have already adequately emphasized the critical role of gender identity confusion in schizophrenia. Yet, the tendency to consider in theory, even if not in practice, that a person's sexual identity is purely biologically determined, and that confusions in sexual identity such as homosexuality are a reflection of the innate bisexuality of all persons stultifies progress.

It has become amply clear that although biological sex provides a very clear directive to proper gender identity, many other factors influence it. Gender attribution and allocation by the parents from birth; the satisfaction of the parents with the child's biological sex; the initial identification of children of both sexes with the mother, and the father's role in blocking the boy's continued identification with her; the model provided by the parent of the same sex as the patient for the child's identification; the worth attributed to the same-sexed parent by the spouse who should be an early love object to the child; the nature of the parents' marital relationship; the advantages or disadvantages of siblings of the opposite sex—all these and still other such factors enter into a person's acceptance, satisfaction, and security with his or her given sex. Consideration of the dynamic interplay of such intra-familial and cultural influences seems essential for proper clarification of the multiplicity of psychopathological problems related to gender identity.

The appreciation of the importance of the family and also of cognitive development to normal and pathological development are many, and we trust we have made it clear, concern all of psychiatry and the understanding of personality development and functioning, and not only schizophrenic disorders. A brief reconsideration of Freud's (1905) Dora case, which he introduced by stating, "Above all our interest will be directed toward the family circumstances"—an orientation he abandoned,[1] and in the end attributed Dora's neurosis to childhood masturbation and constitutional weakness derived from her father's syphilis, may indicate the direction his psychopathological concepts might have taken. Freud left many questions unanswered. What were the consequences of Dora's father's disruption of the generation boundaries when he used Dora, first as something of a replacement for his wife, and then as a means of distracting, assuaging, or "buying off" Mr. K., his mistress's husband? What of the failures of the parental coalition in which her father derogated and neglected his wife, and, at times, handed Dora over to the maternal chaperonage of Mrs. K., who further violated the generation boundaries by making Dora her confidante and roommate, and also by fostering the relationship between Dora and Mr. K.? What of the split feminine role model afforded Dora by a mother who is neglected as a wife and by Mrs. K. who is desirable as a mistress

---

[1]For reasons that are not clear for it was not necessary to renounce it as part of abandonment of his "seduction theory" of the neuroses; Freud may have been retreating to a more clear-cut organic orientation. He wrote, "It is the therapeutic technique alone that is purely psychological; the theory does not by any means fail to point out that the neuroses have an organic basis" (Freud, 1905).

but not as a wife? The continuance of her oedipal strivings into incestuous conflicts surely did not depend upon constitutional factors as much as upon her mother's denigrated position, her father's seductiveness and being placed in a situation with the Ks in which a semi-incestuous relationship to Mr. K. was condoned, and a homosexually toned, quasi-incestuous relatedness to Mrs. K. abetted. Might not the betrayal by her father—her recognition that he was sacrificing her as he did his wife for his own gratification—lead to a renewed identification with her mother, with attendant feelings of worthlessness that led to suicidal preoccupations? The conflicts to which Dora was subjected were far more pervasive and disruptive than the conflict over Mr. K.'s desired or feared advances with their oedipal implications. Dora was no longer a naïve child, and one cannot properly overlook the fact that her serious disturbances arose immediately after learning that Mr. K. had used the same ploy to seduce the K.'s nursemaid, "After all I get nothing from my wife" that he used with Dora—whether successfully or not we really do not know. Might not her use of illness and her specific symptoms have to do with her identification with her tubercular and luetic father? Had she not been taught by her father's example to dissimulate, to use illness as a pretext and as an escape when trapped and unable to resolve opposing motives? Freud recognized and discussed many of these issues, but did not consider them etiologic to Dora's neurosis. An examination of the parental coalition, generation boundaries, gender role models, parental styles of behaving and communicating contributes to an increased understanding of Dora's dilemma, her illness, and her choice of symptoms. Perhaps the essence of the difference in the orientation to psychopathology and psychotherapy we are offering from that of classic psychoanalysis can be found in that Freud believed Dora's telling her parents that Mr. K. has propositioned her was "an action which she had taken when she was already under the influence of a morbid craving for revenge. A normal girl, I am inclined to think, will deal with a situation of this kind by herself." Freud did not seem to consider if a young woman who had grown up under the circumstances he had depicted could have been normal.

We have from our studies of what transpired in the families with schizophrenic offspring been led to the family orientation that Freud renounced, and which has opened the way for a more consistent understanding of personality development and its pathology and a more encompassing grasp of human development.

Bibliography

Abraham, K. (1908), The psycho-sexual differences between hysteria and dementia praecox. In: *Selected Papers of Karl Abraham*. London: Hogarth Press, 1948.

—— (1916), The first pregenital phase of the libido. In: *Selected Papers of Karl Abraham*. London: Hogarth Press, 1948.

Abrahams, J., & Varon, E. (1953), *Maternal Dependency and Schizophrenia: Mothers and Daughters in a Therapeutic Group*. New York: International Universities Press.

Ackerman, N. W. (1954a), The diagnosis of neurotic marital interaction. *Soc. Casew.*, *35*:139-147.

—— (1954b), Interpersonal disturbances in the family: Some unsolved problems in psychotherapy. *Psychiatry, 17*:359-368.

—— (1958), *The Psychodynamics of Family Life*. New York: Basic Books.

—— (1960), Family-focused therapy of schizophrenia. In: *The Out-Patient Treatment of Schizophrenia*, ed. S. Scher & H. Davis. New York: Grune & Stratton.

—— (1961), The schizophrenic patient and his family relationships: A conceptual basis for family-focused therapy of schizophrenia. In: *Mental Patients in Transition, Steps in Hospital-Community Rehabilitation*, ed. M. Greenblatt, D. Levinson, & G. Klerman. Springfield, Ill.: Thomas.

—— (1962), Adolescent problems: A symptom of family disorder. *Fam. Proc., 1*:202-213.

—— Behrens, M. (1956), A study of family diagnosis. *Amer. J. Orthopsychiat., 26*:66-78.

Alanen, Y. O. (1958), The mothers of schizophrenic patients. *Acta Psychiat. Neurol. Scand.*, Suppl. 124.

—— (1960a), Some thoughts on schizophrenia and ego development in the light of family investigations. *Arch. Gen. Psychiat., 3*:650-656.

—— (1960b), Über die Familiensituation der Schizophrenie-Patienten. *Acta Psychother., 8*:89-104.

—— (1966), The family in the pathogenesis of schizophrenic and neurotic disorders. *Acta Psychiatr. Neurol. Scand.*, Suppl. 189, Vol. *24*.

447

——— (1968), From the mothers of schizophrenic patients to interactional family dynamics. *J. Psychiat. Res.*, 6 (Suppl. 1):201-212.

——— (1980), In search of the interactional origin of schizophrenia. In: *The Family: Evaluation and Treatment*, ed. C. K. Holling & J. M. Lewis, New York: Brunner/Mazel.

Alexander, F. (1930), *The Psychoanalysis of the Total Personality: The Application of Freud's Theory of the Ego to the Neuroses*. New York: Nerv. & Ment. Dis. Publ. Co.

Ammar, S., & Ledjri, H. (1972), Les conditions familiales de développement de la Schizophrénie. Tunis: Masson & Cie.

Anthony, E. J. (1968), The developmental precursors of adult schizophrenia. *J. Psychiat. Res.*, 6 (Suppl. 1):293-316.

Ariès, P. (1962), *Centuries of Childhood: A Social History of Family Life*. New York: Knopf.

Arieti, S. (1955), *Interpretation of Schizophrenia*. New York: Brunner.

Arlow, J. (1960), Fantasy systems in twins. *Psychoanal. Quart.*, 29:175-199.

Astrachan, J., & Simon, B. (1963), Study of psychosis in a pair of identical twins. *Arch. Gen. Psychiat.*, 8:582-589.

Bateson, G. (1958), Schizophrenic distortions of communications. In: *Psychotherapy of Chronic Schizophrenic Patients*, ed. C. A. Whitaker. Boston: Little, Brown.

——— (1960), Minimal requirements for a theory of schizophrenia. *Arch. Gen. Psychiat.*, 2:477-491.

——— (1961), The biosocial integration of behavior in the schizophrenic family. In: *Exploring the Base for Family Therapy*, ed. N. W. Ackerman, F. Beatman, & S. Sherman. New York: Family Service Assn. of Amer.

——— Jackson, D., Haley, J., & Weakland, J. (1956), Toward a theory of schizophrenia. *Behav. Sci.*, 1:251-264.

Bauer, F. C. (1953), Folie à trois: A case report. *Psychiat. Quart.*, 27:624-636.

Baxter, J. C., & Arthur, S. C. (1964), Conflict in families of schizophrenics as a function of premorbid adjustment and social class. *Fam. Proc.*, 3:273-279.

——— Becker, J. (1962), Anxiety and avoidance behavior in schizophrenics in response to parental figures. *J. Abnorm. Soc. Psychol.*, 64:432-437.

——— ——— Hooks, W. (1963), Defensive style in the families of schizophrenics and controls. *J. Abnorm. Soc. Psychol.*, 66:512-518.

Beck, S. J. (1960), Families of schizophrenic and of well children: Method, concepts, and some results. *Amer. J. Orthopsychiat.*, 30:247-262.

——— Nunnally, J. C. (1953), Method of social work research in schizophrenia. *J. Psychiat. Soc. Work*, 22:123-128.

Beckett, P. G. S., Robinson, D. B., Frazier, S. H., Steinhilber, R. M., Duncan, G. M., Estes, H. R., Litin, E. M., Grattan, R. T., Lorton, W. L., Williams, G. E., & Johnson, A. M. (1956), Studies in schizophrenia at the Mayo Clinic: 1. The significance of exogenous traumata in the genesis of schizophrenia. *Psychiatry, 19*:137-148.

Behrens, M. I., Rosenthal, A. J., & Chodoff, P. (1968), Communication in lower-class families of schizophrenics: II. Observations and findings. *Arch. Gen. Psychiat., 18*:689-696.

Bell, N. (1962), Extended family relations of disturbed and well families. *Fam. Proc., 1*:175-193.

———— Vogel, E. (1960), Toward a framework for functional analysis of family behavior. Introduction to *A Modern Introduction to the Family*, ed. N. Bell & E. Vogel. Glencoe, Ill.: Free Press.

Beres, D., & Obers, S. J. (1952), The effects of extreme deprivation in infancy on psychic structure in adolescence: A study in ego development. *The Psychoanalytic Study of the Child*, 5:212-235. New York: International Universities Press.

Binswanger, L. (1958a), Insanity as life-historical phenomenon and as mental disease: The case of Ilse. In: *Existence: A New Dimension in Psychiatry and Psychology*, ed. R. May, E. Angel, & H. Ellenberger. New York: Basic Books.

———— (1958b), The case of Ellen West. In: *Existence: A New Dimension in Psychiatry and Psychology*, ed. R. May, E. Angel, & H. Ellenberger. New York: Basic Books.

Bion, W. R. (1954), Notes on the theory of schizophrenia. *Int. J. Psycho-Anal., 35*:113-118.

Blakar, R. M. (1980), Studies of Familial Communication and Psychopathology. Universitetsforlaget, Olso.

Blatt, S. J., & Wild, C. M. (1976) *Schizophrenia: A Developmental Analysis*. New York: Academic Press.

Bleuler, E. (1911), *Dementia Praecox or the Group of Schizophrenias*. New York: International Universities Press, 1950.

———— (1930), Primäre and Sekundäre Symptome der Schizophrenie. Z. *Ges. Neurol. Psychiat., 124*:607-646.

Bleuler, M. (1941), *Krankheitsverlauf, Persönlichkeit und Verwandtschaft Schizophrener und ihre gegenseitigen Beziehungen*. Leipzig: Thieme.

———— (1955), Research and changes in concepts in the study of schizophrenia, 1941-1950. *Bull. Isaac Ray Med. Library, 3*:1-132.

———— (1956), Aspects secrets de la psychiatrie. *L'Evol. Psychiat., 21*:45-50.

———— (1978a) The long-term course of schizophrenic psychoses. In: *The Nature of Schizophrenia*, ed. L. C. Wynne, R. L. Cromwell & S. Matthysee. New York: John Wiley & Sons.

———— (1978b), *Schizophrenic Disorders: Long-Term Patient and Family Studies*. New Haven: Yale University Press.

Block, J., Patterson, V., Block, J., & Jackson, D. D. (1958), A study of the parents of schizophrenic and neurotic children. *Psychiatry*, *21*:387-397.

Blum, G. S., & Rosenzweig, S. (1944), The incidence of sibling and parental deaths in the anamnesis of female schizophrenics. *J. Gen. Psychol.*, *31*:3-13.

Boisen, A. T. (1947), Onset in acute schizophrenia. *Psychiatry*, *10*:159-166.

Boszormenyi-Nagy, I. (1962), The concept of schizophrenia from the perspective of family treatment. *Fam. Proc.*, *1*:103-113.

Bott, E. (1955), Urban families: Conjugal roles and social networks. *Hum. Relat.*, *8*:345-384.

—— (1957), *Family and Social Network*. London: Tavistock Publ.

Bour, P. (1958), Schizophrénie et dissociation familiale. *L'Evol. Psychiat.*, *23*:85-104.

Bowen, M. (1957), Family participation in schizophrenia. Presented at meeting of Amer. Psychiat. Assn.

—— (1960), A family concept of schizophrenia. In: *The Etiology of Schizophrenia*, ed. D. D. Jackson. New York: Basic Books, Chapter 12.

—— Dysinger, R. H., Brodey, W., & Basamania, B. (1957), Study and treatment of five hospitalized families each with a psychotic member. Presented at Amer. Orthopsychiat. Assn. Meeting.

—— —— Basamania, B. (1959), The role of the father in families with a schizophrenic patient. *Amer. J. Psychiat.*, *115*:117-120.

Bowers, M. (1974), *Retreat from Sanity*. New York: Behavioral Publications.

Brecher, S. (1956), The Rorschach reaction patterns of maternally overprotected and maternally rejected schizophrenic patients. *J. Nerv. Ment. Dis.*, *123*:41-52.

Brodey, W. (1959), Some family operations and schizophrenia: A study of five hospitalized families each with a schizophrenic member. *AMA Arch. Gen Psychiat.*, *1*:379-402.

—— (1961), The family as the unit of study and treatment: 3. Image, object and narcissistic relationships. *Amer. J. Orthopsychiat.*, *31*:69-73.

Brody, E. B., & Redlich, F. C., eds. (1952), *Psychotherapy with Schizophrenics*. New York: International Universities Press.

Brody, J. P. (1958), Language in schizophrenia. *Amer. J. Psychother.*, *12*:473-487.

Brown, G. W., Birley, J. L. T., & Wing, J. K. (1972), Influence of family life on the course of schizophrenic disorders: A replication. *Brit. J. Psychiat.*, *121*:241-258.

Brown, R. (1958), *Words and Things*. Glencoe, Ill.: Free Press.

Bruch, H. (1957), Weight disturbances and schizophrenic development. *Congr. Rep. IInd Int. Congr. Psychiat., Zurich*, *2*:190-193.

—— (1959), Studies in schizophrenia. *Acta Psychiat. Neurol. Scand.*, Suppl. 130, Vol. *34*:5-48.

—— (1961), Transformation of oral impulses in eating disorders: a conceptual approach. *Psychiat. Quart., 35*:458-481.

—— Palombo, S. (1961), Conceptual problems in schizophrenia. *J. Nerv. Ment. Dis., 132*:114-117.

—— Touraine, G. (1940), Obesity in childhood: V. The family frame of obese children. *Psychosom. Med., 2*:141-206.

Buell, B. (1953), *Classification of Disorganized Families for Use in Family Oriented Diagnosis and Treatment.* New York: Community Research Associates.

Burgess, E. W. (1926), The family as a unit of interacting personalities. *Family, 7*:3-9.

Burlingham, D. T. (1952), *Twins. A Study of Three Pairs of Identical Twins.* New York: International Universities Press.

Burnham, D. L. (1956), Misperception of other persons in schizophrenia: a structural view of restitution processes, reality representation, and perception. *Psychiatry, 19*:283-303.

—— Gladstone, A. I., & Gibson, R. W. (1967), *Schizophrenia and the Need-Fear Dilemma.* New York: International Universities Press.

Cameron, N. (1938), *Reasoning, Regression and Communication in Schizophrenia. Psychol. Monogr.* No. 221.

—— (1959), The paranoid pseudo-community revisited. *Amer. J. Sociol., 65*:52-58.

—— Magaret, A. (1951), *Behavior Pathology.* Boston: Houghton Mifflin.

Caputo, D. V. (1963), The parents of the schizophrenic. *Fam. Proc., 2*:339-356.

Carr, A. (1963), Observations on paranoia and their relationship to the Schreber Case. *Internat. J. Psycho-Anal., 44*:195-200.

Carroll, J. B. (1959), Language and thought studied across languages: A report of the "Southwest Project." Presented at meeting of Amer. Psychol. Assn.

Caudill, W. (1958), *The Psychiatric Hospital as a Small Society.* Cambridge: Harvard University Press.

—— Stainbrook, E. (1954), Some covert effects of communication difficulties in a psychiatric hospital. *Psychiatry, 17*:27-40.

Chapman, L. J. & Chapman, J. P. (1973), *Disordered Thought in Schizophrenia.* New York: Appleton-Century-Crofts.

Chassell, J. O. (1938), Family constellation in the etiology of essential alcoholism. *Psychiatry, 1*:473-503.

Cheek, F. E. (1964), A serendipitous finding: sex roles and schizophrenia. *J. Abnorm. Soc. Psychol., 69*:392-400.

Chein, I. (1964), *The Road to H: Narcotics, Delinquency and Social Policy.* New York: Basic Books.

Chrzanowski, G. (1957), The family environment of schizophrenic patients. *Congr. Rep. IInd Int. Congr. Psychiat., Zurich*, 4:42-47.

Ciarlo, D. (1967), Word meanings in parents of schizophrenics. *Arch. Gen. Psychiatry*, 17:470-477.

Ciompi, L., & Müller, C. (1976), *Lebensweg und Alter der Schizophrenen*. Berlin: Springer-Verlag.

Clausen, J. A., & Kohn, M. L. (1960), Social relations and schizophrenia. In: *The Etiology of Schizophrenia*, ed. D. D. Jackson. New York: Basic Books.

Cohen, M. B., Baker, G., Cohen, R., Fromm-Reichmann, F., & Weigert, E. (1954), An intensive study of twelve cases of manic-depressive psychosis. *Psychiatry*, 17:103-137.

Conran, M. B. (1976), Schizophrenia as incestuous failure: theoretical implications derived from transference observations of the young male schizophrenic and his mother, concerning the mother-infant relationship. In: *Schizophrenia 75: Psychotherapy, Family Studies, Research*, ed. J. Jorstad & E. Ugelstad. Oslo: Universitetsforlget.

Cornelison, A. R. (1960), Casework interviewing as a research technique in a study of families of schizophrenic patients. *Ment. Hyg.*, 44:551-559.

Cronin, H. J. (1933), Analysis of neuroses of identical twins. *Psychoanal. Rev.*, 20:375-387.

da Silva, G. (1963), The role of the father with chronic schizophrenic patients: a study in group therapy. *Canad. Psychiat. Assn. J.*, 8:190-203.

Delay, J., Deniker, P., & Green, A. (1957), Le milieu familial des schizophrènes: 1. Proposition du problème. *L'Encéphale*, 46:189-232.

——— ——— ——— (1960), Le milieu familial des schizophrènes: 2. Méthode d'approache. *L'Encéphale*, 49:1-21.

——— ——— ——— (1962), Le milieu familial des schizophrènes: 3. Résultats et hypothèses. *L'Encéphale*, 51:5-73.

Demarest, E. W., & Winestine, M. C. (1955), The initial phase of concomitant treatment of twins. *The Psychoanalytic Study of the Child*, 10:336-352. New York: International Universities Press.

Despert, J. L. (1942), Prophylactic aspects of schizophrenia in childhood. *Nerv. Child.*, 1:199-231.

——— (1951), Some considerations relating to the genesis of autistic behavior in children. *Amer. J. Orthopsychiat.*, 21:335-350.

Devoto, A. (1960), *I Precedenti Psicologici dello Schizofrenico*. Florence: Leo S. Olschki.

Dicks, H. V. (1953), Clinical studies in marriage and the family: a symposium on methods. I. Experiences with marital tensions seen in the psychological clinic. *Brit. J. Med. Psychol.*, 26:181-196.

Doane, J., Jones, J. E., Fisher, L., et al. (1982), Parental communication deviance as a predictor of competence in children at risk for adult psychiatric disorder. *Fam. Proc.*, *21*:211-223.

Dworin, J., & Wyant, O. (1957), Authoritarian patterns in the mothers of schizophrenics. *J. Clin. Psychol.*, *13*:332-338.

Dysinger, R. H. (1957), The "action dialogue" in an intense relationship: A study of a schizophrenic girl and her mother. Presented at meeting of Amer. Psychiat. Assn.

Edwards, R. V. (1964), Some schizophrenic mechanisms. *Amer. J. Psychiat.*, *120*:1105-1107.

Ehrenwald, J. (1958), Neurotic interaction and patterns of pseudo-heredity in the family. *Amer. J. Psychiat.*, *115*:134-142.

——— (1963a), Family diagnosis and mechanisms of psychosocial defense. *Fam. Proc.*, *2*:121-131.

——— (1963b), Family dynamics and communication theory. *J. Communication*, *13*:191-198.

Eisenberg, L. (1957), The fathers of autistic children. *Amer. J. Orthopsychiat.*, *27*:715-724.

Ellison, E. A., & Hamilton, D. M. (1949), The hospital treatment of dementia praecox: Part II. *Amer. J. Psychiat.*, *106*:454-461.

Elsasser, G. (1952), *Die Nachkommen geisteskranker Elternpaare*. Stuttgart: Thieme.

Endicott, T. (1958), Personal communication.

Engel, G. L. (1962), *Psychological Development in Health and Disease*. Philadelphia: W. B. Saunders.

Erikson, E. (1950a), Growth and crises of the "healthy personality." In: *Symposium on the Healthy Personality*, Vol. 2: *Problems of Infancy and Childhood*, ed. M. J. E. Senn. New York: Josiah Macy, Jr., Foundation.

——— (1950b), *Childhood and Society*. New York: W. W. Norton.

——— (1956), The problem of ego identity. *J. Amer. Psychoanal. Assn.*, *4*:56-121.

——— (1964), *Insight into Responsibility*. New York: W. W. Norton.

Ernst, K. (1956), Geordnete Familienverhältnisse Späterer Schizophrener im Lichte einer Nachuntersuchung. *Arch. Psychiat. Nervenheilkr.*, *194*:355-367.

Essen-Moller, E. (1941), *Psychiatrische Untersuchungen an einer Serie von Zeillingen*. Copenhagen: Munksgaard.

Fairbairn, W. R. D. (1940), Schizoid factors in the personality. In: *Psycho-Analytic Studies of the Personality*. London: Tavistock Publ., 1952.

——— (1944), Endopsychic structure considered in terms of object relationships. *Internat. J. Psycho-Anal.*, *25*:70-93.

——— (1952), *Psycho-Analytic Studies of the Personality*. London: Tavistock Publ.

Farina, A. (1960), Patterns of dominance and conflict in parents of schizo-phrenic patients. *J. Abnorm. Soc. Psychol., 61*:31-38.

—— Dunham, R. (1963), Measurement of family relationships and their effects. *Arch. Gen. Psychiat., 9*:64-73.

—— Holzberg, J. D. (1968), Interaction patterns of parents and hos-pitalized sons diagnosed as schizophrenic or nonschizophrenic. *J. Abnor. Psychol., 73*:114-118.

—— —— (1970), Anxiety level of schizophrenic and control patients and their parents. *J. Abnor. Psychol., 75*:157-163.

Faris, R. E. L. (1934), Cultural isolation and the schizophrenic personality. *Amer. J. Sociol., 40*:155-164.

—— (1944), Ecological factors in human behavior. In: *Personality and the Behavior Disorders,* Vol. II, ed. J. McV. Hunt. New York: Ronald Press.

Federn, P. (1952), *Ego Psychology and the Psychoses,* ed. E. Weiss. New York: Basic Books.

Feinsilver, D. (1970), Communication in families of schizophrenic patients. Describing common objects as a test of communication between family members. *Arch. Gen. Psychiat., 22*:143-148.

Ferreira, A. J. (1960), The semantics and the context of the schizophrenic's language. *Arch. Gen. Psychiat., 3*:128-138.

Fisher, S., Boyd, I., Walker, D., & Sheer, D. (1959), Parents of schizo-phrenics, neurotics, and normals. *Arch. Gen. Psychiat., 1*:149-166.

—— Mendell, D. (1956), The communication of neurotic patterns over two and three generations. *Psychiatry, 19*:41-46.

Fleck, S. (1953), Vigilance (orienting behavior), conditional reactions and adjustment patterns in schizophrenic and compulsive patients. *Ann. N.Y. Acad. Sci., 56*:342-379.

—— (1960), Family dynamics and origin of schizophrenia. *Psychosom. Med., 22*:333-344.

—— (1962), Residential treatment of young schizophrenics. *Conn. Med., 26*:369-376.

—— (1963), Psychotherapy of families of hospitalized patients. In: *Cur-rent Psychiatric Therapies,* Vol. III, ed. J. Masserman. New York: Grune & Stratton.

—— (1975), The family and psychiatry. In: *Comprehensive Textbook of Psychiatry.* ed. A. Freedman, H. Kaplan, & B. Sadock, Baltimore: Williams & Wilkins.

—— (1978), Schizophrenia. In: *Current Therapy.* ed. H. F. Conn. Phila-delphia: W. B. Saunders.

—— (1980), Family functioning and family pathology. *Psychiat. Annals., 10*:17-35.

—— (1983), A holistic approach to family typology and the axes of DSM-III. *Arch. Gen. Psychiat., 40*:901-906.

———— Cornelison, A. R., Norton, N., & Lidz, T. (1957), The intrafamilial environment of the schizophrenic patient: II. Interaction between hospital staff and families. *Psychiatry, 20*:343-350.

Flugel, J. C. (1921), *The Psycho-Analytic Study of the Family*. London: Hogarth Press.

Foote, N. & Cottrell, L. (1955), *Identity and Interpersonal Competence: A New Direction in Family Research*. Chicago: University of Chicago Press.

Foudraine, J. (1961), Schizophrenia and the family: a survey of the literature 1956-1960 on the etiology of schizophrenia. *Acta Psychother., 9*:82-110.

Frazee, H. E. (1953), Children who later became schizophrenic. *Smith Coll. Stud. Soc. Work, 23*:125-149.

Freeman, R. V., & Grayson, H. M. (1955), Maternal attitudes in schizophrenia. *J. Abnorm. Soc. Psychol., 50*:45-52.

Freeman, T., Cameron, J. L., & McGhie, A. (1958), *Chronic Schizophrenia*. New York: International Universities Press.

Freud, S. (1905), Fragment of an analysis of a case of hysteria. *Standard Edition, 7*:112-122. London: Hogarth Press, 1953.

———— (1911), Psycho-analytic notes on an autobiographical account of a case of paranoia (dementia paranoides). *Standard Edition, 12*:3-82. London: Hogarth Press, 1958.

———— (1913), Totem and taboo. *Standard Edition, 13*:1-161. London: Hogarth Press, 1955.

———— (1916-1917), *A General Introduction to Psychoanalysis*. New York: Boni and Liveright.

———— (1921), Group psychology and the analysis of the ego. *Standard Edition, 18*:67-143. London: Hogarth Press, 1955.

———— (1922), Some neurotic mechanisms in jealousy, paranoia and homosexuality. *Standard Edition, 18*:211-232. London: Hogarth Press, 1955.

———— (1923), The Ego and the Id. *Standard Edition, 19*:3-66. London: Hogarth Press, 1961.

———— (1924a), Neurosis and psychosis. *Standard Edition, 19*:149-153. London: Hogarth Press, 1961.

———— (1924b), The dissolution of the oedipus complex. *Standard Edition, 19*:173-179. London: Hogarth Press, 1961.

———— (1933), New introductory lectures on psychoanalysis. *Standard Edition, 22*. Hogarth Press, London, 1964.

———— (1940), An outline of psycho-analysis. *Standard Edition, 23*. Hogarth Press, London,

Freyhan, F. A. (1951), Study of a schizophrenic family, *Delaware Med. J., 23*:213-217.

Friedman, C. J., & Friedman, A. S. (1970), Characteristics of schizophrenic families during a joint story-telling task. *Fam. Proc., 9*:333-353.

Fromm-Reichmann, F. (1939), Transference problems in schizophrenics. *Psychoanal. Quart.*, *8*:412-426.

———— (1940), Notes on the mother rôle in the family group. *Bull. Menninger Clin.*, *4*:132-145.

———— (1948), Notes on the development of treatment of schizophrenics by psychoanalytic psychotherapy. *Psychiatry*, *11*:263-273.

———— (1950), *Principles of Intensive Psychotherapy*. Chicago: University of Chicago Press.

Frumkin, R. M. (1954), Social factors in schizophrenia. *Sociol. Soc. Res.*, *38*:383-386.

Fujinawa, A. (1960), Die Untersuchungen über die Familienverhältnisse der Schizophrenen. *Psychiat. et Neurol. Japonica* (Tokyo), *62*:1375.

Galvin, J. (1956), Mothers of schizophrenics. *J. Nerv. Ment. Dis.*, *123*:568-570.

Garmezy, N. (1974), Children at risk: the search for the antecedents of schizophrenia. II. Ongoing research programs, issues, and interventions. *Schiz. Bull.*, *9*:55-125.

———— Clarke, A., & Strockner, C. (1961), Child-rearing attitudes of mothers and fathers as reported by schizophrenic and normal control patients. *J. Abnorm. Soc. Psychol.*, *63*:176-182.

———— Farina, A., & Rodnick, E. (1960), The structured situational test: a method for studying family interaction in schizophrenia. *Amer. J. Orthopsychiat.*, *30*:445-452.

Gerard, D. L., & Houston, L. G. (1953), Family setting and the social ecology of schizophrenia. *Psychiat. Quart.*, *27*:90-101.

———— Siegel, J. (1950), The family background of schizophrenia. *Psychiat. Quart.*, *24*:47-73.

Giffin, M., Johnson, A. M., & Litin, E. M. (1954), Antisocial acting out. 2. Specific factors determining antisocial acting out. *Amer. J. Orthopsychiat.*, *24*:668-684.

Glueck, B. C. (1957), *Final Report: Research Project for the Study and Treatment of Persons Convicted of Crimes Involving Sexual Aberrations, June 1952-June 1955*. New York State Department of Mental Hygiene.

Goldberg, E. M. (1953), Experiences with families of young men with duodenal ulcer and "normal" control families: some problems of approach and method. *Brit. J. Med. Psychol.*, *26*:204-214.

Goldfarb, W. (1961), The mutual impact of mother and child in childhood schizophrenia. *Amer. J. Orthopsychiat.*, *31*:738-747.

Goldstein, A. P., & Carr, A. C. (1956), The attitudes of mothers of male catatonic and paranoid schizophrenics toward child behavior. *J. Cons. Psychol.*, *20*:190.

Goldstein, M. J. (1980), Family therapy during the aftercare treatment of acute schizophrenia. In: *Psychotherapy of Schizophrenia*. ed. J. G. Gunderson & L. R. Mosher, New York: Aronson.

———— Rodnick, E. H. (1975), The family's contribution to the etiology of schizophrenia: current status. *Schiz. Bull.*, *14*:48-63.

———— ———— Jones, J., et al. (1978), Familial precursors of schizophrenia spectrum disorders. In: *The Nature of Schizophrenia*. ed. L. Wynne, R. Cromwell, & S. Matthysee, New York: J. Wiley & Sons.

Gottesman, I. & Shields, J. (1975), A critical review of recent adoption, twin, and family studies of schizophrenia. Behavioral genetics perspectives. *Schizo. Bull.*, *2*:360-398.

Green, H. (1964), *I Never Promised You a Rose Garden*. New York: Holt, Rinehart & Winston.

Greenberg, H. P. (1956), *Folie à Deux: An Historical and Clinical Study*. Unpublished thesis written as Registrar at Guy's Hospital, London.

Greenblatt, M., Levinson, D., & Williams, R. H. (1957), *The Patient and the Mental Hospital*. Glencoe, IL: Free Press.

Grinspoon, L., Ewalt, J., & Shader, R. (1972), *Schizophrenia: Pharmacotherapy and Psychotherapy*. Baltimore: Williams & Wilkins.

Grotjahn, M. (1960), *Psychoanalysis and the Family Neurosis*. New York: W. W. Norton.

Group for the Advancement of Psychiatry, Committee on the Family (1954), *Integration and Conflict in Family Behavior*. Report No. 27.

Gunderson, J. G. (1978), The value of psychotherapy of schizophrenia. *McLean Hosp. J.*, *3*:131-145.

Hajdu-Gimes, L. (1940), Contributions to the etiology of schizophrenia. *Psychoanal. Rev.*, *27*:421-438.

Haley, J. (1959a), The family of the schizophrenic: a model system. *J. Nerv. Ment. Dis.*, *129*:357-374.

———— (1959b), An interactional description of schizophrenia. *Psychiatry*, 22:321-332.

———— (1960), Observation of the family of the schizophrenic. *Amer. J. Orthopsychiat.*, *30*:460-467.

———— (1962), Family experiments: a new type of experimentation. *Fam. Proc.*, *1*:265-293.

Handel, G. & Hess, D. (1956), The family as an emotional organization. *Marriage and Family Living*, *18*:99-101.

Hartmann, H. (1934-1935), Psychiatric studies of twins. In: *Essays on Ego Psychology*. New York: International Universities Press, 1964.

———— (1939), *Ego Psychology and the Problem of Adaptation*. New York: International Universities Press, 1958.

———— (1944), Psychoanalysis and sociology. In: *Psychoanalysis Today*, ed. S. Lorand. New York: International Universities Press.

———— (1950), The application of psychoanalytic concepts to social science. *Psychoanal. Quart.*, *19*:385-392.

———— (1953), The metapsychology of schizophrenia. In: *The Psychoanalytic*

Study of the Child, 8:177-197. New York: International Universities Press.

———— Kris, E., & Loewenstein, R. M. (1951), Some psychoanalytic comments on "culture and personality." In: *Psychoanalysis and Culture,* ed. G. B. Wilbur & W. Muensterberger. New York: International Universities Press.

Hassan, S. A. (1974), Transactional and contextual invalidation between the parents of disturbed families. a comparative study. *Fam. Proc.,* 13:53-76.

Hayward, M. L. (1960), Schizophrenia and the double bind. *Psychiat. Quart.,* 34:89-91.

Hendricks, R. C. (1944), Schizophrenia in three brothers. *U.S. Naval Med. Bull.,* 42:1097-1101.

Heston, L. L. (1966), Psychiatric disorders in foster home reared children of schizophrenic mothers. *Brit. J. Psychiat.,* 112:819-825.

Hilgard, J., & Newman, M. (1963a), Early parental deprivation as a functional factor in the etiology in schizophrenia and alcoholism. *Amer. J. Orthopsychiat.,* 33:409-420.

———— ———— (1963b), Parental loss by death in childhood as an etiological factor among schizophrenic and alcoholic patients compared with a non-patient community sample. *J. Nerv. Ment. Dis.,* 137:14-28.

Hill, L. B. (1955), *Psychotherapeutic Intervention in Schizophrenia.* Chicago: University of Chicago Press.

Hill, R. (1954), Marriage and family research: a critical evaluation. *Eugenics Quart.,* 1:58-63.

———— Mark, J., & Wirths, C. S. (1953), *Eddyville's Families: Study of Personal and Family Adjustment Subsequent to the Rapid Urbanization of a Southern Town.* Chapel Hill, NC: Institute for Research in Social Science.

Hirsch, S. R., & Leff, J. P. (1971), Parental abnormalities of verbal communication in the transmission of schizophrenia. *Psychol. Med.,* 1:118-127.

———— ———— (1975), *Abnormalities in Parents of Schizophrenics.* Maudsley Monogr. 22. London: Oxford University Press.

Hobson, J. A. (1964), Identical twins discordant for schizophrenia. *J. Nerv. Ment. Dis.,* 138:432-442.

Hoch, P., & Polatin, P. (1949), Pseudoneurotic forms of schizophrenia. *Psychiat. Quart.,* 23:248-276.

Hollingshead, A., & Redlich, F. (1958), *Social Class and Mental Illness.* New York: J. Wiley & Sons.

Holzberg, J. (1960), The historical traditions of the state hospitals as a force of resistance to the team. *Amer. J. Orthopsychiat.,* 30:87-94.

Hotchkiss, G. D., Carmen, L., Ogilby, A., & Wiesenfeld, S. (1955), Mothers of young male single schizophrenic patients as visitors in a mental hospital. *J. Nerv. Ment. Dis.,* 121:452-462.

Houston, P. E., Cohen, B. D., & Senf, R. (1955), Shifting of set and goal orientation in schizophrenia. *J. Ment. Sci.*, *101*:344-350.

Hubbard, J. P. (1953), Observation of the family in the home. *J. Med. Educ.*, *28*:26-30.

Hutchins, E. (1980), *Culture and Inference: A Trobriand Case Study.* Cambridge: Harvard University Press.

Inhelder, B., & Piaget, J. (1958), *The Growth of Logical Thinking from Childhood to Adolescence.* New York: Basic Books.

Inwood, E. R. (1952), Therapeutic interviewing of hostile relatives. *Amer. J. Psychiat.*, *109*:455-458.

Jackson, D. D. (1954), Some factors influencing the Oedipus Complex. *Psychoanal. Quart.*, *23*:566-581.

———— (1957a), A note on the importance of trauma in the genesis of schizophrenia. *Psychiatry, 20*:181-184.

———— (1957b), The question of family homeostasis. *Psychiat. Quart.* Suppl., *31*:79-90.

———— (1958), The family and sexuality. In: *The Psychotherapy of Chronic Schizophrenic Patients*, ed. C. Whitaker. Boston: Little, Brown.

———— (1959), Family interaction, family homeostasis, and some implications for conjoint family psychotherapy. In: *Individual and Familial Dynamics*, ed. J. Masserman. New York: Grune & Stratton.

———— (1960a), A critique of the literature on the genetics of schizophrenia. In: *The Etiology of Schizophrenia*, ed., D. Jackson, New York: Basic Books.

————, Ed. (1960b), *The Etiology of Schizophrenia.* New York: Basic Books.

———— (1961), Family therapy in the family of the schizophrenic. In: *Contemporary Psychotherapies*, ed. M. Stein. Glencoe, IL: Free Press.

———— (1973), Introduction. In: *The Etiology of Schizophrenia*, ed. D. Jackson. New York: Basic Books.

———— Block, J., Block, J., & Patterson, V. (1958), Psychiatrists' conceptions of the schizophrenogenic parent. *Arch. Neurol. Psychiat.*, *79*:448-459.

———— Haley, J. (1963), Transference revisited. *J. Nerv. Ment. Dis.*, *137*:363-371.

———— Riskin, J., & Satir, V. (1961), A method of analysis of a family interview. *Arch. Gen. Psychiat.*, *5*:321-339.

———— Satir, V. (1961), A review of psychiatric developments in family diagnosis and therapy. In: *Exploring the Base for Family Therapy*, ed. N. W. Ackerman, F. Beatman, & S. Sherman. New York: Family Service Association of America.

———— Weakland, J. (1959), Schizophrenic symptoms and family interaction. *Arch. Gen. Psychiat.*, *1*:618-621.

Jacobs, E. & Mesnikoff, A. (1961), Alternating psychoses in twins. *Amer. J. Psychiat.*, *117*:791-797.

Jensen, T. (1952), Measuring family solidarity. *Amer. Sociol. Rev.*, *17*:727-733.

Johanson, E. (1958), A study of schizophrenia in the male. *Acta Psychiat. Neurol. Scand.*, Suppl. 125.

Johansson, A. (1956), Family dynamics in schizophrenia in the light of psychotherapy. Presented at meeting of Finnish Neuropsychiatric Society.

Johnson, A. M., Giffin, M. E., Watson, J., & Beckett, P. G. S. (1956), Studies in schizophrenia at the Mayo Clinic: II. Observations on ego functions in schizophrenia. *Psychiatry*, *19*:143-148.

—— Szurek, S. A. (1952), The genesis of antisocial acting out in children and adults. *Psychoanal. Quart.*, *21*:323-343.

—— —— (1954), Etiology of antisocial behavior in delinquents and psychopaths. *J. Amer. Med. Assn.*, *154*:814-817.

Jones, D. (1964), Binds and unbinds. *Fam. Proc.*, *3*:323-331.

Jones, J. E. (1977), Patterns of transactional style deviance in the TAT's of parents of schizophrenics. *Fam. Proc.*, *16*:327-337.

—— Rodnick, E. H., Goldstein, M. J., et al. (1977), Parental transactional style deviance as a possible indication of risk for schizophrenia. *Arch. Gen. Psychiat.*, *34*:71-74.

Jones, M. (1953), *The Therapeutic Community: A New Treatment Method in Psychiatry*. New York: Basic Books.

Joseph E. D. (1959), An unusual fantasy in a twin with an inquiry into the nature of fantasy. *Psychoanal. Quart.*, *28*:189-206.

—— (1961), Report of the Panel on "The Psychology of Twins" at the May, 1960 meeting of the American Psychoanalytic Association. *J. Amer. Psychoanal. Assn.*, 9:158-166.

—— Tabor, J. (1961), The simultaneous analysis of a pair of identical twins and the twinning reaction. *The Psychoanalytic Study of the Child*, *16*:275-299. New York: International Universities Press.

Jung, C. G. (1909), *The Psychology of Dementia Praecox*. New York: J. Nerv. Ment. Dis. Publ. Co.

Kahn, S., & Prestwood, A. R. (1954), Group therapy of parents as an adjunct to the treatment of schizophrenic patients. *Psychiatry*, 17:177-185.

Kallmann, F. J. (1946), The genetic theory of schizophrenia: an analysis of 691 schizophrenic twin index families. *Amer. J. Psychiat.*, *103*:309-322.

—— (1952), Comparative twin study on the genetic aspects of male homosexuality. *J. Nerv. Ment. Dis.*, *115*:283-297.

—— (1953), *Heredity in Health and Mental Disorder: Principles of Psychiatric Genetics in Light of Comparative Twin Studies*. New York: W. W. Norton.

———— Bondy, E. (1952), Applicability of the twin study method in the analysis of variations in mate selection and marital adjustment. *Amer. J. Hum. Genet., 4*:209-222.

Kammerer, T., Cahn, R., & Nevers, J. (1957), Etude des mères de schizophrènes. *Congr. Rep. IInd Int. Congr. Psychiat., Zurich, 3*:93-96.

Karon, B., & Rosberg, J. (1958), Study of the mother-child relationship in a case of paranoid schizophrenia. *Amer. J. Psychother., 12*:522-533.

Karpman, B. (1953), Psychodynamics in a fraternal twinship relation. *Psychoanal. Rev., 40*:243-267.

Kasanin, J., Knight, E., & Sage, P. (1934), The parent-child relationship in schizophrenia: I. Over-protection-rejection. *J. Nerv. Ment. Dis., 79*:249-263.

———— & Rosen, Z. (1933), Clinical variables in schizoid personalities. *Arch. Neurol. Psychiat., 30*:538-566.

Katan, M. (1954), The non-psychotic part of the personality in schizophrenia. *Internat. J. Psycho-Anal., 35*:119-128.

Kempler, W., Iverson, R., & Beisser, A. (1962), The adult schizophrenic patient and his siblings. *Fam. Proc., 1*:224-235.

Kendler, K. S. (1983), Overview: a current perspective on twin studies of schizophrenia. *Amer. J. Psychiat., 140*:1413-1425.

Kent, E. (1949), A study of maladjusted twins. *Smith Coll. Stud. Soc. Work, 19*:63-77.

Kernberg, O. (1975), *Borderline Conditions and Pathological Narcissism*. New York: Aronson.

Kety, S. S., Rosenthal, D., Wender, P. H., et al. (1968), The types and prevalence of mental illness in the biological and adoptive families of adopted schizophrenics. In: *The Transmission of Schizophrenia*, ed. D. Rosenthal & S. S. Kety. New York: Pergamon Press.

———— ———— ———— et al., (1975), Mental illness in the biological and adoptive families of adopted individuals who have become schizophrenic: a preliminary report based on psychiatric interviews. In: *Genetic Research in Psychiatry*, ed. R. R. Fieve, D. Rosenthal, & H. Brill. Baltimore: Johns Hopkins University Press.

Khan, M. M. R. (1960), Clinical aspects of the schizoid personality: affects and technique. *Internat. J. Psycho-Anal., 41*:430-437.

———— (1962), The role of polymorph-perverse body experiences and object relations in ego integration. *Brit. J. Med. Psychol., 35*:245-261.

Kisker, K. P. (1960), *Der Erlebniswandel des Schizophrenen: Ein psychopathologischer Beitrag zur Psychonomie schizophrener Grundsituationen*. Berlin: Springer.

———— (1962), Schizophrenie und familie. *Nervenarzt, 33*:13-21.

———— Strötzel, L. (1961a), Zur Vergleichenden Situationsanalyse Beginnender Schizophrenien und Erlebnisreaktiver Fehlentwicklungen bei Jugendlichen. *Arch. Psychiat. Nervenheilkr., 202*:1-30.

———— ———— (1961b), Soziologisch-Psychologische Voraussetzungen und Methodische Probleme einer Psychiatrischen Familienforschung. *Fortschr. Neurol. Psychiat.*, *29*:477-499.

Kizu, M. (1960), A parental study on schizophrenia through Rorschach test. *J. Osaka Med. Coll.* (Osaka, Japan), *20*:1362.

Klein, D. C., & Lindemann, E. (1961), Preventive intervention in individual and family crisis situations. In: *Prevention of Mental Disorders in Children*, ed. G. Caplan. New York: Basic Books.

Klein, M. (1946), Notes on some schizoid mechanisms. *Internat. J. Psycho-Anal.*, *27*:99-110.

Kluckhohn, F. (1952), The American family: past and present and American women. In: *Patterns for Modern Living*. Chicago: Delphian Society.

Knight, R. P. (1937), The dynamics and treatment of chronic alcohol addiction. *Bull. Menninger Clin.*, *1*:233-250.

———— (1953), Borderline states. *Bull. Menninger Clin.*, *17*:1-12.

Kohlberg, L. (1964), Development of moral character and moral ideology. In: *Review of Child Developmental Research*, ed. M. L. Hoffman & L. W. Hoffman. New York: Russell Sage Foundation.

Kohn, M. L., & Clausen, J. A. (1955), Social isolation and schizophrenia. *Amer. Sociol. Rev.*, *20*:265-273.

———— ———— (1956), Parental authority behavior and schizophrenia. *Amer. J. Orthopsychiat.*, *26*:297-313.

Kohut, H. (1971), *The Analysis of the Self.* New York: International Universities Press.

Kolb, L. (1960), Values and limitations of psychoanalysis in a twin study of heterosexual and homosexual identity. Presented at the annual meeting of the Amer. Psychiat. Assn., May.

Kosaka, H. (1960a), A study on the family relationship of schizophrenics. I. *Iryo*, *14*:259-271.

———— (1960b), A study on the family relationship of schizophrenics, II. *Iryo*, *14*:354-360.

Kraepelin, E. (1899), Zur Diagnose und Prognose der Dementia Praecox. *Allg. Z. Psychiat.*, *56*:254.

Kringlen, E. (1964), Schizophrenia in male monozygotic twins. *Acta Psychiat. Neurol. Scand.*, Suppl. 178.

Kronhausen, E., & Kronhausen, P. (1957), The therapeutic family: a family life approach to the rehabilitation of the emotionally disturbed. *Congr. Rep. IInd Int. Congr. Psychiat., Zurich*, *3*:75-79.

Laing, R. D. (1962), *The Self and Others: Further Studies in Sanity and Madness.* London: Tavistock Publ.

Lampron, E. (1933), Children of schizophrenic parents: present mental and social status of 186 cases. *Ment. Hyg.*, *17*:82-91.

Lane, R. C., & Singer, J. L. (1959), Familial attitudes in paranoid schizophrenics and normals from two socioeconomic classes. *J. Abnorm.
Soc. Psychol.*, 59:328-339.

Langfeldt, S. (1953), Some points regarding the symptomatology and diagnosis of schizophrenia. *Acta Psychiat. Neurol. Scand.*, Suppl. 80.

Leach, E. (1966), Anthropological aspects of language: animal categories
and verbal abuse. In: *New Directions in the Study of Language*, ed. E.
Lenneberg. Cambridge: M.I.T. Press.

Leff, J. P. (1976), Schizophrenia and sensitivity to the family environment.
Schiz. Bull., 2:566-574.

Lennard, H. L., Beaulieu, M. R., & Embrey, N. G. (1965), Interaction in
families with a schizophrenic child. *Arch. Gen. Psychiat.*, 12:166-183.

Leonard, M. (1961), Problems in identification and ego development in
twins. *The Psychoanalytic Study of the Child*, 16:300-320. New York:
International Universities Press.

Lewis, J., Beavers, W. R., et al. (1976), *No Single Thread*. New York: Brun-
ner/Mazel.

Lidz, R. W., & Lidz, T. (1950), Eine Interpretation der Grundideen der
Amerikanischen Psychiatrie. *Nervenarzt*, 21:490-494.

———— ———— (1952), Therapeutic considerations arising from the intense
symbiotic needs of schizophrenic patients. In: *Psychotherapy with
Schizophrenics*, ed. E. B. Brody & F. C. Redlich. New York: International Universities Press.

———— ———— (1977), Male menstruation: a ritual alternative to the oedipal
transition. *Internat. J. Psycho-Anal.*, 58:17-31.

Lidz, T. (1939), A study of the effect of right frontal lobectomy on intelligence and temperament. *J. Neurol. Psychiat.*, 2:211-222.

———— (1942), The amnestic syndrome. *Arch. Neurol. Psychiat.*, 47:588-605.

———— (1949), The analysis of a prefrontal lobe syndrome and its theoretic
implications. *Arch. Neurol. Psychiat.*, 62:1-26.

———— (1963a), *The Family and Human Adaptation*. New York: International
Universities Press.

———— (1963b), Family organization and personality structure. In: *The
Family and Human Adaptation*. New York: International Universities
Press.

———— (1963c), The family, language, and ego functions. In: *The Family
and Human Adaptation*. New York: International Universities Press.

———— (1967), The family, personality development and schizophrenia.
In: *The Origins of Schizophrenia*, ed. J. Romano. The Hague: Excerpta
Medica Foundation.

———— (1968), Familie, Sprache und Schizophrenie. *Psyche*, 22:701-719.

———— (1973), *The Origin and Treatment of Schizophrenic Disorders*. New York:
Basic Books.

———— (1978), Egocentric cognitive regression and the family setting of schizophrenic disorders. In: *The Nature of Schizophrenia*, ed. L. Wynne, R. Cromwell, & S. Matthysee. New York: J. Wiley & Sons.

———— (1979), Family studies and changing concepts of personality development. *Can. J. Psychiat., 24*:621-632.

———— Blatt, S. J. (1983), Critique of the Danish-American studies of the biological and adoptive relatives of adoptees who became schizophrenic. *Amer. J. Psychiat., 140*:426-435.

———— ———— Cook, B. (1981), Critique of the Danish-American studies of the adopted-away offspring of schizophrenic parents. *Amer. J. Psychiat., 138*:1063-1068.

———— Carter, J., Lewis, B., & Surratt, C. (1952), Effects of ACTH and cortisone on mood and mentation. *Psychosom. Med., 14*:363-377.

———— Fleck, S. (1960), Schizophrenia, human integration, and the role of the family. In: *The Etiology of Schizophrenia*, ed. D. D. Jackson. New York: Basic Books.

———— ———— (1965), Family studies and a theory of schizophrenia. The American family in crisis. *Forest Hospital Publications*, Vol. 3.

———— Gay, J., & Tietze, C. (1942), Intelligence in cerebral deficit states and schizophrenia measured by Kohs Block Test. *Arch. Neurol. Psychiat., 48*:568-582.

———— Kahn, R. (1946), Toxicity of quinacrine (Atabrine) for the central nervous system: III. An experimental study of human subjects. *Arch. Neurol. Psychiat, 56*:284-299.

———— Lidz, R. W. (1982), Curative factors in the psychotherapy of schizophrenic disorders. In: *Curative Factors in Dynamic Psychotherapy*, ed. S. Slipp. New York: McGraw-Hill.

———— ———— (1984), Oedipus in the Stone Age. *J. Amer. Psychoanal. Assn., 32*:507-527.

———— ———— Rubenstein, R. (1976), An anaclitic syndrome in adolescent amphetamine addicts. *The Psychoanalytic Study of the Child, 31*:317-348. New Haven: Yale University Press.

———— Miller, J., Padget, P., & Stedem, A. (1949), Muscular atrophy and pseudologia fantastica associated with islet cell adenoma of the pancreas. *Arch. Neurol. Psychiat., 62*:304-313.

———— Wild, C., Schafer, S., et al. (1963), Thought disorders in the parents of schizophrenic patients: a study utilizing the Object Sorting Test. *J. Psychiat. Res., 1*:193-200.

Liem, J. H. (1974), Effects of verbal communications of parents and children: a comparison of normal and schizophrenic families. *J. Consult. Clin. Psycholog., 42*:438-450.

———— (1976), Intrafamily communication and schizophrenic thought disorder: an etiological or responsive relationship? *Clin. Psychol., 29*:28-30.

Limentani, D. (1956), Symbiotic identification in schizophrenia. *Psychiatry, 19*:231-236.

Locke, H. J., Sabagh, G., & Thomas, M. (1955), Primary communication, empathy and family unity. Presented at Amer. Sociol. Soc. meeting.

Lomas, P. (1961), Family role and identity formation. *Internat. J. Psycho-Anal.*, *42*:371-380.

Lorenz, M. (1961), Problems posed by schizophrenic language. *Arch. Gen. Psychiat.*, *4*:603-610.

—————— (1963), Criticism as approach to schizophrenic language. *Arch. Gen. Psychiat.*, *9*:235-245.

Lovibond, S. H. (1953), The Object Sorting Test and conceptual thinking in schizophrenia. *Aust. J. Psychol.*, *5*:52-70.

Lu, Y. C. (1962), Contradictory parental expectations in schizophrenia. *Arch. Gen. Psychiat.*, *6*:219-234.

Luxenburger, H. (1934), Die Manifestationswarhrscheinlichkeit der Schizophrenie in Lichte der Zwillingsforschung. *Allg Z Psychiat.*, *103*:174.

Lyketsos, G. (1957), Histories of symbiotic relationship pattern in schizophrenia. *Congr. Rep. IInd Int. Congr. Psychiat.*, *Zurich*, *3*:189-191.

—————— (1959), On the formation of mother-daughter symbiotic relationship patterns in schizophrenia. *Psychiatry*, *22*:161-166.

Macalpine, I., & Hunter, R. A. (1953), The Schreber case: a contribution to schizophrenia, hypochondria, and psychosomatic symptom-formation. *Psychoanal. Quart.*, *22*:328-371.

McConaghy, N. (1959), The use of an Object Sorting Test in elucidating the hereditary factor in schizophrenia. *J. Neurol. Neurosurg. Psychiat.*, *22*:234-245.

McGhie, A. (1961), A comparative study of the mother-child relationship in schizophrenia: I. The interview. *Brit. J. Med. Psychol.*, *34*:195-208.

McKeown, J. E. (1950), The behavior of parents of schizophrenic, neurotic, and normal children. *Amer. J. Sociol.*, *56*:175-179.

Mahler, M. (1968), *On Human Symbiosis and the Vicissitudes of Individuation*. New York: International Universities Press.

—————— Pine, F., & Bergman, A. (1975), *The Psychological Birth of the Infant*. New York: Basic Books.

Main, T. (1951), *Five Year Report of the Cassel Hospital*. London: Hodge & Chilver.

Mangus, A. R. (1952), Family impacts on mental health. *Marriage and Family Living*, *14*:1-6.

Mark, J. D. (1953), The attitudes of mothers of male schizophrenics toward child behavior. *J. Abnorm. Soc. Psychol.*, *48*:185-189.

Matte-Blanco, I. (1957), A study of schizophrenic thinking: its expression in terms of symbolic logic and its representation in terms of multi-dimensional space. *Congr. Rep. IInd Int. Congr. Psychiat.*, *Zurich*, *1*:254-259.

May, P. R. A. (1968), *Treatment of Schizophrenia: A Comparative Study of Five Treatment Methods*. New York: Science House.

Mead, G. H. (1934), *Mind, Self and Society*. Chicago: University of Chicago Press.

Medina, L. von (1937), *Die Konvulsions Therapie der Schizophrenie*. Halle, Germany: Marhold.

Mendell, D., & Fisher, S. (1956), An approach to neurotic behavior in terms of a three generation family model. *J. Nerv. Ment. Dis.*, *123*:171-180.

Mesnikoff, A., Rainer, J. D., Kolb, L. C., & Carr, A. C. (1963), Intrafamilial determinants of divergent sexual behavior in twins. *Amer. J. Psychiat.*, *119*:732-738, 1963.

Meyer, A. (1906), Fundamental concepts of dementia praecox. *Brit. Med. J.*, 2:757-760.

—— (1910), The dynamic interpretation of dementia praecox. *Amer. J. Psychol.*, *21*:385-402.

Meyer-Gross, W., et al. (1955), *Clinical Psychiatry*. London: Cassel.

Meyers, D., & Goldfarb, W. (1961), Studies of perplexity in mothers of schizophrenic children. *Amer. J. Orthopsychiat.*, *31*:551-564.

Meyers, J., & Roberts, B. (1959), *Family and Class Dynamics in Mental Illness*. New York: J. Wiley & Sons.

Midelfort, C. F. (1957), *The Family in Psychotherapy*. New York: McGraw-Hill.

Milici, P., & Von Salzen, C. (1938), Situational schizophrenia. *Psychiat. Quart.*, *12*:650-668.

Miller, H. (1956), *Tropic of Capricorn*. Paris: Obelisk Press.

Miller, N., & Dollard, J. (1941), *Social Learning and Imitation*. New Haven: Yale University Press.

Modell, A. H. (1956), Some recent psychoanalytic theories of schizophrenia. *Psychoanal. Rev.*, *43*:181-194.

Morris, G. O., & Wynne, L. C. (1965), Schizophrenic offspring and parental styles of communication: a predictive study using excerpts of family therapy recordings. *Psychiatry*, *28*:19-44.

Muller, H. J. (1925), Mental traits and heredity. *J. Hered.*, *16*:443-448.

—— (1949), Progress and prospects in human genetics. *Amer. J. Hum. Genet.*, *1*:1-18.

Murphy, B. W. (1952), The genesis of schizoid personality: a study of two cases developing schizophrenia. *Psychiat. Quart.*, *26*:450-461.

Murphy, H. B. M. (1978), Cultural influences on incidence, course, and treatment response. In: *The Nature of Schizophrenia*, ed. L. C. Wynne, R. L. Cromwell, & S. Matthysee. New York: J. Wiley & Sons.

Nakajima, G. (1960), A study of schizophrenics and the intrafamilial relationships. *J. Nagoya Med. Coll.* (Nagoya, Japan), *81*:73.

Newell, H., & Lidz, T. (1946), The toxicity of atabrine to the central nervous system: I. Toxic psychoses. II. Convulsions. *Amer. J. Psychiat.*, *102*:805-818.

Niederland, W. G. (1951), Three notes on the Schreber case. *Psychoanal. Quart.*, *20*:579-591.

———— (1959), Schreber: father and son. *Psychoanal. Quart.*, *28*:151-169.

———— (1960), Schreber's father. *J. Amer. Psychoanal. Assn.*, *8*:492-499.

———— (1963), Further data and memorabilia pertaining to the Schreber case. *Internat. J. Psycho-Anal.*, *44*:201-207.

Nielsen, C. (1954), The childhood of schizophrenics. *Acta Psychiat. Neurol. Scand.*, *29*:281-289.

Nuffield, E. (1954), The schizogenic mother. *Med. J. Australia*, *2*:283-286.

Nydes, J. (1963), Schreber, parricide, and paranoid-masochism. *Internat. J. Psycho-Anal.*, *44*:208-212.

Odenwald, R. P. (1957), The father's role in the development of schizophrenia. *Congr. Rep. IInd Int. Congr. Psychiat., Zurich*, *3*:462-469.

Oltman, J. E., McGarry, J. J., & Friedman, S. (1952), Parental deprivation and "broken home" in dementia praecox and other mental disorders. *Amer. J. Psychiat.*, *108*:685-693.

O'Neal, P., & Robins, L. (1958), Childhood patterns predictive of adult schizophrenia: a 30-year follow-up study. *Amer. J. Psychiat.*, *115*:385-391.

O'Neill, E. (1956), *Long Day's Journey Into Night*. New Haven: Yale University Press.

Opler, M. K. (1957), Schizophrenia and culture. *Sci. Amer.*, *197*:103-110.

———— (1959), The cultural backgrounds of mental health. Introduction to *Culture and Mental Health*, ed. M. Opler. New York: Macmillan.

Orr, D. (1941), A psychoanalytic study of a fraternal twin. *Psychoanal. Quart.*, *10*:284-296.

Osborn, L. A. (1945), Five psychotic sisters. *J. Nerv. Ment. Dis.*, *101*:158-165.

Osgood, C., Suci, G., & Tannenbaum, P. (1957), *The Measurement of Meaning*. Urbana, IL: University of Illinois Press.

Parker, B. (1962), *A Mingled Yarn*. New Haven: Yale University Press.

Parsons, T. (1953), The superego and the theory of social system. In: *Working Papers in the Theory of Action*, ed. T. Parsons, R. Bales, & E. Shils. Glencoe, IL: Free Press.

———— (1954), The incest taboo in relation to social structure and the socialization of the child. *Brit. J. Sociol.*, *5*:101-117.

———— (1958), Social structure and the development of personality: Freud's contribution to the integration of psychology and sociology. *Psychiatry*, *21*:321-340.

———— Bales, R. (1955), *Family, Socialization and Interaction Process*. Glencoe, IL: Free Press.

———— Fox, R. (1952), Illness, therapy, and the modern urban American family. *J. Soc. Issues, 8*:31-44.

Peabody, F. W. (1927), Care of the patient. *J. Amer. Med. Assn., 88*:877-882.

Penrose, L. S. (1945), Survey of cases of familial mental illness. *Dig. Neurol. Psychiat., 13*:644.

Piaget, J. (1926), *The Language and Thought of the Child*. New York: Harcourt, Brace & Co.

———— (1929), *The Child's Conception of the World*. Paterson, NJ: Littlefield, Adams & Co., 1963.

Ping-nie, P. (1960), The use of patient-family-doctor interviews to facilitate the schizophrenic patient's return to the community. *Psychiatry, 23*:199-207.

Plank, R. (1953), The family constellation of a group of schizophrenic patients. *Amer. J. Orthopsychiat., 23*:817-825.

Pollak, O. (1957), Some conceptual steps toward a theoretical framework for studying family situations and child development. *Children, 4*:169-173.

Pollin, W., Stabenau, J., & Tupin, J. (1965), Family studies with identical twins discordant for schizophrenia. *Psychiatry, 28*:60-78.

Pollock, H. M., & Malzberg, B. (1940), Hereditary and environmental factors in the causation of manic-depressive psychoses and dementia praecox. *Amer. J. Psychiat., 96*:1227-1243.

———— ———— & Fuller, R. G. (1939), *Heredity and Environmental Factors in the Causation of Manic-Depressive Psychoses and Dementia Praecox*. Utica, N.Y.: State Hospitals Press.

Prout, C. T., & White, M. A. (1950), A controlled study of personality relationships in mothers of schizophrenic male patients. *Amer. J. Psychiat., 107*:251-256.

———— ———— (1956), The schizophrenic's sibling. *J. Nerv. Ment. Dis., 123*:162-170.

Rapaport, D., Gill, M., & Schafer, R. (1945), *Diagnostic Psychological Testing*. New York: International Universities Press.

Raybin, J. (1969), Homosexual incest. *J. Nerv. Ment. Dis., 148*:105-110.

Redlich, F. C. (1952), The concept of schizophrenia and its implication for therapy. In: *Psychotherapy with Schizophrenics*, ed. E. B. Brody & F. C. Redlich, New York: International Universities Press.

Reichard, S., & Tillman, C. (1950), Patterns of parent-child relationships in schizophrenia. *Psychiatry, 13*:247-257.

Reiss, D. (1967a), Individual thinking and family interaction. I. Introduction to an experimental study of problem solving in families of normals, character disorders, and schizophrenics. *Arch. Gen. Psychiat., 16*:80-93.

——— (1967b), Individual thinking and family interaction. II. A study of pattern recognition and hypothesis testing in families of normals, character disorders, and schizophrenics. *J. Psychiat. Res.*, 5:193-211.

——— (1968a), Individual thinking and family interaction. III. An experimental study of categorization performance in families of normals, those with character disorders and schizophrenia. *J. Nerv. Ment. Dis.*, 146:384-403.

——— (1968b), Family problem solving: two experiments on the relationship between family interaction and individual thinking in families of schizophrenics, normals, and character disorders. *J. Psychiat. Res.*, 6 (Suppl. 1):223-234.

——— (1969), Individual thinking and family interaction. IV. A study of information exchange in families of normals, those with character disorders, and schizophrenics. *J. Nerv. Ment. Dis.*, 149:473-490.

——— (1971), Varieties of consensual experience. III. Contrasts between families of normals, delinquents, and schizophrenics. *J. Nerv. Ment. Dis.*, 152:73-95.

——— Wyatt, R. J. (1975), Family and biologic variables in the same etiologic studies of schizophrenia. a proposal. *Schizo. Bull.*, 14:64-81.

Rhinehart, J. (1961), Genesis of overt incest. *Comprehen. Psychiat.*, 2:338-349.

Richardson, H. B. (1945), *Patients Have Families*. New York: Commonwealth Fund.

Riskin, J. (1963), Methodology for studying family interaction. *Arch. Gen. Psychiat.*, 8:343-348.

Roberts, A. L. (1940), Three schizophrenic brothers. *Med. Bull. Vet. Admin.*, 16:278-279.

Roberts, B. H., & Myers, J. K. (1955), Schizophrenia in the youngest male child of the lower middle class. *Amer. J. Psychiat.*, 112:129-134.

Rosanoff, A. J., Handy, L. M., Plesset, L., & Brush, S. (1934), The etiology of so-called schizophrenic psychoses: with special reference to their occurrence in twins. *Amer. J. Psychiat.*, 91:247-286.

Rosen, J. N. (1948), In panel on Theory and Treatment of Schizophrenia. Summary in *Bull. Amer. Psychoanal. Assn.*, 4:15.

——— (1953), *Direct Analysis: Selected Papers*. New York: Grune & Stratton.

——— (1963), *The Concept of Early Maternal Environment in Direct Psychoanalysis*. Doylestown, PA: Doylestown Foundation.

Rosenbaum, C. P. (1961), Patient-family similarities in schizophrenia. *Arch. Gen. Psychiat.*, 5:120-126.

——— (1970), *The Meaning of Madness*. New York: Science House.

Rosenfeld, H. (1952), Notes on the psycho-analysis of the super-ego conflict of an acute schizophrenic patient. *Internat. J. Psycho-Anal.*, 33:111-131.

———— (1954), Considerations regarding the psycho-analytic approach to acute and chronic schizophrenia. *Internat. J. Psycho-Anal.*, *35*:135-140.

Rosenthal, A. J., Behrens, M. I., & Chodoff, P. (1968), Communication in lower-class families of schizophrenics. I. Methodological problems. *Arch. Gen. Psychiat.*, *18*:464-470.

Rosenthal, D. (1959), Some factors associated with concordance and discordance with respect to schizophrenia in monozygotic twins. *J. Nerv. Ment. Dis.*, *129*:1-10.

———— (1960), Confusion of identity and the frequency of schizophrenia in twins. *Arch. Gen. Psychiat.*, *3*:297-304.

———— (1961a), Sex distribution and the severity of illness in samples of schizophrenic twins. *J. Psychiat. Res.*, *1*:26-36.

———— (1961b), Problems of sampling and diagnosis in the major twin studies of schizophrenia. *J. Psychiat. Res.*, *1*:116-134.

———— Wender, P. H., Kety, S. S., et al. (1968), Schizophrenics' offspring reared in adoptive homes. In: *The Transmission of Schizophrenia*, ed. D. Rosenthal & S. S. Kety. New York: Pergamon Press.

———— ———— ———— et al. (1971), The adopted-away offspring of schizophrenics. *Amer. J. Psychiat.*, *128*:307-311.

Rosman, B., Wild, C., Ricci, J., et al. (1964), Thought disorders in the parents of schizophrenic patients: a further study utilizing the Object Sorting Test. *J. Psychiat. Res.*, *2*:211-221.

Rubinstein, D. (1972), Clinical issues in family therapy of schizophrenics. In: *Psychotherapy of Schizophrenia*, ed. D. Rubinstein & Y. O. Alanen. Amsterdam: Excerpta Medica Foundation.

Rubter, A. E. (1974), *The Family as Patient*. New York: Farrar, Strauss, Giroux.

Ryckoff, I., Day, J., & Wynne, L. C. (1959), Maintenance of stereotyped roles in the families of schizophrenics. *Arch. Gen. Psychiat.*, *1*:109-114.

Sakhel, M. (1936), Zur Methodik der Hypoglykaemic. Behandling von Psychosem. Wien, Ke. Wochochn, *49*:1278-1288.

Sampson, H., Messinger, S., & Towne, R. D. (1961a), Two types of schizophrenic crises in women. *Bull. Menninger Clin.*, *25*:296-306.

———— ———— ———— (1961b), The mental hospital and marital family ties. *Soc. Prob.*, *9*:141-155.

Sander, F. M. (1971), T. S. Eliot's *The Family Reunion*—"schizophrenia" reconsidered. *Fam. Proc. 10*:213-228.

———— (1979), Schizophrenia and the family. In: *Individual and Family Therapy: Toward an Integration*. New York: Aronson.

Sanua, V. D. (1961), Socio-cultural factors in families of schizophrenics: a review of the literature. *Psychiatry, 24*:246-265.

—— (1963), The socio-cultural aspects of schizophrenia: a comparison of Protestant and Jewish schizophrenics. *Internat. J. Soc. Psychiat.,* 9:27-36.

Satir, V. (1963), Schizophrenia and family therapy. In: *Social Work Practice, 1963.* New York: Columbia University Press.

—— (1964), *Conjoint Family Therapy.* Palo Alto: Science and Behavior Books.

Savodnik, I. (1978), The manifest and the scientific imagery. In: *Schizophrenia: Science and Practice,* ed. J. Shershow. Cambridge: Harvard University Press.

Schachtel, E. (1959), The development of focal attention and the emergence of reality. In: *Metamorphosis: On the Development of Affect, Perception, Attention and Memory.* New York: Basic Books.

Schaffer, L., Wynne, L., Day, J., Ryckoff, I., & Halperin, A. (1962), On the nature and sources of the psychiatrist's experience with the family of the schizophrenic. *Psychiatry,* 25:32-45.

Schatzman, M. (1973), *Soul Murder: Persecution in the Family.* New York: Random House.

Scher, J. M. (1957), Indirection: a communicative basis for a theory of schizophrenia. *Congr. Rep. IInd Int. Congr. Psychiat., Zurich,* 3:69-74.

Schlegel, W. S. (1955), *Beiträge zur Sexualforschung.* Stuttgart: Enke.

—— (1957), *Körper und Seele: Eine Konstitutionslehre für Arzte, Juristen, Pädagogen und Theologen.* Stuttgart: Enke.

Schulz, B. (1940a), Kinder Schizophrener Elternpaare. *Z. Neurol. Psychiat., 168*:332-381.

—— (1940b), Kinder von Elternpaaren mit einem Schizophrenen und einem Affektivpsychotischen Partner. *Z. Neurol. Psychiat., 170*:441-514.

Schulz, C. D., & Kilgalen, R. K. (1969), *Case Studies in Schizophrenia.* New York: Basic Books.

Scott, R. D. (1976), "Closure" in family relationships and the first official diagnosis. In: *Schizophrenia 75: Psychotherapy, Family Studies, Research,* ed. J. Jorstad & E. Ugelstad, Oslo: Universitetsforlget.

Searles, H. F. (1958), Positive feelings in the relationship between the schizophrenic and his mother. *Internat. J. Psycho-Anal., 39*:569-586.

—— (1959), The effort to drive the other person crazy: an element in the aetiology and psychotherapy of schizophrenia. *Brit. J. Med. Psychol., 32*:1-18.

Sechehaye, M. (1951), *Symbolic Realization.* New York: International Universities Press.

Semrad, E. V., Menzer, D., Mann, J., & Standish, C. (1952), A study of the doctor-patient relationship in psychotherapy of psychotic patients. *Psychiatry, 15*:377-384.

Shapiro, D. S. (1957), Perceptions of significant family and environmental relationships in aggressive and withdrawn children. *J. Consult. Psychol., 21*:381-385.

Shepherd, I. L., & Guthrie, G. M. (1959), Attitudes of mothers of schizophrenic patients. *J. Clin. Psychol., 15*:212-215.

Silverman, L. H., & Silverman, D. K. (1962), Ego impairment in schizophrenia as reflected in the Object Sorting Test. *J. Abnorm. Soc. Psychol., 64*:381-385.

Simmel, E. (1937), The psychoanalytic sanitorium and the psychoanalytic movement. *Bull. Menninger Clin., 1*:133-143.

Simmons, L. W., & Wolff, H. G. (1954), *Social Science in Medicine*. New York: Russell Sage Foundation.

Singer, M. T. (1963), Personality measurements in the aged. In: *Human Aging*, ed. J. Birren, R. Butler, S. Greenhouse, L. Sokoloff, & M. Yarrow. Bethesda, MD.: Public Health Service Publ. #986.

—— (1978), Attentional processes in verbal behavior. In: *The Nature of Schizophrenia*, ed. L. Wynne, R. Cromwell, & S. Matthysee. New York: J. Wiley & Sons.

—— Wynne, L. (1963), Differentiating characteristics of the parents of childhood schizophrenics, childhood neurotics and young adult schizophrenics. *Amer. J. Psychiat., 120*:234-243.

—— —— (1965a), Thought disorder and family relations of schizophrenics: III. Methodology using projective techniques. *Arch. Gen. Psychiat., 12*:187-200.

—— —— (1965b), Thought disorder and family relations of schizophrenics: IV. Results and implications. *Arch. Gen. Psychiat., 12*:201-212.

—— —— (1976), Schizophrenics, families and communication disorders. Presented at meeting of American College of Psychiatrists, January 31.

Sivadon, P., & Mises, R. (1954), Le milieu familial du schizophrène (Reflections sur un cas clinique). *L'Evol. Psychiat., 19*:147-157.

Slater, E. (1953), *Psychotic and Neurotic Illness in Twins*. London: H.M. Stationery Office.

Sojit, C. M. (1971), The double bind hypothesis and the parents of schizophrenics. *Fam. Proc., 10*:53-74.

Solomon, R., & Bliss, E. L. (1956), Simultaneous occurrence of schizophrenia in identical twins. *Amer. J. Psychiat., 112*:912-915.

Sølvberg, H. A., & Blakar, R. M. (1975), Communication efficiency in couples with and without a schizophrenic offspring. *Fam. Proc., 14*:515-534.

Sonne, J. C., Speck, R. V., & Jungreis, J. (1962), The absent-member maneuver as a resistance in family therapy of schizophrenia. *Fam. Proc., 1*:44-62.

Southard, S. (1957), *The Family and Mental Illness*. Philadelphia: West-minster Press.

Spiegel, J. P. (1954), New perspectives in the study of the family. *Marriage and Family Living*, *16*:4-12.

—— (1957), The resolution of role conflict within the family. *Psychiatry*, *20*:1-16.

—— (1958), Homeostatic mechanisms within the family. In: *The Family in Contemporary Society*, ed. I. Galdston. New York: International Universities Press.

—— Bell, N. W. (1959), The family of the psychiatric patient. In: *American Handbook of Psychiatry*, ed. S. Arieti. New York: Basic Books.

—— Kluckhohn, F. (Chairmen) Committee on the Family, Group for the Advancement of Psychiatry (1954), *Integration and Conflict in Family Behavior*. Report 27. Topeka, Kansas: Group for the Advancement of Psychiatry.

Spitz, R. A. (1937), Familienneurose und Neurotische Familie. *Int. Z. Psychoanal.*, *23*:548-560.

Stabenau, J. R., Tupin, J., Werner, H., & Pollin, W. (1965), Comparative study of families of schizophrenics, delinquents, and normals. *Psychiatry*, *28*:45-59.

Stanton, A. H. (1961), Milieu therapy and the development of insight. *Psychiatry*, Suppl. to Vol. 24, No. 2, pp. 19-29.

—— Schwartz, M. S. (1954), *The Mental Hospital: A Study of Institutional Participation in Psychiatric Illness and Treatment*. New York: Basic Books.

Stierlin, H. (1959), The adaptation to the "stronger" person's reality: some aspects of the symbolic relationship of the schizophrenic. *Psychiatry*, *22*:143-152.

—— (1963a), Treatment dilemmas with psychotic and sociopathic patients. *Brit. J. Med. Psychol.*, *36*:75-84.

—— (1963b), Familie und Schizophrenie. *Nervenarzt, 34*:495-500.

—— (1969), *Conflict and Reconciliation: A Study in Human Relations and Schizophrenia*. Garden City, NJ: Anchor Books.

—— (1972), Family dynamics and separation patterns of potential schizophrenics. In: *Psychotherapy of Schizophrenia*, ed. D. Rubinstein & Y. O. Alanen. Amsterdam: Excerpta Medica Foundation.

—— (1974), *Separating Parents and Adolescents: A Perspective on Running Away, Schizophrenia, and Waywardness*. New York: Quadrangle Press.

—— (1978a), The transmission of irrationality reconsidered. In: *The Nature of Schizophrenia*, ed. L. Wynne, R. Cromwell, & S. Matthysee, New York: J. Wiley & Sons.

—— (1978b), *Delegation und Familie*. Frankfurt: Suhrkamp.

Strauss, A., & Sabshin, M. (1961), Large state mental hospitals. *Arch. Gen. Psychiat.*, *5*:565-577.

Strindberg, A. (1887), The father. In: *Six Plays of Strindberg*. Garden City, NJ: Doubleday Anchor Books, 1955.

——— (1901), *Easter*. Garden City, NJ: Doublday Anchor Books, 1955.

Sullivan, H. S. (1925-1926), Peculiarity of thought in schizophrenia. *Amer. J. Psychiat., 82*:21-86.

——— (1931-32), The modified psychoanalytic treatment of schizophrenia. *Amer. J. Psychiat., 88*:519-540.

——— (1940), Conceptions of modern psychiatry: therapeutic conceptions. *Psychiatry, 3*:87-117.

——— (1946-1947), *The Interpersonal Theory of Psychiatry*, ed. H. Perry & M. Gawel. New York: W. W. Norton, 1953.

Suzuki, K. (1962), The difference in mother-child relationship between schizophrenics and neurotics can be measured using interpersonal check list by Leavy. *Psychiat. et. Neurol. Japonica* (Tokyo), *64*:1103.

Swanson, D. (1961), Six month observation of psychotic identical twins. *Amer. J. Psychiat., 118*:166-168.

Szalita-Pemow, A. (1951), Remarks on pathogenesis and treatment of schizophrenia. *Psychiatry, 14*:295-300.

Szasz, T. (1957), A contribution to the psychology of schizophrenia. *AMA Arch. Neurol. Psychiat.*, 77:420-436.

Szurek, S. A. (1952), Some lessons from efforts at psychotherapy with parents. *Amer. J. Psychiat., 109*:296-302.

Tafuse, H. (1960), A familial study on schizophrenia: an investigation of parent-child relationship chiefly through Rorschach's test. *Psychiat. et. neurol. Japonica* (Tokyo), *62*:737.

Terry, G. C., & Rennie, T. A. C. (1938), Analysis of parergasia. *Nerv. Ment. Dis. Monogr.* 64.

Tienari, P. (1963), Psychiatric illness in identical twins. *Acta Psychiat. Neurol. Scand.*, Suppl. 171.

——— (1975), Schizophrenia in Finnish male twins. In: *Studies of Schizophrenia*, ed. M. H. Lader, Ashford, Kent: Headley Bros.

Tietze, T. (1949), A study of mothers of schizophrenic patients. *Psychiatry, 12*:55-65.

Toman, W. (1961), *Family Constellation*. New York: Springer.

Towne, R. D., & Afterman, J. (1955), Psychosis in males related to parenthood. *Bull. Menninger Clin., 19*:19-26.

——— Sampson, H., & Messinger, S. (1961), Schizophrenia and the marital family: identification crises. *J. Nerv. Ment. Dis., 133*:423-429.

Vaughn, C. E., & Leff, J. P. (1976), The influence of family and social factors on the course of psychiatric illness: a comparison of schizophrenic and depressed neurotic patients. *Brit. J. Psychiat., 129*:125-137.

Vogel, E., & Bell, N. (1960), The emotionally disturbed child as the family scapegoat. In: *A Modern Introduction to the Family*, ed. N. Bell & E. Vogel. Glencoe, IL: Free Press.

Vygotsky, L. D. (1934), Thought in schizophrenia, tr. J. Kasanin. *Arch. Neurol. Psychiat.*, *31*:1063-1077.

Wahl, C. W. (1954), Some antecedent factors in the family histories of 392 schizophrenics. *Amer. J. Psychiat.*, *110*:668-676.

————— (1956), Some antecedent factors in the family histories of 568 male schizophrenics of the United States Navy. *Amer. J. Psychiat.*, *113*:201-210.

Weakland, J. H. (1960), The "double-bind" hypothesis of schizophrenia and three-party interaction. In: *The Etiology of Schizophrenia*, ed. D. D. Jackson. New York: Basic Books.

————— (1962), Family therapy as a research arena. *Fam. Proc.*, *1*:63-68.

————— Fry, W. (1962), Letters of mothers of schizophrenics. *Amer. J. Orthopsychiat.*, *32*:604-623.

————— Jackson, D. D. (1958), Patient and therapist observations on the circumstances of a schizophrenic episode. *AMA Arch. Neurol. Psychiat.*, *79*:554-574.

Weatherly, J., & Deabler, H. L. (1954), Schizophrenia in identical twins one of whom was lobotomized. *J. Nerv. Ment. Dis.*, *120*:262-267.

Weblin, J. (1962), Communication and schizophrenic behavior. *Fam. Proc.*, *1*:5-14.

Wedge, B., & Fry, C. (1955), Schizophrenic reactions as developmental crises. Presented at meeting of Amer. Psychiat. Assn.

Weinberg, S. K. (1955), *Incest Behavior*. New York: Citadel Press.

Weiss, V. W., & Munroe, R. R. (1959), A framework for understanding family dynamics. Parts I & II. *Soc. Casewk.*, *40*:3-9, 80-87.

Wexler, M. (1975), The evolution of a deficiency view of schizophrenia. In: *Psychotherapy of Schizophrenia*, ed. J. Gunderson & L. R. Mosher, New York: Aronson.

White, R. (1963), The Schreber case reconsidered in the light of psychosocial concepts. *Internat. J. Psycho-Anal.*, *44*:213-221.

Whorf, B. (1956), *Language, Thought and Reality: Selected Writings of Benjamin Lee Whorf*, ed. J. Carroll. New York: M.I.T. Press and J. Wiley & Sons.

Wild, C., Shapiro, R., & Goldenberg, L. (1975), Transactional communication disturbances in families of male schizophrenics. *Fam. Proc.*, *14*:131-160.

Will, O. A. (1975), The conditions of being therapeutic. In: *Psychotherapy of Schizophrenia*, ed. J. Gunderson & L. R. Mosher. New York: Aronson.

Willi, J. (1962), Die Schizophrenie in Ihrer Auswirkung auf die Eltern: Untersuchung der Eltern von 15 Jugendlichen Schizophrenen. *Schweiz. Arch. Neurol., Neurochir. Psychiat.*, *89*:426-463.

Williams, T. (1945), *The Glass Menagerie*. New York: New Directions.

Winnicott, D. W. (1956), Primary maternal preoccupation. In: *Collected Papers*. London: Tavistock Publ., 1958.

—— (1960), The theory of the parent-infant relationship. *Internat. J. Psycho-Anal., 41*:585-595.

Wood, E. C., Rakusin, J., & Morse, E. (1960), Interpersonal aspects of psychiatric hospitalization: I. The admission. *Arch. Gen. Psychiat., 3*:632-641.

—— —— —— (1962), Interpersonal aspects of psychiatric hospitalization: II. Some correlations between the admission circumstances and the hospital treatment experience. *Arch. Gen. Psychiat., 6*:55-61.

Wynne, L. C. (1972), Communication disorders and the quest for relatedness in families of schizophrenics. In: *Progress in Group and Family Therapy*, ed. C. J. Sager & H. S. Kaplan. New York: Brunner/Mazel.

—— (1977), Psychopathological aspects of psychoses: nongenetic factors in the family setting. In: *Research on Disorders of the Mind: Progress and Prospects*. Washington, D.C.: U.S. Dept. Health, Educ. Welfare.

—— (1981), Current concepts about schizophrenics and family relationships. *J. Nerv. Ment. Dis., 169*:82-89.

—— Day, J., Hirsch, S., & Ryckoff, I. (1957), The family relations of a set of monozygotic quadruplet schizophrenics. *Congr. Rep. IInd Int. Congr. Psychiat., Zurich*, 2:43-49.

—— Jones, J. E., Al-Khayyal, M., et al. (1982), Familial risk factors in psychopathology. In: *Preventive Intervention in Schizophrenia. Are We Ready?*, ed. M. Goldstein. Washington, D.C.: U.S. Dept. Health & Human Services.

—— Ryckoff, I., Day, J., & Hirsch, S. (1958), Pseudo-mutuality in the family relations of schizophrenics. *Psychiatry, 21*:205-220.

—— Singer, M. T. (1963a), Thought disorder and family relations of schizophrenics: I. A research strategy. *Arch. Gen. Psychiat., 9*:191-198.

—— —— (1963b), Thought disorder and family relations of schizophrenics: II. A classification of forms of thinking. *Arch. Gen. Psychiat., 9*:199-206.

—— —— Toohey, M. (1976), Communication in the adoptive parents of schizophrenics. In: *Schizophrenia 75: Psychotherapy, Family Studies, Research*, ed. J. Jorstad & E. Ugelstad, Oslo: Universitetsforlget.

—— Toohey, M., & Doane, J. (1979), Family studies. In: *Disorders of the Schizophrenic Syndrome*, ed. L. Bellak. New York: Basic Books.

Zelditch, M. (1955), Role differentiation in the nuclear family: a comparative study. In: *Family, Socialization and Interaction Process*, ed. T. Parsons & R. Bales. Glencoe, IL: Free Press.

Index of Names

Abraham, K., 4, 127
Abrahams, J., 71, 219
Ackerman, N. W., 3, 153, 169
Alanen, Y. O., 3, 16, 38, 71, 85, 99,
    120, 219, 220, 249, 256, 262,
    314, 377, 410, 414, 418
Aristophanes, 295
Arlow, J., 315, 319
Astrachan, 314

Bales, R., 3, 131, 133, 153, 154, 169,
    227, 234
Bateson, G., 3, 40, 120, 186, 187,
    199, 377, 382, 414, 420, 442
Blakar, R. M., 207, 414
Bleuler, E., 217, 375, 401, 421
Bleuler, M., 29, 432
Bleuler, M., 29, 432
Bliss, E. L., 296, 314, 325
Bondy, E., 295
Borden, Lizzie, 412
Bott, E., 169
Bowen, M., 3, 38, 199, 316, 377,
    392, 414
Bowers, M., 422, 430
Brody, E. B., 127
Brown, R., 408
Bruch, H., 372, 442
Buell, B., 153, 157
Burlingham, D. T., 315
Burnham, D. L., 404

Cameron, N., 209, 422
Cancro, R., 412
Carter, J., 6

Chassell, J. O., 422
Ciarlo, D., 187, 353
Ciompi, L., 432
Clausen, J. A., 330, 331
Community Research Associates,
    153–154
Cornelison, A. R., 11, 70, 125, 151,
    168, 187, 209, 219, 230, 262,
    294, 327, 363
Cottrell, L., 169
Cronin, H. J., 296, 325

Day, J., 377
Deabler, H. L., 296, 314
Delay, J., 3, 10, 38, 85, 122, 377,
    414
Demarest, E. W., 296
Deniker, P., 3
Dicks, H. V., 169
Dollard, J., 209
Downey, T. W., 400

Ellison, E. A., 133
Endicott, T., 232
Engel, G. L. 404
Erikson, E., 126
Essen-Moller, E., 314

Fairbairn, W. R. D., 127
Faris, M. T., 330, 331
Federn, P., 127
Fleck, S., 8, 70, 124, 151, 168, 187,
    209, 219, 230, 262, 294, 316,
    327, 393, 400, 402, 410, 440,
    442
Flechsig, 433

Subject Index

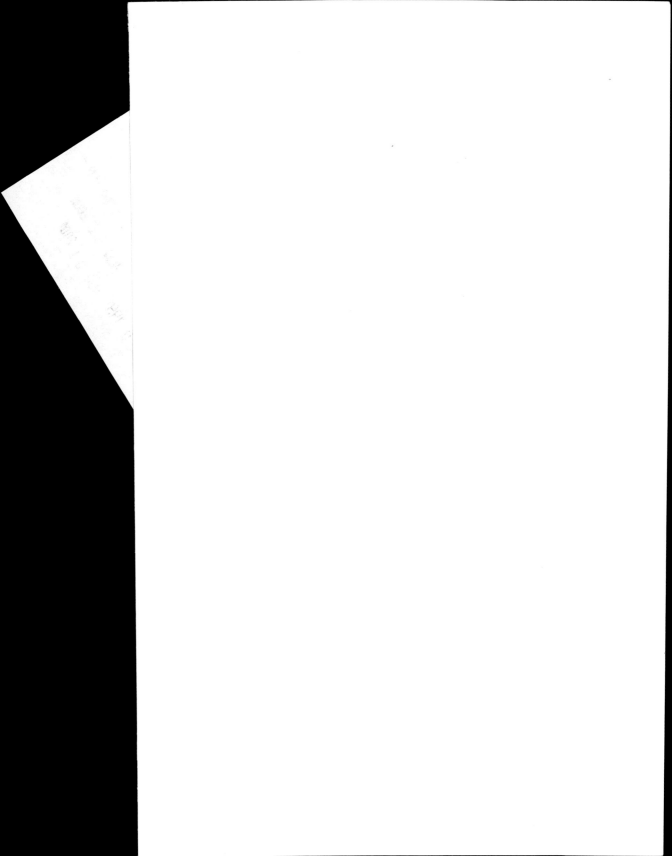